NELSON·GCSE
MATHS

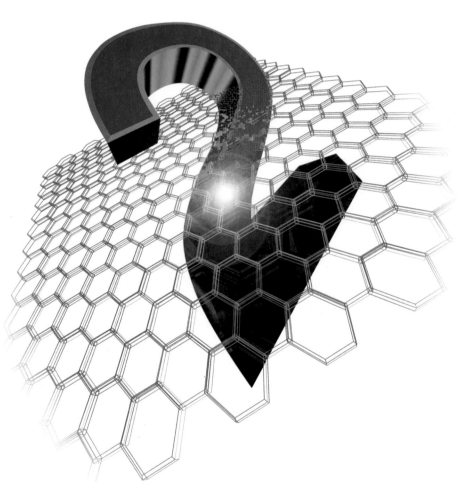

HIGHER 2

BARBARA BALL·DEREK BALL — SERIES EDITORS

CHRISTINE ATKINSON·WENDY FISHER·MARGARET POSTON

Thomas Nelson & Sons Ltd
Nelson House
Mayfield Road
Walton-on-Thames
Surrey KT12 5PL

First published by Thomas Nelson & Sons Ltd 1999
ISBN 0-17-431486-8
9 8 7 6 5 4 3 2 1
03 02 01 00 99

Printed in Spain

Acquisition: Jean Carnall
Editorial: Jenny Lawson, First Class Publishing
Production: Liz Carr
Design & Illustration: Ian Foulis & Associates
Cover design: R&B Creative Services

The authors and publishers are grateful to the following schools involved in trials of material from this series:

Worle School, Avon; Holte School, Birmingham; The Woodrush School, Birmingham; Hayle Community College, Cornwall; Ash Green School, Coventry; Stainburn School, Cumbria; The Deanes School, Essex; Cirencester Kingshill School, Glos.; Pontllanfraith High School, Gwent; The Hayling School, Hants; Swakeleys School, Hillingdon; Crown Hills Community College, Leicester; Hampstead School, London; St Martin's in the Fields High School, London; Kenton School, Newcastle upon Tyne; Walbottle High School, Newcastle upon Tyne; Belfast Royal Academy, Northern Ireland; The Bluecoat School, Nottingham; Bretton Woods School, Peterborough; Eccles C of E School, Salford; Our Lady of Mount Carmel High, Salford; Ludlow C of E School, Salop; St Richard Gwyn R.C. School, South Glam; Headlands School, Wilts.

Some of the revision questions on pages 169–294 have been reproduced from past examination papers, as cited in the text. Copyright in these questions is held by the examination boards, and the publishers would like to thank the Midland Examining Group (MEG), Northern Examinations and Assessment Board (NEAB), Northern Ireland Council for the Curriculum, Examinations and Assessment (CCEA), Southern Examining Group (SEG), London Examinations, a division of Edexcel Foundation, and the Welsh Joint Education Committee (WJEC) for permission to reproduce this material. The answers supplied to these questions are, however, the responsibility of the authors.

CONTENTS

1

EXTENDING NUMBER SYSTEMS

This chapter is about:

- using rules of indices for integers and fractions
- expressing roots and reciprocals in index form
- calculations in standard form with and without a calculator
- rational numbers as terminating or recurring decimals
- converting recurring decimals to fractions
- rational and irrational numbers
- simplifying expressions involving surds.

Powers, roots and indices

DISCUSSION POINT

- Why does $b^3 \times b^5 = b^8$?
- What values for a, b, c, d would fit the pattern in this table?

x	−3	−2	−1	0	1	2	3	4
2^x	d	c	b	a	2	4	8	16

- What is 2^{-5}? How is it related to 2^5?
- What values would fit the pattern here?

x	−3	−2	−1	0	1	2	3	4
5^x					5	25	125	625

- What is the reciprocal of 5^4 as a power of 5?
- What is the value of $2^{-3} \times 2^5$?
- What are the values of these?

$2^2 \div 2^{-2}$ $5^3 \times 5^{-2}$ $5^2 \div 5^0$

$(2^3)^4$ $(5^2)^{-3}$ $\left(\frac{2}{5}\right)^{-1}$

These are two of the **laws of indices**.

- $a^m \times a^n = a^{m+n}$
- $a^m \div a^n = a^{m-n}$

If these laws are followed, these results can be deduced.

- $a^0 = 1$
- $a^{-n} = \dfrac{1}{a^n}$
- $(a^3)^2 = a^3 \times a^3 = a^6$
- $(a^3)^{-2} = \dfrac{1}{(a^3)^2} = \dfrac{1}{a^6} = a^{-6}$
- In general, $(a^m)^n = a^{mn}$

EXERCISE 1

1 Evaluate these expressions.

(a) 3^4 (b) 2^8 (c) $5^2 + 3^2$ (d) $(5+3)^2$

(e) 6^0 (f) 204^0 (g) 23^{-1} (h) 7^{-2}

(i) 10^{-3} (j) $(-2)^3$ (k) $(-2)^{-3}$ (l) $(-5)^0$

(m) $\left(\frac{1}{2}\right)^0$ (n) $\left(\frac{3}{4}\right)^{-2}$ (o) $\left(1\frac{1}{2}\right)^{-3}$ (p) $(-1)^{-1}$

2 Express each of these in the form 3^x.

(a) $3^2 \times 3^4$ (b) $3^5 \times 3^{-3}$ (c) $3^7 \div 3^2$ (d) $3^6 \div 3^{-3}$

(e) 27×3^2 (f) $\dfrac{3^3 \times 3^{-8}}{9}$ (g) $(3^4)^2$ (h) $(3^5)^{-2}$

3 Simplify these expressions.

(a) $x^4 \times x^5$ (b) $x^7 \times x^{-4}$ (c) $y^{-3} \times y^5$ (d) $5p^6 \times 2p^3$

(e) $\dfrac{15w^{12}}{3w^5}$ (f) $t^9 \div t^{-3}$ (g) $v^{-5} \div v^3$ (h) $\dfrac{r^{16} \times r^{-5}}{r^9}$

4 Write each of these as a power of one number.

(a) $2^x \times 2^y$ (b) $3^a \times 3^{2b}$ (c) $2^m \times 4^n$ (d) $9^x \times 27^y$

(e) $\sqrt{5^{2m}}$ (f) $\sqrt{7^{2p} \times 49^{2q}}$

5 Solve these equations.

(a) $2^x = 32$ (b) $5^x = 1$ (c) $7^x = \frac{1}{49}$ (d) $3^x = \frac{1}{27}$

(e) $\dfrac{2^x \times 2^5}{2^7} = 2^3$ (f) $10^x \times 10^3 = \frac{1}{100}$

DISCUSSION POINT

- What is the value of $2^{\frac{1}{2}} \times 2^{\frac{1}{2}}$?

  What does $2^{\frac{1}{2}}$ mean?

- Look at this pattern of powers of 2. Fill in the gaps.

x	0	$\frac{1}{2}$	1	$\frac{3}{2}$	2	$\frac{5}{2}$	3
2^x	1		2		4		8

- What meanings can be given to these?

  $5^{\frac{1}{2}}$ $\qquad$ $2^{\frac{1}{3}}$ $\qquad$ $3^{\frac{1}{4}}$ $\qquad$ $10^{\frac{1}{5}}$ $\qquad$ $2^{\frac{2}{3}}$ $\qquad$ $3^{0.75}$

- Is it true that $9^{-\frac{1}{2}} = \dfrac{1}{9^{\frac{1}{2}}}$?

- Explain why $8^{\frac{5}{3}} = 32$

$a^{\frac{1}{q}}$ means $\sqrt[q]{a}$ $\qquad\qquad\qquad\qquad$ $a^{\frac{p}{q}}$ means $(\sqrt[q]{a})^p$ or $\sqrt[q]{(a^p)}$

EXERCISE 2

1 Evaluate these expressions.

(a) $4^{\frac{1}{2}}$ $\qquad$ (b) $9^{-\frac{1}{2}}$ $\qquad$ (c) $16^{\frac{3}{2}}$ $\qquad$ (d) $100^{\frac{1}{2}}$

(e) $81^{\frac{1}{4}}$ $\qquad$ (f) $125^{\frac{2}{3}}$ $\qquad$ (g) $25^{-\frac{1}{2}}$ $\qquad$ (h) $144^{-\frac{1}{2}}$

(i) $27^{\frac{2}{3}}$ $\qquad$ (j) $8^{-\frac{1}{3}}$ $\qquad$ (k) $64^{-\frac{2}{3}}$ $\qquad$ (l) $(-8)^{\frac{2}{3}}$

2 Evaluate

(a) $(-27)^{-\frac{1}{3}}$ $\qquad$ (b) $\left(\frac{9}{16}\right)^{\frac{1}{2}}$ $\qquad$ (c) $\left(\frac{25}{9}\right)^{-\frac{3}{2}}$ $\qquad$ (d) $\left(3\frac{3}{8}\right)^{-\frac{2}{3}}$

(e) $\left(6\frac{1}{4}\right)^{\frac{3}{2}}$ $\qquad$ (f) $25^{-\frac{1}{2}} \times 125^{\frac{1}{3}}$ $\qquad$ (g) $16^{-\frac{3}{2}} \times 8^{\frac{4}{3}}$ $\qquad$ (h) $36^{\frac{3}{2}} \times 27^{-\frac{4}{3}}$

(i) $14^{-2} \div 49^{-\frac{3}{2}}$ $\qquad$ (j) $1000^{-\frac{2}{3}} \div 25^{-\frac{3}{2}}$

3 Evaluate

(a) $\sqrt[3]{4} \times 16^{\frac{1}{3}}$ $\qquad\qquad\qquad\qquad$ (b) $\sqrt{3} \times \sqrt{(3^3)}$

(c) $\sqrt[6]{3} \times \sqrt[4]{9} \times \sqrt[9]{27}$ $\qquad\qquad$ (d) $\dfrac{\sqrt[3]{25^4} \times \sqrt[3]{25}}{\sqrt[6]{25}}$

4 Express each of these as a power of x.

(a) $x^2 \times \sqrt{x}$ $\qquad$ (b) $\dfrac{x^3}{\sqrt{x}}$ $\qquad$ (c) $(\sqrt{x})^5$ $\qquad$ (d) $\dfrac{(\sqrt{x})^3}{x^5}$

5 Simplify these expressions.

(a) $\left(x^{\frac{4}{3}}\right)^6$ $\qquad$ (b) $\left(p^{\frac{3}{2}}\right)^4$ $\qquad$ (c) $\left(b^{\frac{2}{5}}\right)^{-10}$

6 (a) Find $8^{\frac{2}{3}}$ in two different ways.

(b) Write $a^{\frac{4}{3}}$ in two different ways.

(c) Write $p^{\frac{5}{2}}$ in two different ways.

7 Solve these equations.

(a) $25^x = 5$ (b) $27^x = 3$ (c) $8^x = \frac{1}{2}$ (d) $4^x = 8$

8 (a) If $x = 3$, arrange these in order of size, starting with the smallest.

$$x^2 \qquad\qquad x^{-2} \qquad\qquad x^{\frac{1}{2}} \qquad\qquad \frac{1}{x}$$

(b) Repeat part (a) with $x = \frac{1}{2}$.

(c) Repeat part (a) with $x = 1$.

9 (a) On the same axes, draw graphs of $y = 2^x$ and $y = x^2$ for x between 0 and 5.

(b) For which positive values of x is $x^2 > 2^x$?

Standard form without a calculator

DISCUSSION POINT

Check that you understand how these calculations can be done without a calculator.

$(3 \times 10^3) \times (2 \times 10^5) = 6 \times 10^8$ $(9 \times 10^{10}) \times (3 \times 10^3) = 2.7 \times 10^{14}$

$(8 \times 10^7) \div (4 \times 10^4) = 2 \times 10^3$ $(5 \times 10^8) \times (3 \times 10^{-4}) = 1.5 \times 10^5$

$(5 \times 10^8) \div (2 \times 10^{-4}) = 2.5 \times 10^{12}$ $\sqrt{9 \times 10^{10}} = 3 \times 10^5$

$(3 \times 10^{-6}) \div (5 \times 10^2) = 6 \times 10^{-9}$ $\sqrt{1.6 \times 10^5} = 4 \times 10^2$

$(6 \times 10^3) + (4 \times 10^5) = 4.06 \times 10^5$ $(2 \times 10^3) - (3 \times 10^1) = 1.97 \times 10^3$

$(8 \times 10^{12}) - (7 \times 10^{11}) = 7.3 \times 10^{12}$

EXERCISE 3

1 Evaluate these, giving your answer in standard form.

(a) $(2 \times 10^4) \times (4 \times 10^6)$ (b) $(3 \times 10^5) \times (4 \times 10^7)$

(c) $(3.5 \times 10^{-2}) \times (2 \times 10^6)$ (d) $(2.5 \times 10^6) \times (6 \times 10^{-8})$

(e) $(6.4 \times 10^{-7}) \times (2 \times 10^{-4})$ (f) $(3.2 \times 10^{15}) \times (4 \times 10^{-23})$

2 Evaluate these, giving your answer in standard form.

(a) $(4 \times 10^6) \div (2 \times 10^4)$ (b) $(7 \times 10^9) \div (2 \times 10^{13})$

(c) $(3 \times 10^5) \div (4 \times 10^2)$ (d) $(3.5 \times 10^{-2}) \div (2 \times 10^6)$

(e) $(6.4 \times 10^{-7}) \div (2 \times 10^{-4})$ (f) $(3.2 \times 10^{15}) \div (4 \times 10^{-23})$

3 Evaluate these, giving your answer in standard form.

(a) $\sqrt{4 \times 10^8}$ (b) $\sqrt{9 \times 10^{14}}$ (c) $\sqrt{2.5 \times 10^{15}}$ (d) $\sqrt{4 \times 10^{-8}}$

(e) $\sqrt{9 \times 10^{-16}}$ (f) $\sqrt{3.6 \times 10^{-17}}$

4 Evaluate these, giving your answer in standard form.

(a) $\sqrt{(3.2 \times 10^9) \times (2 \times 10^{16})}$ (b) $\sqrt{(1.96 \times 10^{15}) \div (4 \times 10^{23})}$

5 Evaluate these, giving your answer in standard form.

(a) $(4 \times 10^7) + (5 \times 10^7)$ (b) $(3 \times 10^5) + (8 \times 10^5)$

(c) $(6 \times 10^{-2}) - (4 \times 10^{-2})$ (d) $(6 \times 10^9) - (9 \times 10^8)$

(e) $(4.63 \times 10^5) - (4.23 \times 10^5)$ (f) $(4.543 \times 10^{-2}) - (4.539 \times 10^{-2})$

(g) $(2.3 \times 10^3) + (3.4 \times 10^4)$ (h) $(4.7 \times 10^{-2}) + (5.3 \times 10^2)$

(i) $(9.3 \times 10^5) - (3.9 \times 10^2)$ (j) $(4.2 \times 10^4) - (8.9 \times 10^{-1})$

Standard form with a calculator

EXERCISE 4

Use a calculator for these questions. Check that you know how to enter numbers in standard form efficiently.

1 Calculate these expressions. Give your answers in standard form, rounded to 2 significant figures.

(a) $(4.9 \times 10^3) \times (6.3 \times 10^6)$ (b) $(5.89 \times 10^{-3}) \times (7.28 \times 10^{-4})$

(c) $(7.38 \times 10^5) \div (9.47 \times 10^9)$ (d) $(6.59 \times 10^{-7}) \div (4.28 \times 10^{-10})$

(e) $\sqrt{(4.65 \times 10^5) \div (8.421 \times 10^{-2})}$ (f) $\sqrt{(3.6 \times 10^{12}) \div (1.8 \times 10^{-14})}$

2 Calculate these expressions. Give your answers in standard form, rounded to 2 significant figures.

(a) $(3.4 \times 10^4) + (5.7 \times 10^6)$ (b) $(3.4 \times 10^4) - (5.7 \times 10^6)$

(c) $(7.52 \times 10^7) + (4.6 \times 10^4)$ (d) $(7.52 \times 10^7) - (4.6 \times 10^4)$

(e) $(6.53 \times 10^{-4}) + (9.403 \times 10^{-5})$ (f) $(6.53 \times 10^{-4}) - (9.403 \times 10^{-5})$

An AU (Astronomical Unit) is about 150 million kilometres.

3 (a) The planet Pluto is 39.44 AU from the Sun.
Find the distance from the Sun in kilometres in standard form.
Round your answer to 2 significant figures.

(b) The planet Saturn is 1.429×10^9 km from the Sun.
Find this distance in AU, correct to 2 significant figures.

4 The total thickness of the pages in a dictionary is 5 cm.
The last page is numbered 1792. Find, in metres, the thickness of one page.
Give your answer in standard form to a sensible degree of accuracy.

5 The diameter of a molecule of oil is about 2×10^{-9} m.
Approximately how many layers of molecules of oil are there in an oil tank, if the depth of oil in the tank is 3.5 m? Give your answer in standard form.

There are 5280 feet in a mile.

6 Jason's hair grows at the rate of about $\frac{1}{2}$ inch per month.
Express this in miles per hour in standard form.

Writing rational numbers as terminating or recurring decimals

You have seen that when a fraction is turned into a decimal, the decimal either terminates or recurs (*Book 1*, Chapter 1, page 10).

Example

$\frac{5}{8} = 0.625$ terminates but $\frac{5}{11} = 0.454545...$ recurs.

A **rational number** is a number that can be written as $\frac{p}{q}$ where p and q are whole numbers or **integers**.

In other words, a rational number is a number which can be written as a fraction. Most of the numbers commonly used are rational numbers. Here are some examples.

$5\frac{1}{3}$ 17   −3   6.27

These are rational because

$5\frac{1}{3} = \frac{16}{3}$ $17 = \frac{17}{1}$ $-3 = \frac{-3}{1}$ $6.27 = \frac{627}{100}$

Later in this chapter (on page 11), it will be explained that many numbers are *not* rational.

DISCUSSION POINT

Convert these rational numbers to decimals.

$\frac{3}{25}$ $\frac{5}{6}$ $\frac{4}{9}$ $\frac{5}{16}$ $\frac{8}{13}$

Why must every rational number, when it is written in decimal form, either terminate or recur? In other words, why is it impossible for the decimal form of a fraction to have an endless string of digits which never repeats?

EXERCISE 5

1 Express $\frac{1}{7}$, $\frac{2}{7}$, $\frac{3}{7}$, $\frac{4}{7}$, $\frac{5}{7}$ and $\frac{6}{7}$ as recurring decimals.

2 Study your answers to Question 1. How are they related? How many different remainders occur when dividing by 7?

3 Copy and complete this wheel diagram, which summarises the answers to Question 1.

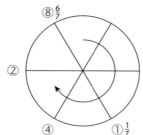

The number of digits in the repeating pattern is called the **period** of the recurring decimal.

4 (a) Find the recurring decimals for $\frac{1}{13}, \frac{2}{13}, \frac{3}{13} ..., \frac{12}{13}$.

  (b) Two wheels are needed to summarise the answers to part (a).
      Draw these wheels.

5 (a) Write $\frac{1}{11}, \frac{2}{11}, \frac{3}{11}, \frac{4}{11}, \frac{5}{11}, \frac{6}{11}, \frac{7}{11}, \frac{8}{11}, \frac{9}{11}$, and $\frac{10}{11}$ as recurring decimals.

  (b) How many wheels are needed to summarise the family of elevenths?
      Draw these wheels.

6 Express $\frac{1}{17}$ as a recurring decimal.
  Draw the wheel for the family of seventeenths.

Recurring decimals

Explore patterns in the decimal representation of sets of fractions, such as these:

◆ The fractions $\frac{1}{3}, \frac{1}{7}, \frac{1}{11}, \frac{1}{13}, \frac{1}{17}, ...$, which are of the form $\frac{1}{p}$ where p is a prime number

◆ The fractions $\frac{1}{6}, \frac{1}{14}, \frac{1}{22}, ...$, which are of the form $\frac{1}{2p}$

◆ The fractions $\frac{1}{11}, \frac{1}{111}, \frac{1}{1111}, ...$

◆ Fraction families such as $\frac{1}{14}, \frac{2}{14}, \frac{3}{14}, ...$

◆ Any other sets of fractions.

Converting recurring decimals to fractions

DISCUSSION POINT

The previous section was about this theorem.

Every rational number can be written as a terminating or a recurring decimal.

It is possible to show that the *converse* of this theorem is also true.

Every terminating or recurring decimal is a rational number.

• How is 0.42 converted back to $\frac{21}{50}$?

• How would you convert 3.142 into the form $\frac{\text{integer}}{\text{integer}}$?

• What about $5.\dot{4}$?

• The recurring decimal $x = 0.12121212...$ has a period of 2.
  What are $10x$, $100x$ and $1000x$?
  Which of them can you use to show that $x = \frac{12}{99}$?

• The recurring decimal $y = 0.247247247...$ has a period of 3.
  What are $10y$, $100y$ and $1000y$?
  Use one of them to help you to express y as a rational number.

EXERCISE 6

1 Convert these terminating decimals to rational numbers in their simplest form.

(a) 1.5   (b) 3.4   (c) –0.6   (d) –5.25

(e) 0.375   (f) –0.27

2 Write each of these as rational numbers in their simplest form.

(a) 7.625   (b) $9\frac{1}{5}$ (c) –4.32   (d) $5.\dot{6}$

(e) 23   (f) $7.\dot{0}\dot{9}$

3 Convert these recurring decimals to rational numbers in their simplest form.

(a) $0.\dot{7}$ (b) $8.\dot{2}$ (c) $0.\dot{2}8\dot{5}$ (d) $6.\dot{1}\dot{3}$

(e) $-4.4\dot{5}$ (f) $0.\dot{6}15\dot{8}$ (g) $0.61\dot{5}$ (h) $0.13\dot{6}$

(i) $0.21\dot{6}$ (j) $3.4\dot{5}\dot{6}$

Irrational numbers

There are some numbers which cannot be written as rational numbers, as this section will show. Such numbers are called **irrational numbers**.

EXERCISE 7

1 Look at this diagram.

(a) Use Pythagoras' theorem to show that the lengths of OB, OC, OD, OE are √2, √3, √4 = 2 and √5 respectively.

(b) On A4 paper, make an accurate drawing of this diagram using a scale of 5 cm to 1 unit.

(c) Use compasses to mark off the lengths OB, OC and OE along a number line drawn to the same scale as your diagram in part (b). From this, estimate the values of √2, √3 and √5.

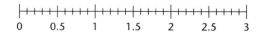

(d) Show that the squares of your answers to part (c) are not *exactly* 2, 3 and 5 respectively.

Later we shall see that no recurring decimal could be √2 either.

2 (a) An estimate of √2 is 1.414. Imagine multiplying 1.414 × 1.414.
What is the last digit of the answer?
How many digits would the answer have after the decimal point?
Why can the answer *not* be exactly 2?

(b) A better estimate of √2 is 1.4142.
What is the right-hand digit of 1.4142 × 1.4142?
Why can the answer *not* be exactly 2?

(c) Extend this idea to explain why no *terminating* decimal could be √2.

3 For thousands of years people have been trying to find accurate ways of calculating the circumference of a circle. They all knew it was 3-and-a-bit times the diameter – but how big was the 'bit'?
These are some of the values used by early civilisations.

Babylonian $\frac{25}{8}$

Egyptian $\frac{256}{81}$

Greek $\frac{22}{7}$ and $\frac{377}{120}$

Chinese $\frac{355}{113}$

Indian √10

(a) Use your calculator to find decimal forms for these values.

(b) Write down all the figures that your calculator gives for π.

(c) List the civilisations in order, starting with the one with the closest estimate to π and ending with the one with the least close estimate.

In the fifteenth century, π was known to 15 decimal places by Indian mathematicians. By the early eighteenth century, European mathematicians could use complicated formulae to find π to 100 decimal places.

4 This is π to 15 decimal places.
3.141592653589793
You clearly cannot get this value by measuring! People are still working to find more and more digits of π. Computers are used for this, of course. One way to calculate π is to draw polygons with more and more sides inside a circle.

(a) Here is a regular hexagon drawn inside a circle.
The perimeter of the hexagon is an approximation to the circumference of the circle.
What approximate value does this give for π?

(b) Vertices can be added to produce a regular dodecagon.
Pythagoras' theorem can then be used to find the lengths of the sides.
What approximate value does this give for π?

(c) Repeat this process as far as you want. A spreadsheet can be used.

Until about the sixth century BC, the Ancient Greek mathematicians
thought that positive rational numbers were enough for all their
arithmetical and geometrical problems. Then they were very disturbed to
find that this was not the case. They discovered that √2 is *not* a rational
number. Some historians say that it stopped them making progress in
arithmetical ideas and led to their great interest in geometrical
constructions. Exercise 8 is about proving that √2 is not rational.

EXERCISE 8

Providing a
mathematically
rigorous justification

1 $7^2 = 49$ and $15^2 = 225$. If you experiment with square odd numbers, the
answer always seems to be odd.
Every odd number can be expressed using the formula $2n + 1$, where n is
an integer. Use this to *prove* that the square of an odd number is always odd.

2 Prove that the square of an even number is always even.

3 To prove that √2 is *not* rational, we can show that it is impossible to write
√2 as a fraction, $\frac{p}{q}$, in its lowest terms (where p and q are integers).
Suppose it was possible.
   (a) Explain why p and q cannot both be even.
   (b) Show that $\sqrt{2} = \frac{p}{q}$ means that $2q^2 = p^2$.
   (c) Use part (b) and Question 1 to explain why p *must* be even.
   (d) p is even and so it can be written as $2r$ (r is an integer).
   Show that the equation connecting q and r is $q^2 = 2r^2$.
   (e) Use part (d) to explain why q *must* be even.
   (f) Explain why parts (c) and (e) mean that √2 cannot be written as a
   fraction $\frac{p}{q}$ in its lowest terms.

Question 3 proves that $\sqrt{2}$ cannot be written as a fraction in its lowest terms. This means that $\sqrt{2}$ cannot be written as a fraction *at all*, because *any* fraction can be cancelled to give a fraction in its lowest terms. So $\sqrt{2}$ is not a rational number. In other words, $\sqrt{2}$ is **irrational**.

In a very similar way, it can be proved that $\sqrt{3}$, $\sqrt{5}$ and so on are irrational numbers. So are $\sqrt[3]{2}$, $\sqrt[5]{7}$ and so on.

You need to know that these numbers are irrational:

- $\sqrt{2}$, $\sqrt{3}$, $\sqrt{5}$, and the square root of any other number which is not a square number
- $\sqrt[3]{2}$, $\sqrt[3]{3}$, $\sqrt[3]{4}$ and the cube root of any other number which is not a cube number
- $\sqrt[n]{x}$ if x and n are integers and x is not an exact nth power

You also need to know that π is irrational. (This is very hard to prove!)

This Discussion Point is only for you if you are interested in proving that some more numbers are irrational.

Providing a mathematically rigorous justification

DISCUSSION POINT

- How do we know that the number $0.101\,001\,000\,100\,001\,000\,001...$, where the number of zeros increases by one each time, is irrational?
- Use the method of Question 3 in Exercise 8 to prove that $\sqrt{3}$ cannot be written as a fraction in its lowest terms.
- Use the method of Question 3 in Exercise 8 to prove that $\sqrt[3]{5}$ cannot be written as a fraction in its lowest terms.

Surds

Surds are numbers containing irrational roots. These are examples of surds.

$$\sqrt{10} \qquad \sqrt{2}+3 \qquad 7\sqrt{5} \qquad \sqrt{12}-\sqrt{5} \qquad \sqrt{\tfrac{7}{6}} \qquad \sqrt[3]{11} \qquad \sqrt[3]{4}-\sqrt[3]{3}$$

When the exact answer to a question is a surd like one of these, mathematicians often find it helpful to leave it in this exact form rather than using a calculator to evaluate it.

DISCUSSION POINT

Use squaring to check which of these numbers are exactly equal.

$\sqrt{\tfrac{18}{25}}$	$\dfrac{\sqrt{2}}{3}$	$\sqrt{\tfrac{3}{8}}$	$6\sqrt{2}$
$\dfrac{\sqrt{6}}{4}$	$\sqrt{32}$	$\sqrt{125}$	$4\sqrt{2}$
$\dfrac{3}{2}$	$\sqrt{\tfrac{9}{4}}$	$3\sqrt{2}$	$\sqrt{3}\times\sqrt{6}$
$\dfrac{3\sqrt{2}}{5}$	$\sqrt{72}$	$\dfrac{\sqrt{50}-\sqrt{8}}{9}$	

1 Show that the length of AG in this cuboid is exactly $5\sqrt{14}$ cm.

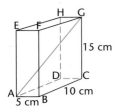

2 Look at these two triangles

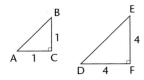

(a) Find AB in surd form.

(b) Find DE in surd form in two different ways (using Pythagoras' theorem *and* using similarity).
Check that the two ways give the same answer.

3 Look at these two triangles.

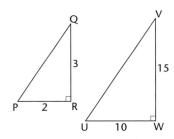

(a) Find PQ in surd form.

(b) Find UV in surd form in two different ways (using Pythagoras' theorem *and* using similarity).
Check that the two ways give the same answer.

4 Show, by squaring, that these are all equal.

$$\sqrt{\frac{5}{4}} \qquad \frac{\sqrt{5}}{2} \qquad \frac{5}{2\sqrt{5}}$$

5 Some of these expressions are equal to others. Find which are equal.

$$\frac{3}{\sqrt{3}} \qquad \frac{6}{\sqrt{2}} \qquad \sqrt{3} \qquad 2\sqrt{3} \qquad 3\sqrt{2} \qquad \frac{6}{\sqrt{3}}$$

6 Write each of these expressions as a multiple of √2 or √3 or √5.

    (a) $\sqrt{12}$ (b) $\sqrt{50}$ (c) $\sqrt{75}$ (d) $\sqrt{27}$

    (e) $\sqrt{48}$ (f) $\sqrt{800}$ (g) $\sqrt{8000}$ (h) $\sqrt{2700}$

7 Simplify each of these expressions.

    (a) $\sqrt{50} - \sqrt{8}$ (b) $\sqrt{75} + \sqrt{12}$ (c) $\sqrt{20} - \sqrt{5}$ (d) $\sqrt{12} \times \sqrt{27}$

    (e) $\sqrt{12} \times \sqrt{75}$ (f) $\sqrt{20} \times \sqrt{45}$

8 Simplify each of these expressions.

    (a) $\dfrac{\sqrt{18}}{\sqrt{2}}$ (b) $\dfrac{\sqrt{10}}{\sqrt{6}}$ (c) $\dfrac{\sqrt{10} - \sqrt{8}}{\sqrt{2}}$ (d) $\dfrac{\sqrt{27}}{\sqrt{6} + \sqrt{15}}$

For Question 9, use the facts that √2 is about 1.414, √3 is about 1.732 and √5 is about 2.236.

9 (a) Using $\sqrt{32} = 4\sqrt{2}$, find an approximate value for $\sqrt{32}$.

    (b) Find an approximate value for these expressions.

        (i) $\sqrt{72}$ (ii) $\sqrt{50}$ (iii) $\sqrt{300}$ (iv) $\sqrt{45}$

        (v) $\sqrt{200}$ (vi) $\sqrt{2000}$

DISCUSSION POINT

Check that you understand how these are worked out.

- $\dfrac{\sqrt{18}}{\sqrt{2}} = \dfrac{\sqrt{18} \times \sqrt{2}}{\sqrt{2} \times \sqrt{2}} = \dfrac{6}{2} = 3$

- $\dfrac{5}{\sqrt{7}} = \dfrac{5 \times \sqrt{7}}{\sqrt{7} \times \sqrt{7}} = \dfrac{5\sqrt{7}}{7}$

- $(3 + 4\sqrt{2}) + (5 - 7\sqrt{2}) = 8 - 3\sqrt{2}$

- $(4 - \sqrt{5}) - (2 + 3\sqrt{5}) = 2 - 4\sqrt{5}$

- $(7 + \sqrt{2})(7 - \sqrt{2}) = 49 - 7\sqrt{2} + 7\sqrt{2} - 2 = 47$

- $(3 + \sqrt{2})(5 - \sqrt{7}) = 15 - 3\sqrt{7} + 5\sqrt{2} - \sqrt{14}$

- $(7 + \sqrt{5})^2 = 49 + 14\sqrt{5} + 5 = 54 + 14\sqrt{5}$

Removing a surd from a denominator is called **rationalising**.

Example:

$\dfrac{3}{\sqrt{5}} = \dfrac{3 \times \sqrt{5}}{\sqrt{5} \times \sqrt{5}} = \dfrac{3\sqrt{5}}{5}$

EXERCISE 10

1 Rationalise the denominator in each of these expressions.

    (a) $\dfrac{5}{\sqrt{6}}$ (b) $\dfrac{2}{\sqrt{2}}$ (c) $\dfrac{12}{\sqrt{3}}$ (d) $\dfrac{10}{\sqrt{5}}$

2 Find the odd one out.

    $\dfrac{2}{3\sqrt{2}}$ $\dfrac{2}{\sqrt{3}}$ $\dfrac{\sqrt{2}}{3}$ $\dfrac{20}{30\sqrt{2}}$ $\dfrac{12}{9\sqrt{8}}$

3 Simplify these expressions.

(a) $(5 + 3\sqrt{2}) + (3 - \sqrt{2})$ (b) $(2\sqrt{3} - 4) + (6\sqrt{3} + 7)$

(c) $(5 + 3\sqrt{2}) - (3 - \sqrt{2})$ (d) $(2\sqrt{3} - 4) - (6\sqrt{3} + 7)$

(e) $(5 + 3\sqrt{2})(3 - \sqrt{2})$ (f) $(2\sqrt{3} - 4)(6\sqrt{3} + 7)$

(g) $(2 + \sqrt{5})(5 + 3\sqrt{2})$ (h) $(2 + \sqrt{5})(2 - \sqrt{5})$

(i) $(4 + \sqrt{3})^2$ (j) $(3 - \sqrt{7})^2$

(k) $(3\sqrt{2} - 5)^2$

4 Find the value of x in each of these equations.

(a) $(3 + 5\sqrt{2}) + x = 8 + 12\sqrt{2}$ (b) $(3 + 5\sqrt{2}) + x = 8$

(c) $(7 - 3\sqrt{5}) - x = 10 + 6\sqrt{5}$ (d) $(3 + \sqrt{2})(3 - x) = 7$

5 In this equation, x and y are integers. Find their values.
$(2 + \sqrt{3})(5 + \sqrt{x}) = 16 + y\sqrt{3}$

6 (a) Multiply out $(\sqrt{2} + \sqrt{3})^2$. Use your answer to decide whether $\sqrt{2} + \sqrt{3}$ is greater or less than $\sqrt{2 + 3}$.

(b) Is $\sqrt{a} + \sqrt{b}$ greater or less than $\sqrt{a + b}$?

7 If $a = \sqrt{10} - 2$, show that $a^2 + 4a = 6$.

8 If $x = \dfrac{1 + \sqrt{5}}{2}$, find x^2 and show that $x^2 = x + 1$.

Justifying a generalisation

DISCUSSION POINT

Sometimes a surd is more difficult to remove from the denominator.
You can use the difference of two squares.

Rationalise the denominator in each of these.

$$\frac{5}{\sqrt{3} + 1} \qquad \frac{5 + \sqrt{2}}{5 - \sqrt{2}}$$

EXERCISE 11

1 Rationalise the denominator in each of these expressions.

(a) $\dfrac{6}{\sqrt{2} - 1}$ (b) $\dfrac{5}{3 + \sqrt{2}}$ (c) $\dfrac{\sqrt{3} + 2}{\sqrt{2} + 3}$ (d) $\dfrac{3 - 2\sqrt{2}}{3 + 2\sqrt{2}}$

2 Simplify each of these expressions.

(a) $\dfrac{4}{\sqrt{5} - 1} - \dfrac{4}{\sqrt{5} + 1}$ (b) $\dfrac{3 + \sqrt{7}}{3 - \sqrt{7}} + \dfrac{3 - \sqrt{7}}{3 + \sqrt{7}}$

3 Find the odd one out.

$$\frac{4}{\sqrt{6} - 2} \qquad 2\sqrt{6} + 4 \qquad \frac{2\sqrt{2}}{\sqrt{3} - 1} + \frac{2\sqrt{2}}{\sqrt{3} + 1} + 4 \qquad \frac{4}{\sqrt{6} + 2}$$

More practice with manipulating surds and rationalising denominators is provided on pages 52, 117 and 163.

The real numbers

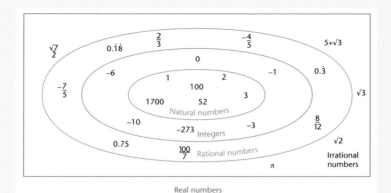

Real numbers

The first kind of numbers you learnt about were the counting numbers or natural numbers used by the earliest civilisations.

Natural numbers: 1, 2, 3, 4, …,

When measuring temperature or when finding an answer to 6 − 6 or 5 − 8, for example, we need zero and the negative numbers. These, together with the positive numbers, are called the integers. Seventh-century Hindu mathematicians had the rules now used for working with these.

Integers: …, −4, −3, −2, −1, 0, 1, 2, 3, …

Sharing out, and division generally, needs fractions or rational numbers, which can be positive or negative (or zero). Egyptian hieroglyphic inscriptions show the use of reciprocals; the Ancient Greeks used ratios in their geometry.

Some rational numbers: $\frac{2}{3}$, $-\frac{4}{5}$, 4

The irrational numbers are also needed for calculations on the circle, for Pythagoras' Theorem, for trigonometry, for solving $(x + 1)^2 = 7$, and so on. The Hindus accepted these as proper numbers, unlike the Ancient Greeks.

Some irrational numbers: $\sqrt{2}$, $3\sqrt{5}$, $\sqrt{7} - \sqrt{3}$, $\sqrt[3]{3}$, π

The notation we use today took time to develop. For example, +, − and √ were only adopted in the early sixteenth century.

It took until the nineteenth century to become clear about the idea that the rationals and the irrationals together make a continuous 'number line'; in other words, that they are interleaved with no gaps, making the real numbers.

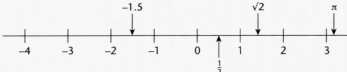

Every number you have met so far has its place on this number line.

- What positive number added to $3 + 2\sqrt{7}$ makes the answer rational?
- What number subtracted from $4 - 3\sqrt{2}$ makes the answer rational?
- What number multiplied by $7 + 2\sqrt{5}$ makes the answer rational?

EXERCISE 12

1 **(a)** Show the positions of each of these on the same number line.

-4 -0.45 $\sqrt{7}$ $\sqrt{2}$ $\sqrt{2} + 1$ $\frac{4}{3}$ $\sqrt{2} - 1$ $\frac{8}{4}$ π 2π

(b) Show the positions of the numbers in part (a) on a copy of this diagram.

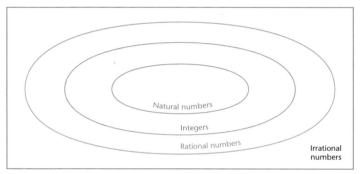

Real numbers

2 Find a possible number for x in each of these expressions.

(a) $(3 + 2\sqrt{3}) + x$ is rational   **(b)** $(5 + 2\sqrt{2}) + x$ is a multiple of $\sqrt{2}$

(c) $(6 + 3\sqrt{5}) - x$ is rational   **(d)** $\sqrt{5} \times x$ is rational

(e) $(2 + 4\sqrt{3}) \times x$ is rational   **(f)** $\sqrt{7} \times x = 21$

(g) $\dfrac{\sqrt{45}}{x} = \sqrt{5}$

3 Which of these numbers are rational? Which are irrational?

$\dfrac{4\pi}{\pi}$ $\dfrac{3\pi}{2}$ $\dfrac{\sqrt{18}}{\sqrt{2}}$ $\dfrac{\sqrt{3}}{\sqrt{18}}$ 0.45 $0.454\,5454...$

4 **(a)** x and y are different rational numbers. $x + y$ is an integer.
Give an example for x and y.

(b) x and y are different irrational numbers. Give an example to make
(i) $x + y$ a rational   **(ii)** $x - y$ a rational   **(iii)** $x \times y$ a rational
(iv) $x \div y$ an integer   **(v)** $x \div y$ an irrational

5 **(a)** Can the sum of two rational numbers be irrational?

(b) Can the product of two rational numbers be irrational?

(c) Can the square of a rational number be irrational?

(d) Can the square of an irrational number be irrational?

6 (a) Use your calculator to check that $1.4142 < \sqrt{2} < 1.4143$.

(b) Write inequalities like the one in part (a) for $\sqrt{3}$ and $\sqrt{5}$.

7 (a) Write down three irrational numbers that are between 3 and 5.

(b) Write down three irrational numbers that are between $\sqrt{3}$ and $\sqrt{5}$.

8 The Fibonacci sequence starts 1, 1, 2, 3, 5, 8, 13, 21, ...

(a) Find the next four terms of this sequence.

(b) Find the ratios of successive terms for the first 12 terms, i.e. $\frac{1}{1} = 1$, $\frac{2}{1} = 2$, $\frac{3}{2} = 1.5$, $\frac{5}{3} = $ etc.

(c) The sequence of answers in part (b) gets closer and closer to the irrational number $\frac{1 + \sqrt{5}}{2}$.

Which answers are greater than this irrational number? Which are less?

DISCUSSION POINT

- What type of number is required to solve each of these equations?

$$x + 14 = 35 \qquad x + 23 = 8 \qquad 3x = 7 \qquad x^2 = 4 \qquad x^2 = 11 \qquad (x + 1)^2 = 7$$

- Why are the real numbers no help for solving the equation $x^2 = -4$?

Sixteenth-century European mathematicians began to realise that it was useful to assume that there *were* answers to equations such as $x^2 = -4$. They called these **imaginary numbers** or 'numeri ficti'.

Now mathematicians write $\sqrt{-1}$ as **i** (some physicists use **j** instead) and $\sqrt{-4}$ can be written as 2i. Mathematicians, electrical engineers and people doing aerodynamics for example, work with **complex numbers** like 4 + 5i. These are 'two-dimensional' numbers, and physicists also use four-dimensional and eight-dimensional numbers: quaternions and octonions.

Who knows where our expanding knowledge will take us?!

CHAPTER SUMMARY

Rules of indices

> You need to be able to use these results and to work with numbers in standard form without the help of a calculator.

Rule	Example	Rule	Example
$a^m \times a^n = a^{m+n}$	$5^5 \times 5^{-9} = 5^{-4}$	$a^{-n} = \frac{1}{a^n}$	$2^{-3} = \frac{1}{8}$
$a^m \div a^n = a^{m-n}$	$7^2 \div 7^{-4} = 7^6$	$(a^m)^n = a^{mn}$	$(3^5)^2 = 3^{10}$
$a^0 = 1$	$4^0 = 1$	$a^{\frac{p}{q}} = (\sqrt[q]{a})^p = \sqrt[q]{a^p}$	$27^{\frac{2}{3}} = (27^{\frac{1}{3}})^2 = 3^2 = 9$

Types of number

Natural numbers (counting numbers): 1, 2, 3, 4, ...

Integers: ..., −4, −3, −2, −1, 0, 1, 2, 3, 4, ...

Rational numbers are all the numbers that can be written as $\dfrac{\text{integer}}{\text{integer}}$.
E.g. $\frac{2}{3}$, $-\frac{8}{5}$
Rational numbers include the integers (e.g. $3 = \frac{6}{2}$).

Irrational numbers are numbers that *cannot* be written as $\dfrac{\text{integer}}{\text{integer}}$.
E.g. π, $\sqrt{2}$, $2\sqrt{3} - 5$, $\sqrt[3]{7}$

Real numbers are all the numbers which are represented by points on the number line. They include rational and irrational numbers.

Terminating and recurring decimals

All rational numbers can be expressed as terminating or recurring decimals. Fractions in which the denominator contains only powers of 2 and 5 produce decimals which terminate.

$\frac{5}{8} = 0.625$ $\qquad\qquad$ $\frac{37}{100} = 0.37$ $\qquad\qquad$ $\frac{9}{25} = 0.36$

All other fractions produce recurring decimals.

$\frac{2}{3} = 0.\dot{6}$ $\qquad\qquad$ $\frac{3}{7} = 0.\dot{4}2857\dot{1}$ $\qquad\qquad$ $\frac{7}{12} = 0.58\dot{3}$

Turning a recurring decimal into a fraction

Example: What is $0.\dot{1}\dot{2}$ as a fraction?

$$x = 0.12121212...$$
$$100x = 12.12121212... \text{ (multiply by } 10^2 = 100 \text{, because the period is 2)}$$

Subtract: $99x = 12$
So: $\qquad x = \frac{12}{99} = \frac{4}{33}$
So, $0.\dot{1}\dot{2} = \frac{4}{33}$.

To turn the recurring decimal $0.\dot{3}8461\dot{5}$ into a fraction, you multiply by 10^6.
To turn the recurring decimal $0.34\dot{0}\dot{5}$ into a fraction, you multiply by 10^3.

Calculating with surds

$\sqrt{ab} = \sqrt{a} \times \sqrt{b}$

$\sqrt{\dfrac{a}{b}} = \dfrac{\sqrt{a}}{\sqrt{b}}$

But $\sqrt{a} + \sqrt{b} \neq \sqrt{a + b}$

and $\sqrt{a} - \sqrt{b} \neq \sqrt{a - b}$

Rationalising the denominator

E.g. $\dfrac{3}{\sqrt{5}} = \dfrac{3 \times \sqrt{5}}{\sqrt{5} \times \sqrt{5}} = \dfrac{3\sqrt{5}}{5}$

TRANSFORMATIONS AND VECTORS

Nelson GCSE Maths   TRANSFORMATIONS AND VECTORS (HIGHER)

This chapter is about:

- transformations: reflection, rotation, translation, enlargement (including with a negative scale factor)

- constructions involving reflection and rotation, using ruler and compasses

- combinations of transformations

- proofs using congruence and similarity

- combining vectors

- using vectors to solve problems.

Revisiting transformations

▶ Resource Sheet B: *Transformations*

EXERCISE 1

1 (a) Plot the hexagon with vertices A(2, 1), B(2, –2), C(5, –3), D(7, 0), E(7, 3) and F(5, 3).
   Plot the line $y = x$.
   (b) Reflect ABCDEF in the mirror line $y = x$, labelling the image A′B′C′D′E′F′.
   (c) If the point with coordinates (p, q) is reflected in $y = x$, what are the coordinates of the image?

Draw axes like these on squared paper for Question 1.

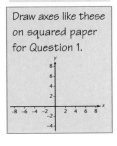

2 (a) Plot the quadrilateral with vertices E(5, 0), F(2, 1), G(1, 3) and H(4, 4).
   (b) Rotate EFGH through 180° about (–1, 2) as centre, labelling the image $E_1F_1G_1H_1$.
   (c) Rotate EFGH through 90° clockwise about (–1, 2) as centre, labelling the image $E_2F_2G_2H_2$.
   (d) What single transformation maps $E_1F_1G_1H_1$ on to $E_2F_2G_2H_2$?
   (e) Add a fourth quadrilateral to the diagram, so that the whole has rotational symmetry of order 4.

Draw axes like these on squared paper for Question 2.

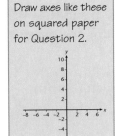

3 (a) Plot the triangle with vertices P(2, –1), Q(3, – 4) and R(1, –3).

(b) Translate PQR by $\binom{0}{3}$, labelling the image $P_1Q_1R_1$.

(c) Translate PQR by $\binom{-4}{3}$, labelling the image $P_2Q_2R_2$.

(d) What single transformation maps $P_2Q_2R_2$ on to $P_1Q_1R_1$?

(e) What transformation maps $P_1Q_1R_1$ back to PQR?

(f) What transformation maps $P_2Q_2R_2$ back to PQR?

4 In this diagram, the reflection in $y = x$ maps Δ1 to Δ2.

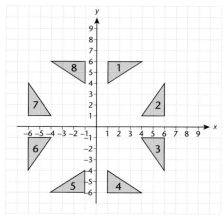

Which transformation maps

(a) Δ1 to Δ4? **(b)** Δ1 to Δ3? **(c)** Δ2 to Δ5? **(d)** Δ5 to Δ2?

(e) Δ6 to Δ5? **(f)** Δ7 to Δ2? **(g)** Δ8 to Δ7? **(h)** Δ8 to Δ6?

5 Find the images of the points (6, 2), (–3, 4), (–2, – 4) and (p, q) under these transformations.

(a) Reflection in the x-axis

(b) Reflection in the y-axis

(c) Reflection in the line $y = x$

(d) Reflection in the line $y = -x$

(e) Rotation of 180° about the origin

(f) Anticlockwise rotation of 90° about the origin

(g) Translation of $\binom{-4}{3}$

6 (a) Plot the quadrilateral with vertices at E(5, 0), F(2, 1), G(1, 3) and H(4, 4).

(b) Enlarge EFGH by scale factor 3 with centre (0, 0), labelling the image $E_1F_1G_1H_1$.

(c) Mark J(3, 2) inside EFGH, and its image J_1 inside $E_1F_1G_1H_1$.

(d) What is the image of (p, q) after enlargement by scale factor 3 with centre the origin?

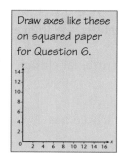

7 In each of these diagrams, the red shape is the image of the blue shape following an enlargement.

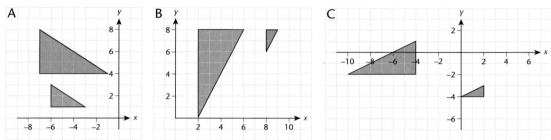

State the scale factor and centre for each enlargement.

Draw axes like these on squared paper for Question 8.

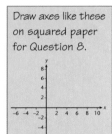

8 **(a)** Plot the triangle with vertices at P(2, –1), Q(3, –4), R(1, –3).
   (b) Enlarge PQR by scale factor 3 with centre (0, –4), labelling the image $P_1Q_1R_1$.
   (c) Enlarge PQR by scale factor 3 with centre (4, –5), labelling the image $P_2Q_2R_2$.
   (d) Describe the transformation that maps $P_1Q_1R_1$ on to $P_2Q_2R_2$.
   (e) Suppose enlargements with the same centres had been applied to triangle PQR, but this time both with scale factor 4.
   What transformation would map $P_1Q_1R_1$ on to $P_2Q_2R_2$ now?

For Question 9, you need Resource Sheet B: Transformations.

9 In each diagram on Resource Sheet B, the object is unshaded and the image is shaded. For each object, find the transformation that maps it on to its image.

Remember to give
• the centre and scale factor for an enlargement
• the mirror line equation for a reflection
• the centre, angle and direction for a rotation
• the vector for a translation.

10 Find as many different transformations as you can which map the blue square on to the red square.

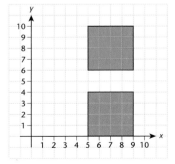

Nelson GCSE Maths   TRANSFORMATIONS AND VECTORS (HIGHER)

DISCUSSION POINT

Given a point and a line, it is sometimes useful
to be able to construct a line through the given
point and perpendicular to the given line.
Discuss how to do this, using ruler and compasses.

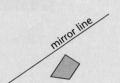

This picture shows an object and a mirror line.
Discuss how to construct the image, using ruler
and compasses.

This picture shows an object and its image after reflection.
Discuss how to construct the mirror line, using ruler and compasses.

This picture shows an object and a centre of rotation.
The rotation is to be 70° clockwise.
Discuss how to construct the image, using ruler and compasses.

Centre•
70°

This picture shows an object and its image after a rotation.
Discuss how to construct the centre of the rotation using ruler and
compasses, and, hence, to find the angle of rotation.

▶ Compasses
▶ Protractor
▶ Resource Sheet C:
   *Constructing
   reflections and
   rotations*

EXERCISE 2

1 On each of the diagrams A and B on Resource Sheet C, use ruler and
compasses to construct the image *after* reflection in the given mirror line.

2 On each of the diagrams C and D on Resource Sheet C, use ruler and
compasses to construct the mirror line.

3 On each of the diagrams E and F on Resource Sheet C, use ruler,
compasses and protractor to construct the image after rotation about the
given centres and through the given angle.

4 On each of the diagrams G and H on Resource Sheet C, use ruler and
compasses to construct the centre of rotation. State the angle of rotation.

Combining reflections and rotations

DISCUSSION POINT

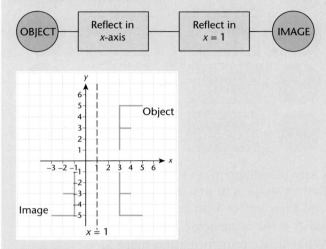

What *single* transformation is equivalent to this combination of transformations?

Nelson GCSE Maths TRANSFORMATIONS AND VECTORS (HIGHER)

EXERCISE 3

► Resource Sheet A: *Isometric dot*

1 (a) Draw the triangle with vertices A(3, 1), B(4, 4) and C(6, 2) on squared paper.

(b) Reflect triangle ABC in the mirror line $y = -1$, labelling the image triangle $A_1B_1C_1$.

(c) Reflect triangle $A_1B_1C_1$ in the mirror line $x = 2$, labelling the image triangle $A_2B_2C_2$.

(d) What single transformation maps triangle ABC on to triangle $A_2B_2C_2$?

Draw axes like these on squared paper for Question 1.

2 (a) Draw the triangle with vertices A(3, 1), B(4, 4) and C(6, 2).

(b) Reflect triangle ABC in the x-axis, labelling the image triangle $A_1B_1C_1$.

(c) Reflect triangle $A_1B_1C_1$ in $x = -2$, labelling the image triangle $A_2B_2C_2$.

(d) What single transformation maps triangle ABC on to triangle $A_2B_2C_2$?

Draw axes like these on squared paper for Question 2.

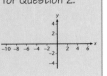

3 Find by experiment the single transformation that is equivalent to this combination.

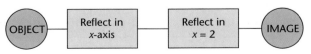

4 Find a single transformation equivalent to each of these combinations.

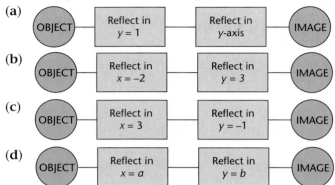

(a) OBJECT — Reflect in $y = 1$ — Reflect in y-axis — IMAGE

(b) OBJECT — Reflect in $x = -2$ — Reflect in $y = 3$ — IMAGE

(c) OBJECT — Reflect in $x = 3$ — Reflect in $y = -1$ — IMAGE

(d) OBJECT — Reflect in $x = a$ — Reflect in $y = b$ — IMAGE

5 (a) Copy this diagram on to isometric dot paper.
Reflect shape S in line m to get S_1
and then reflect S_1 in line n to get S_2.

(b) What is the acute angle between lines m and n?

(c) What single transformation maps S
to S_2 directly?

(d) How is this transformation connected to
the angle found in part (b)?

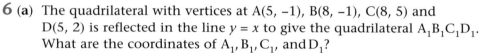

6 (a) The quadrilateral with vertices at A(5, –1), B(8, –1), C(8, 5) and
D(5, 2) is reflected in the line $y = x$ to give the quadrilateral $A_1B_1C_1D_1$.
What are the coordinates of $A_1, B_1, C_1,$ and D_1?

(b) What is the image of (p, q) after reflection in $y = x$?

(c) $A_1B_1C_1D_1$ is reflected in the x-axis to give $A_2B_2C_2D_2$.
What are the coordinates of $A_2, B_2, C_2,$ and D_2?

(d) What is the image of (p, q) after both these transformations?

(e) What single transformation is equivalent to these two transformations?

7 Find the single transformation equivalent to each of these combinations.

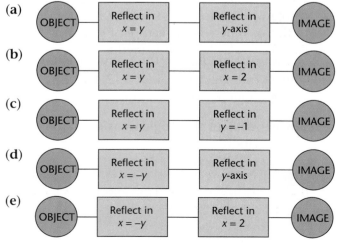

(a) OBJECT — Reflect in $x = y$ — Reflect in y-axis — IMAGE

(b) OBJECT — Reflect in $x = y$ — Reflect in $x = 2$ — IMAGE

(c) OBJECT — Reflect in $x = y$ — Reflect in $y = -1$ — IMAGE

(d) OBJECT — Reflect in $x = -y$ — Reflect in y-axis — IMAGE

(e) OBJECT — Reflect in $x = -y$ — Reflect in $x = 2$ — IMAGE

(f)

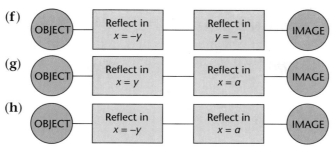

(g)

(h)

8 When point P is reflected in line *l*, the image point is P_1.
When point P_1 is reflected in line *m*, the image point is P_2.
The angle between XP and *l* is *u*.
The angle between XP_2 and *m* is *v*.

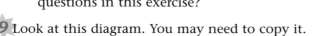

(a) Explain why the angle between *l* and *m* is *u* + *v*.

(b) Express angle PXP_2 in terms of *u* and *v*.

(c) How does this result relate to your answers to earlier questions in this exercise?

9 Look at this diagram. You may need to copy it.

(a) A rotation through 180° transforms flag 1 to flag 2.
Where is the centre of rotation?

(b) Flag 1 can also be transformed to flag 2 by two successive reflections.

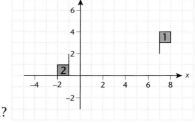

   (i)   If the mirror line of the first reflection is *x* = 3, what is the mirror line of the second reflection?

   (ii) If the mirror line of the first reflection is *y* = *x* – 1, what is the mirror line of the second reflection?

   (iii) Make a general statement about pairs of reflections which produce the same rotation.

10 Look at this diagram. You may need to copy it.

(a) A rotation through 90° transforms flag 3 to flag 4. Where is the centre of rotation?

(b) Flag 3 can also be transformed to flag 4 by two successive reflections.

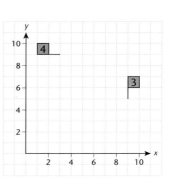

   (i)   If the mirror line of the first reflection is *y* = *x*, what is the mirror line of the second reflection?

   (ii) If the mirror line of the first reflection is *y* = 4, what is the mirror line of the second reflection?

   (iii) Make a general statement about pairs of reflections which produce the same rotation.

DISCUSSION POINT

In this diagram, the blue F has been reflected to the red F and the red F has been reflected to the orange F.

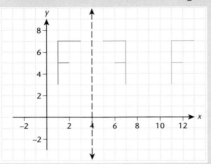

This describes the successive reflections.

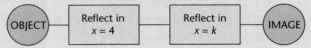

- What is the value of *k*?
- What single transformation is equivalent to this combination of reflections?

Look at this frieze pattern. Imagine it continuing for ever in both directions.

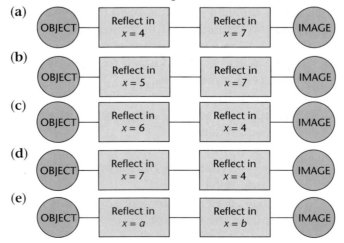

How could it be produced using just the two mirror lines, *m* and *n*?

In this exercise and in Exercise 5, you might need to experiment by drawing diagrams. You could use the F shape in the DISCUSSION POINT above.

EXERCISE 4

1 What transformation is equivalent to each of these?

(a)

OBJECT — Reflect in *x* = 4 — Reflect in *x* = 7 — IMAGE

(b)

OBJECT — Reflect in *x* = 5 — Reflect in *x* = 7 — IMAGE

(c)

OBJECT — Reflect in *x* = 6 — Reflect in *x* = 4 — IMAGE

(d)

OBJECT — Reflect in *x* = 7 — Reflect in *x* = 4 — IMAGE

(e)

OBJECT — Reflect in *x* = *a* — Reflect in *x* = *b* — IMAGE

2 What transformation is equivalent to each of these?

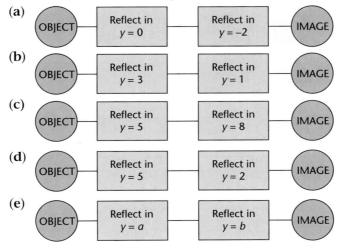

(a) OBJECT — Reflect in $y = 0$ — Reflect in $y = -2$ — IMAGE

(b) OBJECT — Reflect in $y = 3$ — Reflect in $y = 1$ — IMAGE

(c) OBJECT — Reflect in $y = 5$ — Reflect in $y = 8$ — IMAGE

(d) OBJECT — Reflect in $y = 5$ — Reflect in $y = 2$ — IMAGE

(e) OBJECT — Reflect in $y = a$ — Reflect in $y = b$ — IMAGE

3 What transformation is equivalent to each of these?

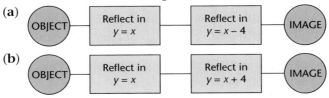

(a) OBJECT — Reflect in $y = x$ — Reflect in $y = x - 4$ — IMAGE

(b) OBJECT — Reflect in $y = x$ — Reflect in $y = x + 4$ — IMAGE

EXERCISE 5

1 What transformation is equivalent to each of these?

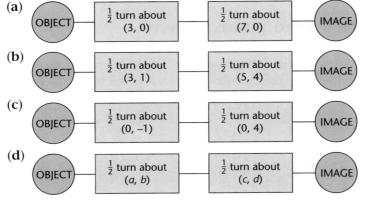

(a) OBJECT — $\frac{1}{2}$ turn about $(3, 0)$ — $\frac{1}{2}$ turn about $(7, 0)$ — IMAGE

(b) OBJECT — $\frac{1}{2}$ turn about $(3, 1)$ — $\frac{1}{2}$ turn about $(5, 4)$ — IMAGE

(c) OBJECT — $\frac{1}{2}$ turn about $(0, -1)$ — $\frac{1}{2}$ turn about $(0, 4)$ — IMAGE

(d) OBJECT — $\frac{1}{2}$ turn about (a, b) — $\frac{1}{2}$ turn about (c, d) — IMAGE

2 What transformation is equivalent to each of these?

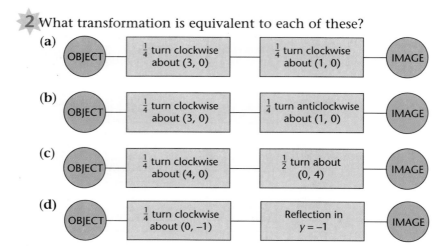

(a) OBJECT — $\frac{1}{4}$ turn clockwise about (3, 0) — $\frac{1}{4}$ turn clockwise about (1, 0) — IMAGE

(b) OBJECT — $\frac{1}{4}$ turn clockwise about (3, 0) — $\frac{1}{4}$ turn anticlockwise about (1, 0) — IMAGE

(c) OBJECT — $\frac{1}{4}$ turn clockwise about (4, 0) — $\frac{1}{2}$ turn about (0, 4) — IMAGE

(d) OBJECT — $\frac{1}{4}$ turn clockwise about (0, –1) — Reflection in $y = -1$ — IMAGE

3 What single transformation is equivalent to a combination of two $\frac{1}{4}$ turns
    (a) about the same centre and in the same direction?
    (b) about the same centre and in opposite directions?
    (c) about different centres $(a, 0)$ and $(b, 0)$ and in the same direction?
    (d) about different centres $(a, 0)$ and $(b, 0)$ and in opposite directions?

4 What single transformation is equivalent to a $\frac{1}{4}$ turn and $\frac{1}{2}$ turn
    (a) about the same centre?
    (b) about different centres $(p, 0)$ and $(0, p)$?

5 What single transformation is equivalent to
    (a) $\frac{1}{2}$ turn about $(p, 0)$ and reflection in $x = p$?
    (b) $\frac{1}{4}$ turn about $(p, 0)$ and reflection in $x = p$?

Making a generalisation

Negative enlargement

In both these diagrams, the red shape is the image of the blue shape after an enlargement with negative scale factor.

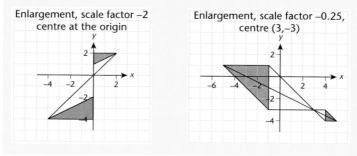

Enlargement, scale factor –2 centre at the origin

Enlargement, scale factor –0.25, centre (3,–3)

DISCUSSION POINT

In each of these pictures, the red shape is the image of the blue shape after enlargement.

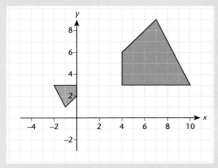 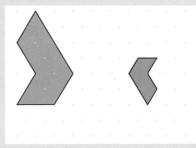

Where is the centre of enlargement?
What is the scale factor?

▶ Resource Sheet D: *Negative enlargements*

EXERCISE 6

1 The red shape is the image of the blue shape after enlargement.

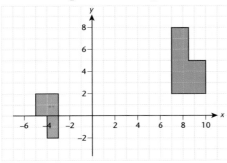

Where is the centre of enlargement?
What is the scale factor?

2 (a) Draw axes with $-10 \leq x \leq 10$ and $-12 \leq y \leq 16$.

(b) Draw a triangle with vertices E(–3, 2), F(0, 4) and G(1, –1).
Draw the image of the triangle after enlargement with centre the origin and scale factor –3.

(c) On the same set of axes, draw the quadrilateral with vertices P(0, –3), Q(3, 0), R(1, 2) and S(–1, –1).
Draw its image after the same enlargement as in part (a).

3 (a) Copy these axes and the quadrilateral labelled A on to squared paper.

(b) Enlarge A with scale factor –2 and with the origin as centre. Label the image B.

(c) Enlarge A with scale factor –3 and with the point (2, 3) as centre. Label the image C.

(d) Enlarge A with scale factor –0.5 and with the point (3, 0) as centre. Label the image D.

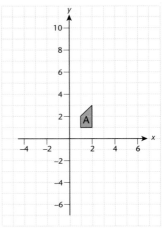

For Question 4, you need a copy of Resource Sheet D: Negative enlargements.

4 (a) Enlarge W with scale factor –2 about point A. Label the image X.

(b) Enlarge X with scale factor –1.5 about point B. Label the image Y.

(c) Enlarge Y with scale factor –$\frac{1}{3}$ about point C. Label the image Z.

(d) What is the scale factor of the enlargement that maps Z to W?

5 In each of these diagrams, the shape Q is the image of shape P after an enlargement. For each diagram, give the coordinates of the centre of enlargement and state the scale factor.

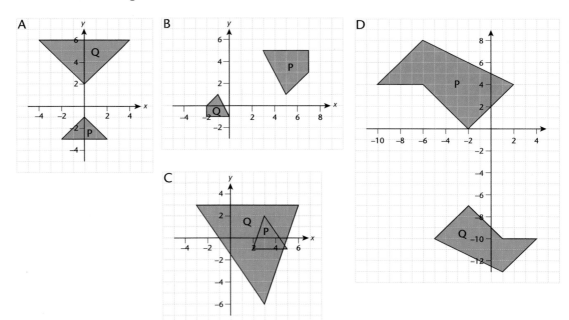

Combining enlargements

1 (a) Draw axes with $-2 \le x \le 10$ and $0 \le y \le 10$.
  (b) Draw the triangle with vertices A(6, 4), B(8, 6) and C(2, 8).
  (c) Draw the image of ABC after enlargement with centre (0, 0) and scale factor $\frac{1}{2}$. Label this $A_1B_1C_1$.
  (d) Draw the image of $A_1B_1C_1$ after enlargement with centre (2, –1) and scale factor 2. Label this $A_2B_2C_2$.
  (e) What single transformation maps ABC to $A_2B_2C_2$?

2 (a) Draw axes with $-10 \le x \le 4$ and $-6 \le y \le 12$.
  (b) Draw the triangle with vertices E(–3, 2), F(0, 4) and G(1, –1).
  (c) Draw the image of EFG after enlargement with centre (0, 1) and scale factor 3. Label this $E_1F_1G_1$.
  (d) Draw the image of $E_1F_1G_1$ after enlargement with centre (3, –2) and scale factor $\frac{1}{3}$. Label this $E_2F_2G_2$.
  (e) What single transformation maps EFG to $E_2F_2G_2$?

In Questions 3 to 6, you might need to experiment by drawing diagrams.

3 What single transformation is equivalent to each of these?
  (a) Enlargement with scale factor $\frac{1}{2}$ and centre (0, 0) followed by enlargement with scale factor –2 with the same centre
  (b) Enlargement with scale factor $\frac{1}{2}$ and centre (0, 0) followed by enlargement with scale factor –2 and centre (0, –2)

4 (a) What single transformation is equivalent to an enlargement with scale factor –2, followed by an enlargement with scale factor $-\frac{1}{2}$ with the same centre?
  (b) What single transformation is equivalent to an enlargement with scale factor k, followed by an enlargement with scale factor $\frac{1}{k}$ with the same centre?

Making a generalisation

5 (a) What single transformation is equivalent to an enlargement with scale factor 2, followed by an enlargement with scale factor –3 with the same centre?
  (b) What single transformation is equivalent to an enlargement with scale factor h, followed by an enlargement with scale factor k with the same centre?

6 (a) What single transformation is equivalent to an enlargement with scale factor 2, followed by an enlargement with scale factor –3 with different centres?
  (b) What single transformation is equivalent to an enlargement with scale factor h, followed by an enlargement with scale factor k with different centres? For what values of h and k is there an exception? What happens in this exceptional case?

Making a generalisation

Properties of transformations

DISCUSSION POINT

Often we apply transformations to objects. Really, a transformation transforms the whole plane.

When a plane is rotated or reflected the shapes of objects in the plane are not changed.

- When a plane is rotated, objects keep the same **orientation**.
- When it is reflected, their **orientation** is changed.

Discuss what is meant by **orientation**.

Discuss and complete this table.

Transformation	Objects and images			Corresponding edges of objects and images parallel?	Fixed points?
	congruent?	same orientation?	same area?		
Rotation	Yes	Yes			
Reflection	Yes	No			
Translation					
Enlargement					

Making a generalisation

EXERCISE 8

1 State which points are fixed after each of these transformations of the plane.
  (a) Reflection in $y = x$
  (b) Rotation about $(-2, -1)$
  (c) Translation by $\left(\begin{smallmatrix} 3 \\ -2 \end{smallmatrix}\right)$
  (d) Enlargement with scale factor -3, centre $(0, 0)$
  (e) Enlargement with scale factor $\frac{1}{2}$, centre $(2, 4)$
  (f) Reflection in $y = x + 1$ followed by reflection in the y-axis
  (g) $\frac{1}{2}$ turn rotation about the origin followed by translation by $\left(\begin{smallmatrix} 2 \\ 4 \end{smallmatrix}\right)$

2 A polygon has a smallest angle of 40°.
  Say what the smallest angle of its image will be after each of the transformations in Question 1.

3 A polygon has a perimeter of 20 cm.
  Say what the perimeter of its image will be after each of the transformations in Question 1.

4 A polygon has an area of 50 cm².
  Say what the area of its image will be after each of the transformations in Question 1.

Matrices and transformations

You know that, for example, reflection in the x-axis transforms the point (x, y) to the point $(x, -y)$.

This can be expressed like this:

$$\begin{pmatrix} x_1 \\ y_1 \end{pmatrix} = \begin{pmatrix} 1 & 0 \\ 0 & -1 \end{pmatrix}\begin{pmatrix} x \\ y \end{pmatrix} = \begin{pmatrix} x \\ -y \end{pmatrix}$$

$\begin{pmatrix} 1 & 0 \\ 0 & -1 \end{pmatrix}$ is called a matrix.

Matrix multiplication works in such a way that $\begin{pmatrix} 1 & 0 \\ 0 & -1 \end{pmatrix}\begin{pmatrix} x \\ y \end{pmatrix} = \begin{pmatrix} x \\ -y \end{pmatrix}$

So, $\begin{pmatrix} 1 & 0 \\ 0 & -1 \end{pmatrix}$ describes reflection in the x-axis.

♦ Investigate the relationship between transformations and matrices.

♦ Include in this investigation finding out about matrix multiplication.

♦ You might want to include in your investigation, not only reflections, rotations, translations and enlargements, but also stretches and shears.

Congruent triangles

Examining
generalisations

DISCUSSION POINT

You might have met these ideas before in the COURSEWORK OPPORTUNITY on page 261 of *Book 1*.

A triangle has three angles and three sides. The sizes of the angles and the lengths of the sides provide six facts about a triangle. Usually, knowing just three of these facts about a triangle 'fixes' the triangle.

For example, knowing the lengths of the three sides fixes the triangle.

• What other sets of three facts about the angles and sides of a triangle fix it?

• Which sets of three facts do *not* fix it? Explain why this is so.

If a set of facts which fixes a triangle is *the same* for two triangles, this proves that the triangles are congruent.

Nelson GCSE Maths   TRANSFORMATIONS AND VECTORS (HIGHER)

EXERCISE 9

1 These two triangles are congruent.

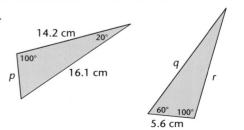

Find the values of p, q and r.

2 Two students constructed a triangle from this data.
AB = 8.4 cm, ∠BAC = 50°, BC = 7.6 cm
Draw diagrams to show that they might have constructed different triangles.

3 Each of these pairs of triangles are congruent.

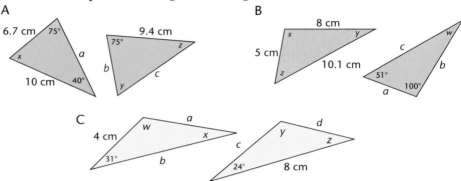

For each pair, state the size of any sides and angles which you can deduce from the congruence.

4 In triangle ABC, sides AB and AC are equal in length.
D is the mid-point of BC. Draw a sketch and prove that triangles ABD and ACD are congruent. Deduce that the base angles of an isosceles triangle are equal.

5 ABCD is a square. The lines BP and DQ are parallel.
Prove that triangles ABP and CDQ are congruent.

6 ABCD is a rectangle. Parallel lines through A and C meet diagonal BD at H and K.

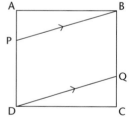

Prove that triangles ABH and CDK are congruent.
Deduce that AHCK is a parallelogram.

7 ABCD is a quadrilateral. Its diagonals bisect each other at E. (In other words, AE = EC and BE = ED.)

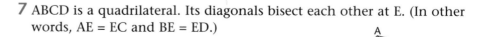

Use congruent triangles to prove that the opposite sides of the quadrilateral ABCD are parallel.

8 ABC and ADE are two congruent isosceles triangles.
Prove that triangles ABD and ACE are congruent.
Deduce that BD = CE.

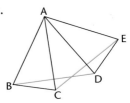

9 ABC is a triangle. BCD, ACE and ABF are equilateral triangles.

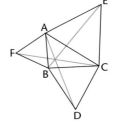

Use congruent triangles to prove that
the lengths AD, BE and CF are equal.

Similarity

Two shapes are similar if they are exactly the same shape, even though
they may be different sizes. It is important to understand that the use of
this word in mathematics is more precise than in everyday language.

Shapes that are related by enlargement are similar.

DISCUSSION POINT
• How can you tell that these triangles are similar?

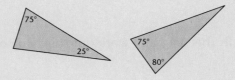

• These triangles are similar. Their equal angles are indicated.

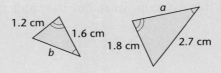

What are the values of *a* and *b*?

EXERCISE 10

1 (a) Show that these two rectangles are similar.

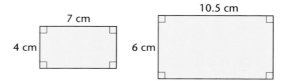

(b) Show that these two rectangles are *not* similar.

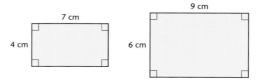

2 (a) Explain how you know that these two triangles are similar.
(b) Calculate the value of *d*.

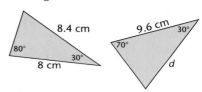

3 The larger of these triangles can be obtained from the smaller by an enlargement.
  (a) What is the scale factor of the enlargement?
  (b) Work out the values of *a* and *b*.

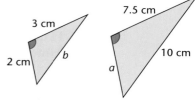

4 In this diagram, work out the value of *x*.

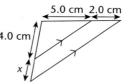

5 In this diagram, work out the value of *y*.

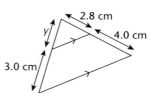

6 In this diagram, work out the value of *d*.

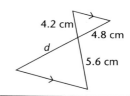

7 In this diagram, work out the value of x.

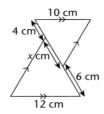

8 Look at this diagram.
  (a) Prove that triangles AED and ABC are similar.
  (b) Which angle is equal to $\angle ABC$?

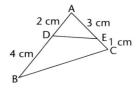

9 This diagram shows a regular pentagon with three of its diagonals.
  (a) Prove that ABCF is a rhombus.
  (b) Prove that triangles EFD and ACF are similar.
  (c) Prove that $d(d - 1) = 1$.
  (d) Use trial and improvement to find the length of each diagonal, correct to 2 decimal places.

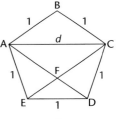

10 (a) In this diagram, Q is the mid-point of PR.
  (i) Use similarity to prove that RT = 2QU.
  (ii) Prove that S is the mid-point of RT.
  (iii) How many of triangle PQU will fit inside triangle PRT?

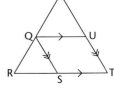

  (b) In this diagram, CB = 3BA.
  (i) Use similarity to prove that CE = 4BF.
  (ii) Prove that ED:EC = 1:4.
  (iii) How many of triangle ABF will fit inside triangle ACE?

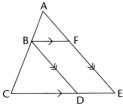

11 You may already know that by folding A3 paper in half you can make two A4 sheets. You may also know that the A3 and A4 rectangles are similar.
  (a) Use the fact that the rectangles are similar to write down an equation for a.
  (b) Solve the equation to find a.

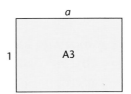

Combining vectors

DISCUSSION POINT

In this diagram, the blue octagon can
be translated to the green one by vector
u and the green octagon can then be
translated to the red one byvector **v**.
Or the blue one can betranslated straight
to the red one by vector **w**.

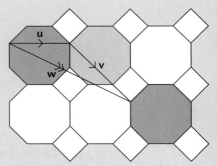

We can write **w = u + v**.

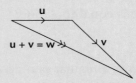

The addition of two vectors
is defined by using an
addition triangle.

As you have seen earlier in this chapter, vectors are often written using
columns of numbers. Here is the addition triangle for adding the
vectors $\mathbf{y} = \begin{pmatrix} 2 \\ 3 \end{pmatrix}$ and $\mathbf{z} = \begin{pmatrix} 5 \\ 2 \end{pmatrix}$.

- How can vectors given as columns of numbers be
  added without drawing an addition triangle?

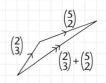

The addition triangle can also be used to subtract vectors. There are two
ways of doing this. Discuss them.

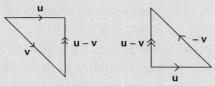

- Draw the addition triangle for **y – z**.
- What do you think 2**y**, 3**z** and –4**y** mean?
- Draw addition triangles for 3**y** + 2**z** and **z** – 2**y**.

In this exercise,
vectors are defined
as shown here.

$\mathbf{r} = \begin{pmatrix} 8 \\ -2 \end{pmatrix}$ $\mathbf{s} = \begin{pmatrix} 14 \\ -8 \end{pmatrix}$

$\mathbf{t} = \begin{pmatrix} -9 \\ -6 \end{pmatrix}$ $\mathbf{u} = \begin{pmatrix} 3 \\ 2 \end{pmatrix}$

$\mathbf{v} = \begin{pmatrix} 5 \\ 1 \end{pmatrix}$ $\mathbf{w} = \begin{pmatrix} 4 \\ -1 \end{pmatrix}$

$\mathbf{x} = \begin{pmatrix} -7 \\ 4 \end{pmatrix}$ $\mathbf{y} = \begin{pmatrix} -5 \\ -6 \end{pmatrix}$

$\mathbf{z} = \begin{pmatrix} -4 \\ 5 \end{pmatrix}$

EXERCISE 11

1 Which of the vectors **r, s, t, u, v, w, x, y** and **z** are parallel?

2 (a) Draw addition triangles for **u + v** and **v + u**.

   (b) Draw addition triangles for **w + x** and **x + w**.

   (c) Comment on your answers.

Use squared paper for
Questions 2 to 6.

3 Draw addition triangles for $u - v$, $w - y$, $x - z$ and $s - r$.

4 (a) Draw diagrams to show $(u + v) + w$ and $u + (v + w)$.
   (b) Comment on your answers to part (a).
   (c) What is the value of $u + v + w$?

5 Draw addition triangles for $3u + x$, $2u - v$ and $3z - 2x$.

6 Find **a** in each of these equations.
   (a) $a + s = r$ **(b)** $2a + u = y$ **(c)** $x - a = z$ **(d)** $2w + 3a = 4v$

Velocity vectors

A pilot is trying to fly a plane due East at 300 km/h, but a wind from the South at 60 km/h is blowing it off course. What happens?

In 1 hour, the plane travels 300 km East, but is blown 60 km North by the wind.

So, it actually travels about 305 km on a bearing of 079°.

The **velocity** of an object measures both the speed of the object and its direction. Velocity is a vector. So, velocities can be added like vectors.

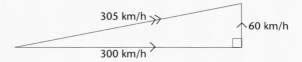

When velocities are added, the answer is called the **resultant velocity**. So, for the plane in the example above, the resultant velocity is 305 km/h on a bearing of 079°.

▷ Protractor

Exercise 12

1 A plane is travelling at 480 km/h due West.
Then a wind of 70 km/h blows from the South.
What is the resultant velocity?
Remember to give the speed and direction.

2 A plane is travelling at 250 km/h due North.
Then a wind of 60 km/h blows from the South East.
Find the resultant velocity.

> For each of the questions in this exercise, draw a labelled vector addition triangle with arrows.

If the triangle is
right-angled, solve
the problem using
Pythagoras'
theorem and
trigonometry.
Otherwise, draw the
triangle to scale:

3 A boat can travel at 5 m/s in still water.
It is being steered across a river at right angles
to the bank.
There is a current of 2 m/s.
(a) What is the resultant velocity?
(b) The river is 80 m wide.
How far downstream is the boat carried?

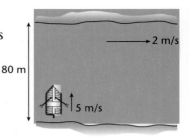

80 m

4 A boat is being steered across a river at right angles to the bank.
In still water, it can travel at 4 m/s. There is a current of 1.5 m/s.
(a) What is the resultant velocity?
(b) The river is 20 m wide.
How far is the boat carried downstream?

5 A boat is being steered across a river at 70° to the bank against the
current, as shown.
The speed of the boat in still water is 6 m/s
and the speed of the current is 1.5 m/s.
What is the resultant velocity?

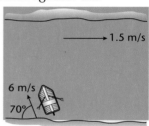

6 A plane can travel at 250 km/h in still air.
A wind of 50 km/h is blowing from the West.
The pilot wants to travel North.
In which direction should the pilot head the plane?
How fast will the plane travel relative to the ground?

7 A boat which can travel at 3 m/s on still water, is being used to cross a river
with a current of 1 m/s.
(a) In what direction must it be steered so as to land at the point directly
opposite its start?
(b) The river is 30 m wide.
How long does the crossing take?

8 A boat which can travel at 2.5 m/s in still water, is being used to cross a
river with a current of 1.5 m/s.
(a) In what direction must it be steered so as to land at the point directly
opposite its start?
(b) The river is 20 m wide. How long does the crossing take?

9 A plane can travel at 350 km/h in still air. A wind of 60 km/h is blowing
from the South East. The pilot wants to travel East.
(a) In which direction should the pilot head the plane?
(b) How fast will the plane travel relative to the ground?

10 A boat is travelling with a resultant velocity of 20 knots on a bearing of
048°. There is a current of 5 knots in the direction 076°.
What would the boat's velocity be in the absence of the current?

Force vectors

DISCUSSION POINT

Forces can also be added like vectors.

If forces of 12 newtons and 18 newtons are acting on an object at 120° to
each other, their resultant is found by adding them as vectors.

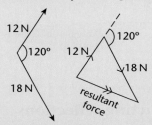

Draw this diagram to scale to find the resultant force.

EXERCISE 13

1 Forces of 8N and 6N are acting on an object at 90° to each other.
What is the size of the resultant force, and what angle does it
make with the force of 6N?

2 Forces of 10N and 7N act on an object as shown.
What is the size of the resultant force, and what angle does
it make with the force of 7N?

3 Forces of 9N and 3N act on an object as shown.
What is the size of the resultant force, and what angle
does it make with the force of 9N?

4 The resultant of these two forces is 13N.
  (a) Find X.
  (b) At what angle to the force of 5N does the resultant act?

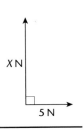

Constructing a perpendicular from a point P on to a line

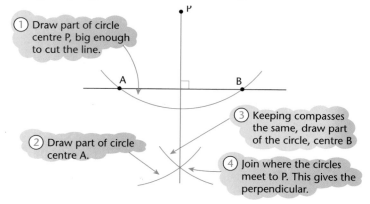

P

① Draw part of circle centre P, big enough to cut the line.

② Draw part of circle centre A.

③ Keeping compasses the same, draw part of the circle, centre B

④ Join where the circles meet to P. This gives the perpendicular.

A   B

Constructing reflections

To construct the image of this blue object in the mirror line, drop perpendiculars from each vertex on to the mirror line.
Then, extend the perpendiculars so that they meet the mirror line at their mid-points.

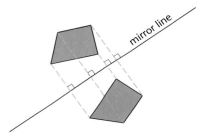

mirror line

Finding the centre of rotation

Join a pair of corresponding vertices (e.g. AA_1).
Construct the perpendicular bisector of AA_1 (see page 246 of the Revision Section).
Repeat for another pair of vertices.

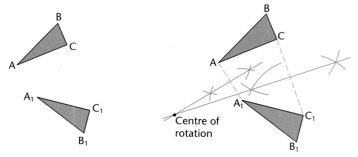

Centre of rotation

The centre of rotation is where these perpendicular bisectors intersect.

Negative enlargements

In each of these diagrams, the red shape is the image of the blue shape after a negative enlargement.

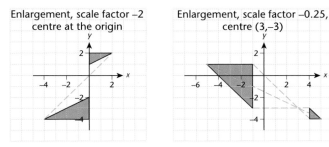

Finding the centre of enlargement

Join pairs of corresponding vertices. The lines meet at the centre of enlargement. This works for both positive and negative enlargements.

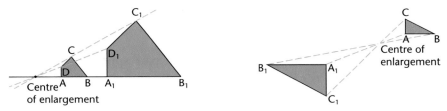

Combining transformations

Two reflections in intersecting lines,
AB and AC, meeting at angle θ,
are equivalent to a rotation of 2θ about A.

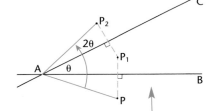

Two reflections in parallel lines produce a translation which is twice the distance between the lines and perpendicular to them.

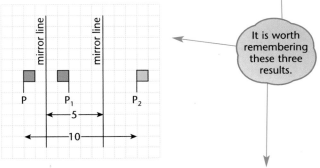

It is worth remembering these three results.

Two enlargements with the same centre and with scale factors h and k, are equivalent to an enlargement with the same centre and with scale factor hk. This works for both positive and negative scale factors.

Properties of transformations

This table summarises the effect of different types of transformation of the plane.

Transformation	Objects and images			Corresponding edges of objects and images parallel?	Fixed points?
	congruent?	same orientation?	same area?		
Rotation	Yes	Yes	Yes	Yes	One, centre of rotation
Reflection	Yes	No	Yes	Yes	All points on mirror line
Translation	Yes	Yes	Yes	Yes	None
Enlargement	No	Yes	No; $\times k^2$ where scale factor is k	Yes	One, centre of enlargement

Congruent triangles

Triangles are congruent if
- all three pairs of sides are equal
- two pairs of angles and a pair of corresponding sides are equal
- two pairs of sides are equal and the pair of angles between these sides are equal.

In general, two pairs of sides equal and a pair of corresponding angles *not* between these sides is insufficient to ensure congruence.

Here are two different triangles satisfying the same three conditions.

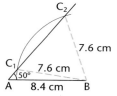

$AB = 8.4\,\text{cm}$
$\angle BAC = 50°$
$BC = 7.6\,\text{cm}$

However, two sides and a non-included right angle are sufficient to ensure congruence.

Similar triangles

A pair of triangles are similar when
- their angles are equal

- all three of the sides of one are the same ratio to the corresponding sides of the other (the ratio is the 'scale factor of the enlargement')

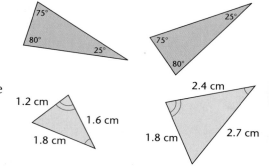

- two pairs of sides are in the same
  ratio and the included angles are equal.

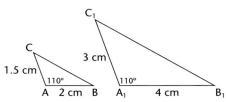

Combining vectors

The following are always true:

$\mathbf{u} + \mathbf{v} = \mathbf{v} + \mathbf{u}$ $(\mathbf{u} + \mathbf{v}) + \mathbf{w} = \mathbf{u} + (\mathbf{v} + \mathbf{w})$

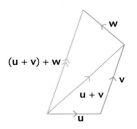

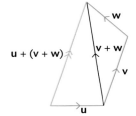

If $\mathbf{u} = \begin{pmatrix} 4 \\ 2 \end{pmatrix}$ and $\mathbf{v} = \begin{pmatrix} 3 \\ -5 \end{pmatrix}$ then $\mathbf{u} + \mathbf{v} = \begin{pmatrix} 7 \\ -3 \end{pmatrix}$ and $\mathbf{v} - \mathbf{u} = \begin{pmatrix} 3 \\ -5 \end{pmatrix} - \begin{pmatrix} 4 \\ 2 \end{pmatrix} = \begin{pmatrix} -1 \\ -7 \end{pmatrix}$

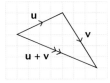

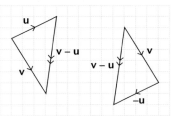

These results can be used to find resultant velocities and resultant forces.
This diagram shows what happens to a boat being steered across a river 80 m
wide at 5 m/s in a current of 2 m/s.

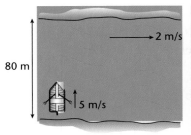

Velocity triangle	Distance triangle
2 m/s 68°	32 m 68°
5 m/s 5.4 m/s 68°	80 m 68°
Boat travels at 5.4 m/s at 68° to the downstream bank.	Boat ends up 32 m on the downstream opposite bank.

3 QUADRATIC EQUATIONS

This chapter is about:

- revision of factorising
- completing the square
- using completing the square to find greatest and least values and to draw graphs
- quadratic equations, solved by factorising, by completing the square and by the formula
- working with irrationals in the context of quadratic expressions
- solving problems using quadratic equations.

Factorising quadratic expressions

In *Book 1* on page 46, you learnt to factorise quadratic expressions. Exercise 1 is to remind you.

EXERCISE 1

1 Factorise these expressions.
   (a) $x^2 + 5x + 6$ **(b)** $x^2 - 5x + 6$ **(c)** $x^2 - 7x + 6$
   (d) $x^2 + 7x + 6$ **(e)** $x^2 - 5x - 6$ **(f)** $x^2 + x - 6$

2 Factorise these expressions.
   (a) $x^2 + 11x + 10$ **(b)** $x^2 - 11x + 10$ **(c)** $x^2 - 7x + 10$
   (d) $x^2 + 7x + 10$ **(e)** $x^2 - 3x - 10$ **(f)** $x^2 + 9x - 10$

3 Factorise these expressions.
   (a) $x^2 + 8x + 12$ **(b)** $x^2 - 7x + 12$ **(c)** $x^2 + 13x + 12$
   (d) $x^2 - x - 12$ **(e)** $x^2 + 11x - 12$ **(f)** $x^2 - 4x - 12$

4 Factorise these expressions.
   (a) $2x^2 + 7x + 3$ **(b)** $2x^2 - 5x + 3$ **(c)** $2x^2 + x - 3$
   (d) $2x^2 - 5x - 3$

5 Factorise these expressions.
   (a) $4x^2 - 9x + 5$ **(b)** $4x^2 + 21x + 5$ **(c)** $4x^2 - 12x + 5$
   (d) $4x^2 + 8x - 5$ **(e)** $4x^2 - x - 5$ **(f)** $4x^2 + 19x - 5$

6 Factorise these expressions.

(a) $x^2 + 2x + 1$ (b) $x^2 - 8x + 16$

(c) $x^2 + 10x + 25$ (d) $x^2 - 20x + 100$

7 In each of these, find the values of m and n.

(a) $x^2 + mx + 25 = (x + n)^2$ (b) $x^2 - 10x + m = (x - n)^2$

(c) $4x^2 - mx + 49 = (2x - n)^2$ (d) $9x^2 + 24x + m = (3x + n)^2$

<table>
<tr><td>For Question 8,
take out a common
factor first.</td></tr>
</table>

8 Factorise these expressions.

(a) $2x^2 + 16x + 32$ (b) $3x^2 - 36x + 108$

(c) $5x^2 + 80x + 320$ (d) $7x^2 - 42x + 63$

9 Factorise these expressions.

(a) $9x^2 - 3x - 2$ (b) $6x^2 + 13x + 6$

(c) $10x^2 - 31x + 15$ (d) $20x^2 - 144x - 45$

(e) $30x^2 - 61x + 30$ (f) $15x^2 - 32x - 60$

Completing the square

DISCUSSION POINT

Look at your answers to Question 6 in Exercise 1.

Each of the expressions is a perfect square.

In Question 8, each of the expressions is a multiple of a perfect square.

This is what happens when we square $(x + a)$.

$(x + a)^2 = x^2 + 2ax + a^2$ The constant a^2 is the square of half the coefficient of x.

In a number of mathematical contexts, it is useful to have a perfect square to factorise. Given a quadratic expression which is *not* a perfect square, it is often possible to think of it as a perfect square by adjusting the constant. This process is called **completing the square**.

The expression $x^2 + 6x$ is not a perfect square, but it would become a perfect square if 9 is added.

$x^2 + 6x = x^2 + 6x + 9 - 9$ Halve the coefficient of x ($6 \div 2 = 3$) and then
$= (x + 3)^2 - 9$ square it, ($3^2 = 9$).

Now try completing the square with these.

- $x^2 - 8x$ • $x^2 + 14x - 5$ • $x^2 - 10x + 12$
- $x^2 + 3x - 2$ • $2x^2 + 16x - 7$

EXERCISE 2

1 Complete the square for each of these expressions.

(a) $x^2 + 4x$ (b) $x^2 - 6x$ (c) $x^2 + 2x$

(d) $x^2 - 16x$ (e) $x^2 + 14x$ (f) $x^2 - 20x$

2 Complete the square for each of these expressions.

(a) $x^2 + 12x + 8$ (b) $x^2 - 18x + 20$ (c) $x^2 - 6x + 10$

(d) $x^2 + 10x + 30$ (e) $x^2 + 2x - 3$ (f) $x^2 - 8x - 7$

3 Complete the square for each of these expressions.

(a) $x^2 + 3x$ (b) $x^2 - 5x$ (c) $x^2 + x + 1$

(d) $x^2 - 7x - 3$ (e) $x^2 + 9x + 3.25$ (f) $x^2 - 11x - 6.75$

4 Complete the square for each of these expressions.

(a) $2x^2 + 12x$ (b) $3x^2 - 12x$ (c) $5x^2 + 10x + 3$

(d) $7x^2 - 70x + 50$ (e) $4x^2 + 56x - 5$ (f) $10x^2 - 20x + 17$

5 Complete the square for each of these expressions.

(a) $-x^2 - 2x$ (b) $-x^2 + 12x - 6$ (c) $-3x^2 - 18x$

(d) $2x^2 + 6x + 2$ (e) $3x^2 - 15x - 7$ (f) $-5x^2 + 15x + 3$

6 Sometimes, if the coefficient of x^2 is a perfect square, you can complete the square by 'spotting it', without taking out the coefficient of x^2 as a factor first.

Complete the square for each of these in any way you want.

(a) $4x^2 + 12x$ (b) $9x^2 - 30x$

(c) $16x^2 + 40x$ (d) $36x^2 - 60x$

Using 'completing the square'

DISCUSSION POINT

Consider the expression $x^2 - 6x + 12$.

- Put different values of x into this expression.
  What answers does this give you?
- Which values of x give a positive value?
- Which give a negative value?
- Prove your conclusions by completing the square.
- What is the *least* value of x this expression can have?

EXERCISE 3

1 Write down the least value each of these expressions can have.

(a) $(x - 7)^2 + 30$ (b) $(x + 9)^2 - 17$ (c) $2(x - 13)^2 + 15$

(d) $(x - 23)^2$ (e) $3(x - 7.5)^2 - 6.25$ (f) $5(x + 9.5)^2 + 8.75$

2 Find the greatest value each of these expressions can have.

(a) $8 - (x - 6)^2$ (b) $10 - x^2$ (c) $20 - 3(x + 5)^2$

(d) $-(x + 1)^2$ (e) $-2(x + 4)^2 - 19$ (f) $-13 - 13(x + 13)^2$

3 Complete the square for each of these expressions.
Hence, find the least value each expression can have.

(a) $x^2 + 2x + 4$ (b) $x^2 - 6x + 20$ (c) $x^2 - 4x + 1$

(d) $x^2 + 10x$ (e) $2x^2 + 16x - 15$ (f) $3x^2 - 30x + 80$

4 Complete the square for each of these expressions.
Hence, find the greatest value each expression can have.

(a) $-x^2 + 8x + 3$ (b) $-x^2 - 6x - 5$ (c) $12x - x^2$

(d) $3 - 4x - x^2$ (e) $-2x^2 - 20x - 12$ (f) $5 + 14x - 7x^2$

5 Which of these expressions are positive for *all* values of x?

(a) $x^2 - 4x + 5$ (b) $x^2 + 6x + 5$ (c) $x^2 + 20x$

(d) $350 + 100x - x^2$ (e) $x^2 + 8x + 16$ (f) $2x^2 - 12x + 20$

DISCUSSION POINT

- Draw a sketch graph for each of these equations.

$y = x^2$

$y = x^2 + 5$

$y = x^2 - 3$

$y = (x - 2)^2$

$y = (x + 3)^2 + 3$

What are the coordinates of the minimum point of each graph?

- Consider the equation $y = x^2 + 4x + 7$. Complete the square.
Hence sketch the graph of $y = x^2 + 4x + 7$.
What are the coordinates of the minimum point of this graph?

- Sketch the graph of $y = 4 - (x - 2)^2$

EXERCISE 4

1 Sketch the graphs of these equations.
State the coordinates of the minimum or maximum point.

(a) $y = (x - 3)^2 + 4$ (b) $y = (x + 4)^2 - 5$ (c) $y = 2(x - 1)^2 + 3$

(d) $y = -(x + 2)^2$ (e) $y = 5 - (x - 3)^2$ (f) $y = -2(x + 1)^2 - 6$

2 Sketch the graphs of these equations by completing the square.
State the coordinates of the minimum point.

(a) $y = x^2 + 4x + 1$ (b) $y = x^2 - 2x + 3$

(c) $y = x^2 - 8x - 3$ (d) $y = x^2 - 6x + 10$

3 Sketch the graphs of these equations by completing the square.
State the coordinates of the maximum point.

(a) $y = -x^2 + 6x + 5$ (b) $y = -x^2 + 4x - 3$

(c) $y = 6x - x^2$ (d) $y = -5 - 4x - x^2$

• At how many points does a quadratic graph meet the *x*-axis?
• How does knowing the coordinates of a minimum point or a maximum point help?

The number of points at which a graph meets the *x*-axis tells you the number of real solutions of the associated quadratic equation (see page 54).

Solving quadratic equations by factorising

In *Book 1* on page 232, you learnt how to solve quadratic equations by factorising. The method only works if the quadratic expression does factorise! Here is an example to remind you.

Solve $\qquad x^2 - 5x - 6 = 0$

$\qquad\qquad (x - 6)(x + 1) = 0$

Either $x - 6 = 0$ or $x + 1 = 0$.

Solutions are $x = 6$ and $x = -1$.

EXERCISE 5

1 Solve these quadratic equations by factorising.

(a) $x^2 - 3x + 2 = 0$ 　　　　　　(b) $x^2 + 5x = 0$

(c) $x^2 - 5x - 36 = 0$ 　　　　　(d) $x^2 + 6x + 9 = 0$

(e) $3x^2 + 4x + 1 = 0$ 　　　　　(f) $4x^2 + 4x + 1 = 0$

(g) $2x^2 + 5x + 2 = 0$ 　　　　　(h) $3x^2 - 10x + 3 = 0$

2 Solve these equations by factorising.

(a) $x^2 + 4 = 5x$ 　　　　　　　(b) $4x + 12 = x^2$

(c) $x + \dfrac{25}{x} = 10$ 　　　　　　(d) $x(x + 3) = 4$

(e) $x(6x - 23) = 35$ 　　　　　(f) $33x - \dfrac{20}{x} = 49$

(g) $x = \dfrac{11}{x - 10}$ 　　　　　　(h) $\dfrac{20}{x} - \dfrac{96}{x^2} = 1$

> In Question 2, you will need to rearrange the equations before you can factorise them.

3 Some of these quadratic equations can be solved by factorising. Some cannot. Solve them where possible.

(a) $x^2 + 37x + 36 = 0$ 　　　　(b) $x^2 - 35x + 36 = 0$

(c) $x^2 - 35x - 36 = 0$ 　　　　(d) $x^2 - 5x - 36 = 0$

(e) $x^2 + 12x - 36 = 0$ 　　　　(f) $x^2 - 12x + 36 = 0$

(g) $x^2 + 36x = 0$ 　　　　　　(h) $x^2 - 20x - 36 = 0$

Solving quadratic equations by completing the square

When quadratic equations do not factorise, we need to use another method to solve them. Methods discussed in *Book 1* were drawing graphs and using trial and improvement. Neither of these methods give exact solutions.

Sometimes the solution of a quadratic equation is straightforward, even though it does not factorise. Here is an example.

$x^2 - 6 = 0$

$\quad x^2 = 6$

$\quad x = \pm\sqrt{6}$

If we want to give a decimal approximation to the solutions, we can use a calculator.

The solutions are $x = 2.45$ and $x = -2.45$, correct to 2 decimal places.

The method just used can be adapted even when the equation is not so straightforward. Completing the square is used. This is explored next.

DISCUSSION POINT

- Consider this equation.

  $x^2 + 6x + 7 = 0$

  This equation does not factorise.

  Discuss how completing the square can be used to convert the equation to this.

  $(x + 3)^2 = 2$

  The two solutions can now be found. What are they?

- Now solve these equations by completing the square.

  $x^2 + 8x - 3 = 0$ $\qquad\qquad\qquad$ $2x^2 - 8x - 5 = 0$

In this exercise, you can leave your answers as surds. Or you can write the solutions as decimals, say, correct to 2 decimal places.

EXERCISE 6

1 Solve these quadratic equations by completing the square.

(a) $x^2 + 2x - 1 = 0$ $\qquad$ (b) $x^2 + 4x + 1 = 0$

(c) $x^2 - 6x + 3 = 0$ $\qquad$ (d) $x^2 - 8x - 5 = 0$

2 Solve these quadratic equations by completing the square.

(a) $x^2 - 3x - 5 = 0$ $\qquad$ (b) $x^2 + x - 1 = 0$

(c) $x^2 - 5x + 3 = 0$ $\qquad$ (d) $x^2 + 7x + 4 = 0$

3 These equations can be solved by factorising, but solve them by completing the square.

(a) $x^2 - 8x + 12 = 0$ $\qquad$ (b) $x^2 + 20x + 36 = 0$

(c) $x^2 - 22x - 75 = 0$ $\qquad$ (d) $x^2 + 14x - 72 = 0$

In Questions 4 and 5, you will need to rearrange the equations before you can complete the square.

4 Solve these quadratic equations by completing the square.

(a) $4x = x^2 + 2$

(b) $x^2 = 2x + 4$

(c) $x(x + 6) = 2$

(d) $x + \dfrac{10}{x} + 8 = 0$

5 Solve these equations.

(a) $x(x - 3) = 7$

(b) $5x - 2 = x^2$

(c) $x^2 + 7 = 18x$

(d) $\dfrac{100}{x} = x - 50$

6 Solve these equations.

(a) $2x^2 + 16x - 17 = 0$

(b) $3x^2 - 12x + 4 = 0$

(c) $5x^2 + 100x + 100 = 0$

(d) $2x^2 - 6x - 7 = 0$

EXERCISE 7

1 Solve these quadratic equations, either by factorising or by completing the square. For each equation, when you have found the two solutions, find their sum and their product.

(a) $x^2 + 9x + 14 = 0$

(b) $x^2 - 8x + 15 = 0$

(c) $x^2 + 5x - 36 = 0$

(d) $x^2 - 5x - 6 = 0$

2 Solve these quadratic equations by completing the square.
Leave your answers in surd form. For each equation, find the sum and the product of the two solutions.

(a) $x^2 - 12x + 10 = 0$

(b) $x^2 - 2x - 12 = 0$

(c) $x^2 + 6x + 4 = 0$

(d) $x^2 + 10x - 8 = 0$

Making a generalisation

3 (a) What patterns do you notice in your answers to Questions 1 and 2?

(b) Make up some equations of your own to provide further examples of the pattern.

(c) What happens if the coefficient of x is not 1?

The word real was explained in Chapter 1 on page 15.

4 Some of these equations have real solutions; some do not.
Complete the square and, then, solve the equations where possible.

(a) $x^2 + 6x + 7 = 0$

(b) $x^2 - 2x + 3 = 0$

(c) $x^2 + 4x + 5 = 0$

(d) $x^2 - 10x + 16 = 0$

(e) $x^2 + 10x + 34 = 0$

(f) $x^2 - 10x - 34 = 0$

5 Mathematicians often find it useful to find solutions to quadratic equations even when the solutions are not real. As explained in Chapter 1 (page 17), they write i for $\sqrt{-1}$. The numbers produced in this way are called **complex numbers**.

(a) Check that you understand that the equation $x^2 - 2x + 3 = 0$ has solutions $1 \pm i\sqrt{2}$.

(b) Write the solution to other equations in Question 4 as complex numbers.

The formula for solving quadratic equations

DISCUSSION POINT

Proving the formula for solving a quadratic equation

- How would you solve this equation by completing the square?
$3x^2 + 11x + 5 = 0$

- The method of completing the square can be applied to solving this general quadratic equation:

$ax^2 + bx + c = 0$

Follow the same process of completing the square to show that these are the solutions to this equation:

$$x = \frac{-b + \sqrt{(b^2 - 4ac)}}{2a} \text{ and } x = \frac{-b - \sqrt{(b^2 - 4ac)}}{2a}$$

This can also be written as:

$$x = \frac{-b \pm \sqrt{(b^2 - 4ac)}}{2a}$$

- Use this formula, with $a = 3$, $b = 11$ and $c = 5$, to check that it gives the same solutions to $3x^2 + 11x + 5 = 0$ as you obtained by completing the square.

EXERCISE 8

1 Solve these equations by using the formula.
Give your answers correct to 2 decimal places.

(a) $x^2 + 7x - 23 = 0$ (b) $x^2 - 19x + 38 = 0$

(c) $3x^2 - 11x - 5 = 0$ (d) $5x^2 + 13x + 7 = 0$

(e) $7x^2 - 22x + 13 = 0$ (f) $8x^2 + 9x - 19 = 0$

2 Solve these equations by using the formula.
Give your answers correct to 2 decimal places.

(a) $x(x + 9) = 17$ (b) $3x(2x - 7) = 19$

(c) $x(x - 8) = 23 - 2x(x + 5)$ (d) $3x + \frac{3}{x} = 13$

(e) $20x - 5 = 13x^2$ (f) $\frac{x}{7} - \frac{7}{x} = 1$

3 Sometimes it is difficult to spot the factors of a quadratic expression.
If so, you can use the formula to find the roots of the equation and then deduce the factors. Do this for these expressions.

(a) $x^2 - 51x + 144$ (b) $x^2 + 22x - 555$

(c) $x^2 + 66x + 1008$ (d) $20x^2 + 13x - 72$

(e) $200x^2 - 471x + 180$ (f) $72x^2 + 371x + 432$

4 The solutions of the equation $x^2 + 6x - 11 = 0$ can be written as $x = a + b\sqrt{5}$ and $x = a - b\sqrt{5}$ where a and b are integers. Find the values of a and b.

5 The solutions of the equation $5x^2 - 12x + 6 = 0$ can be written as $x = a + b\sqrt{6}$ and $x = a - b\sqrt{6}$ where a and b are rational numbers. Find the values of a and b.

6 (a) Use the formula to solve the equation $3x^2 - 9x + 5 = 0$.
   (b) By putting $y^2 = x$ and using your answer to part (a), find all the solutions of the equation $3y^4 - 9y^2 + 5 = 0$.

7 Find the real solutions of these equations, giving your answers correct to 2 decimal places where necessary.
   (a) $y^4 - 13y^2 + 36 = 0$ **(b)** $4y^4 - 101y^2 + 25 = 0$ **(c)** $x^4 - 3x^2 - 4 = 0$
   (d) $z^4 + 6z^2 + 8 = 0$ **(e)** $y^6 - 4y^3 + 3 = 0$ **(f)** $y^6 - y^3 - 6 = 0$
   (g) $z^4 - 6z^2 + 9 = 0$ **(h)** $x^6 + 10x^3 + 25 = 0$

8 Using your answers to Question 7, say at how many points the graph of each of these meets the x-axis.
   (a) $y = x^4 - 13x^2 + 36$ **(b)** $y = 4x^4 - 101x^2 + 25$ **(c)** $y = x^4 - 3x^2 - 4$
   (d) $y = x^4 + 6x^2 + 8$ **(e)** $y = x^6 - 4x^3 + 3$ **(f)** $y = x^6 - x^3 - 6$
   (g) $y = x^4 - 6x^2 + 9$ **(h)** $y = x^6 + 10x^3 + 25$

The number of solutions of a quadratic equation

Justifying a
generalisation

DISCUSSION POINT

You are given a quadratic equation. So you know the values of a, b and c to put into the formula.

• How can you use the formula to tell you whether the quadratic equation has real roots?

• How can you use the formula to tell you whether the equation has two roots or one root?

• How can you use the formula to tell you whether the equation has rational or irrational roots?

• If you put y equal to the left-hand side of the quadratic equation and draw a graph, what does the graph tell you about the roots of the equation?

Mathematicians are inclined to say that *all* quadratic equations have two roots. The roots are not always real; they are certainly not always rational. When a quadratic equation has one root, mathematicians will call this a *repeated* root (because when the quadratic expression is factorised, there is a repeated factor).

EXERCISE 9

1 Use the formula to find out which of these equations have *two* real roots, which have *one* real root and which have *no* real roots. *You do not need to find the roots.*

(a) $x^2 + 7x + 11 = 0$ (b) $3x^2 - 13x + 15 = 0$ (c) $9x^2 - 96x + 256 = 0$

(d) $8x^2 + 5x - 9 = 0$ (e) $13x^2 - 32x + 19 = 0$ (f) $8x^2 + 21x + 14 = 0$

2 Use the formula to find out which of these equations have *rational* roots, which have *irrational* roots and which have *no* real roots at all. (You do not need to find the roots.)

(a) $3x^2 + 13x + 12$ (b) $4x^2 - 21x + 16$ (c) $5x^2 + 24x + 16$

(d) $7x^2 - 26x + 15$ (e) $5x^2 + 25x + 18$ (f) $4x^2 - 17x + 19$

(g) $7x^2 - 20x + 17$ (h) $3x^2 - 20x + 12$ (i) $4x^2 - 12x - 7$

(j) $3x^2 + 8x - 9$ (k) $4x^2 - 7x - 5$ (l) $4x^2 + 15x - 4$

COURSEWORK OPPORTUNITY

Families of quadratics

Look at these quadratic expressions.

$x^2 + 2x + 6$ $x^2 + 3x + 6$ $x^2 + 4x + 6$ $x^2 + 5x + 6$ $x^2 + 6x + 6$

These are all members of the family of quadratic expressions of the form $x^2 + ax + 6$.

Explore this family.

♦ You could find greatest and least values.

♦ You could solve the quadratic equation when the expression is equated to zero.

♦ You could investigate the graphs.

♦ What is the same for all these expressions? What is different?

Explore other families of quadratic expressions in a similar way.

Problems involving quadratic equations

Each of the questions in Exercise 10 involves solving a quadratic equation. Some will factorise and others will not. Solve them in whatever way you like.

EXERCISE 10

1 A rectangle has one side 10 cm longer than the other.
The area of the rectangle is 100 cm².
Find the sides of the rectangle, correct to 2 decimal places.

2 Two numbers differ by 2. The squares of the numbers differ by 100.
Call the smaller number x.
Write down an equation for x, and solve it to find possible values for the two numbers.

3 Two numbers differ by 10. Their product is 95 more than their sum.
Call the smaller of the numbers x.
Write down an equation for x, and solve it to find possible values for
the two numbers.

4 A mother is 21 years older than her daughter.
They work out the product of their ages.
They also work out that, in 10 years time, the product of their ages will
have increased by 610.
Taking the age of the daughter now to be y years, find an equation for y.
Solve the equation to find the daughter's and mother's ages.

5 The dimensions of a rectangle are 5 cm and 7 cm.
A border of uniform width is drawn all round the rectangle to produce a
larger rectangle.
The total area of the border is 100 cm².
Find the width of the border, correct to 2 decimal places.

6 A parallelogram has an interior angle of 30°.
Its area is 100 cm² and its perimeter is 70 cm.
Find the lengths of its sides, correct to 1 decimal place.

7 The perimeter of a right-angled triangle is 10 cm.
Two of its sides differ in length by 2 cm.
Find all possible triangles satisfying these conditions.

8 The shape of a window is a rectangle with a semicircle on one of its sides.
The area of the window is 1 m² and the
total height of the window is 1 metre.
If r metres is the radius of the semicircle,
show that r satisfies this equation.
$(2 - \frac{\pi}{2}) r^2 - 2r + 1 = 0$
Hence find r. Find also the perimeter of the
window, correct to the nearest centimetre.

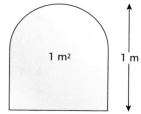

9 A golden rectangle is a rectangle which remains the same shape after a
square has been removed from it. So, rectangle B is similar to rectangle A.

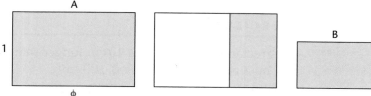

If the ratio of the sides of a golden rectangle is ϕ, show that ϕ satisfies
this equation.
$\phi(\phi - 1) = 1$
Hence find the value of ϕ, correct to 3 decimal places.

Nelson GCSE Maths   QUADRATIC EQUATIONS (HIGHER)

10 A man invests a sum of money in a savings account which pays a fixed rate of interest of r% at the end of each year. He makes no withdrawal for 2 years and finds that, after 2 years, the *total* increase in his savings is 12%. Show that r satisfies this equation.

$$0.0001r^2 + 0.02r - 0.12 = 0$$

Hence, find the rate of interest correct to the nearest 0.01 per cent.

DISCUSSION POINT

Another method of solving a quadratic equation is to use **iteration**.

To find one of the solutions of the quadratic equation $x^2 - 8x - 5 = 0$, the equation can be rearranged like this:

$$x^2 - 8x - 5 = 0$$
$$\Rightarrow \quad x(x - 8) = 5$$
$$\Rightarrow \quad x = \frac{5}{x - 8}$$

Now, define a sequence of numbers x_1, x_2, x_3, x_4, ... using this **iterative formula**.

$$x_{n+1} = \frac{5}{x_n - 8}$$

So, a number in the sequence (x_{n+1}) is found by subtracting 8 from the previous number in the sequence (x_n) and dividing 5 by your answer.

Suppose you start with the number 12. The next number in the sequence is

$$\frac{5}{12 - 8} = 1.25$$

- What are the next four numbers in this sequence? (If you have an ANS button on your calculator you will find it very useful here.)

This sequence rapidly approaches one of the solutions of the equation $x^2 - 8x - 5 = 0$. You can use it to find this solution correct to any desired degree of accuracy.

- Use it to find the solution correct to 3 decimal places. (You can check your solution by substituting it into the equation.)

- Show that another rearrangement of the equation leads to this iterative formula:

$$x_{n+1} = \frac{5}{x_n} + 8$$

- Use this rearrangement to find the other solution to the quadratic equation.

Different arrangements will produce different results. Some do not work at all. Others produce one or other of the solutions.

- Try different arrangements and see what happens.

- Now try solving other quadratic equations using iteration.

Completing the square

$x^2 + 6x = x^2 + 6x + 9 - 9$
$\qquad = (x + 3)^2 - 9$

> Halve the coefficient of x and square it.

$x^2 - 10x + 12 = x^2 - 10x + 25 - 25 + 12$
$\qquad\qquad = (x - 5)^2 - 13$

$2x^2 + 8x + 10 = 2(x^2 + 4x) + 10$

> Factorise first

$\qquad\qquad = 2(x + 2)^2 - 8 + 10$
$\qquad\qquad = 2(x + 2)^2 + 2$

Using 'completing the square'

Writing $x^2 - 10x + 12$ as $(x - 5)^2 - 13$ helps us to deduce that $x^2 - 10x + 12$ has a minimum value of -13 when $x = 5$.

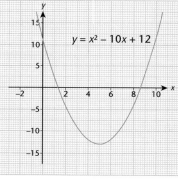

The graph of $y = x^2 - 10x + 12$ is a parabola (congruent to $y = x^2$) with a minimum point at $(5, -13)$.

From $2x^2 + 8x + 10 = 2(x + 2)^2 + 2$, we can deduce that $2x^2 + 8x + 10$ has a minimum value of 2 when $x = -2$.

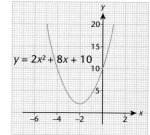

The graph of $y = 2x^2 + 8x + 10$ is congruent to the graph of $y = 2x^2$ and has a minimum point at $(-2, 2)$.

Solving equations by factorising

Example

$\qquad 2x^2 + 9x - 5 = 0$
$\Rightarrow (2x - 1)(x + 5) = 0$
$\Rightarrow \quad$ either $2x - 1 = 0$ or $x + 5 = 0$
$\Rightarrow \qquad\qquad\qquad x = \frac{1}{2}$ or $\qquad x = -5$

Equations may need to be rearranged before they can be factorised.

Example 1

$$x(x - 5) = 36$$
$$\Rightarrow x^2 - 5x - 36 = 0$$
$$\Rightarrow (x - 9)(x + 4) = 0$$
$$\Rightarrow \qquad x = 9$$
$$\text{or } x = -4$$

Example 2

$$x + \frac{25}{x} = 10$$
$$\Rightarrow \qquad x^2 + 25 = 10x$$
$$\Rightarrow \quad x^2 - 10x + 25 = 0$$
$$\Rightarrow \qquad (x - 5)^2 = 0$$
$$\Rightarrow \qquad x = 5$$

Solving quadratic equations by completing the square

Example

$$x^2 + 6x + 7 = 0$$

This equation does not factorise. So we complete the square.

$$x^2 + 6x + 9 - 2 = 0$$
$$(x + 3)^2 = 2$$

Now take the square root of both sides.

$$x + 3 = \pm\sqrt{2}$$

So the two solutions are $x = -3 + \sqrt{2}$ and $x = -3 - \sqrt{2}$.

These are the *exact* solutions. Decimal approximations can be found using a calculator to evaluate $\sqrt{2}$.

Solving quadratic equations by using the formula

If $ax^2 + bx + c = 0$ then $x = \dfrac{-b \pm \sqrt{(b^2 - 4ac)}}{2a}$

Example

$$3x^2 + 11x - 5 = 0$$

Here, $a = 3$, $b = 11$ and $c = -5$. So,

$$x = \frac{-11 \pm \sqrt{11^2 - (-60)}}{6}$$
$$\Rightarrow x = \frac{-11 \pm \sqrt{181}}{6}$$
$$\Rightarrow x = -4.08 \text{ or } x = 0.41 \text{ (to 2 decimal places)}$$

Roots of quadratic equations

Consider the equation $ax^2 + bx + c = 0$.

- If $b^2 - 4ac > 0$, this equation has two real roots and the graph of $y = ax^2 + bx + c$ crosses the x-axis twice.
- If $b^2 - 4ac$ is a perfect square, these roots are rational. Otherwise, they are irrational.
- If $b^2 - 4ac = 0$, the equation has one real root (sometimes called a repeated root, because, when the quadratic is factorised, it has a repeated factor). The graph of $y = ax^2 + bx + c = 0$ touches the x-axis.
- If $b^2 - 4ac < 0$, the equation does not have real roots (it does have two complex number roots). The graph of $y = ax^2 + bx + c$ does not meet the x-axis.

4

STATISTICS AND PROBABILITY

This chapter is about:

- counting systematically and counting populations
- sampling techniques
- random numbers
- using probability to solve problems
- designing and criticising questionnaires
- standard deviation of a grouped frequency distribution
- correlation and lines of best fit
- analysing and comparing sets of data.

Counting systematically

DISCUSSION POINT

In a normal set of dominoes, there are 28 dominoes. Here are four of them.

There is one domino for each pair of 'numbers', where the numbers range from 0 (blank) to 6 (six dots).
Can you explain why there are 28 dominoes, without listing them all?

In some sets of dominoes, the numbers are from 0 to 9.
How many dominoes are there in such sets?

EXERCISE 1

1 A game requires square tiles of this design.
   (a) Each of the triangles on each tile is to be coloured red, blue or yellow.
       One tile is needed for each possible way of colouring to produce a complete set. Here are two of the tiles in the set.
       How many tiles are there altogether?

(b) For a different game, the tiles are coloured red, blue, yellow and green.
How many tiles are there in a complete set of these tiles?

(c) Suppose the tiles are coloured using *n* colours.
How many tiles are there in a complete set?

For Questions 2 and 3, two tiles are different if one cannot be placed on top of the other so that they match exactly.

2 A different set of tiles consists of triangular tiles like these.

Each region of the tile is numbered using the numbers 0, 1, 2, 3, 4, 5 and 6.
(a) How many tiles are there altogether?
(b) How many tiles would there be if the numbers 0, 1, 2, ..., *n* were used?

3 In another set, square tiles have this design.

The colours red, blue, yellow and green are used to produce the tiles.
Here are three of the tiles in the set.

(a) How many tiles are there altogether?
(b) How many tiles would there be if *n* different colours were used?

Counting populations

▶ Resource Sheet E:
How many?
▶ Resource Sheet F:
*Heights of Y11
students*

EXERCISE 2

1 One day, 100 fish are pulled from a small lake. They are tagged and then returned to the lake. Two days later, 150 fish are pulled from the lake and 17 of them are tagged.
(a) Estimate the number of fish in the lake.
(b) Suppose 18 of the fish are tagged instead of 17.
What is the new estimate of the number of fish?
(c) How could you improve the accuracy of the estimate?
Why might you *not* want to do this?

For Question 2, you need a copy of the Resource Sheet E: How many?

2 This question is about how you can use sampling to estimate the number of dashes on the Resource Sheet.
(a) Cut a 2 cm square hole out of a piece of card to make a sampling window.
(b) Drop the card on to the Resource Sheet and count the number of dashes visible through the hole.
(c) Use this to estimate the number of dashes on the Resource Sheet.
(d) Do this a number of times and hence improve your estimate.
(e) Compare your estimate with those of other people.
Does the method seem to produce a reasonably accurate estimate?

Nelson GCSE Maths   STATISTICS AND PROBABILITY (HIGHER)

3 A botanist wants to count the number of wild flowers of a certain type growing in a meadow. Suggest how this might be done.

For Questions 4 and 5, you need a copy of Resource Sheet F: Heights of Y11 students. These questions are about estimating the heights of the students, using sampling.

4 (a) This is how to find your starting position on the Resource Sheet. Select a row at random by opening this book at random dividing the page number by 12 and using the remainder. Select a position in that row by choosing another page at random and dividing the page number by 8 instead of by 12.

(b) Select a sample of size 5 by writing down the five heights in the same row as your starting position with your starting position in the middle. (If your starting position is near or at the end of a row, still keep it in the middle by using results at the other end of the row.)

(c) Find the mean of this sample.

(d) Repeat this process a number of times and record the mean of each of your samples.

5 Repeat Question 4, but this time select a *column* at random (by dividing by 8 instead of by 12) and then a position in that column. Select the sample of size 5 from one column instead of from one row.

DISCUSSION POINT

Compare the answers several people have obtained for Questions 4 and 5. Are you surprised by them?

Sampling techniques

The method of sampling using a window is only successful if the items being sampled are randomly distributed in space or in time. This means that there is no predictable pattern to the way in which the items occur.

When a sample is used to make statements about a population, it needs to be as **representative** as possible of that population. If it is not representative, then it is a **biased sample**.

In **simple random sampling**, every item has the same chance of being chosen. Each item in the population is assigned a number and these numbers are then drawn out of a hat or selected in some other way through the use of random numbers. One way of generating random numbers is to use a **table of random numbers**. Another is to use the random number key on a calculator.

In **systematic sampling**, each item in the population is assigned a number and then every 10th or 20th (or whatever) item is chosen.

Calculator with random number button
Resource Sheet F: *Heights of Y11 students*

EXERCISE 3

1 Suppose you are interested in finding out whether traditionally popular sports are still as popular as they used to be, and you decide to collect some information.
Your sample could be all the people who play football at the same club as you.
(a) Why is this sample *not* a good one?
(b) Suggest a better sample.

2 Suppose you are interested in finding out whether more of the food shopping is being done by men nowadays, and you decide to collect some information about it.
Your sample could be all the people in the local supermarket between 10 a.m. and 10.30 a.m. on a particular Thursday.
(a) Why is this sample *not* a good one?
(b) Suggest a better sample.

3 The council of a small town wants to discover people's opinions concerning a new road, planned to pass round the town through the nearby countryside.
Comment on the suitability of each of these methods of collecting a sample of opinions.
A: Names are randomly selected from the telephone directory
B: Motorists in the town are stopped and asked their opinions
C: People are invited to write in for a questionnaire about the proposals
D: Every 100th name on the electoral register for the town is selected
E: People leaving the shopping centre in town are asked their opinion

4 How might you select an unbiased sample of
(a) students in Y11 in your school?
(b) people who live in your street?
(c) books in your school library to find out how often they are borrowed?

5 A headteacher wants to check if teachers in her school are setting homework. Suggest how she might do this.

6 Here is a part of a table of random numbers.

| 88 | 14 | 29 | 46 | 18 | 39 | 52 | 27 | 43 | 96 | 16 |
| 14 | 98 | 75 | 03 | 75 | 37 | 13 | 84 | 93 | 16 | 13 |

(a) Explain how you could use it to select a random sample of size 5 from a group of 50 people.
(b) Explain how you could use it to select a random sample of size 5 from a group of 43 people.

Questions 7, 8, 9
and 10 are about
using random
numbers to select
a random sample
of the students'
heights from the
Resource Sheet F:
Heights of Y11
students.

7 There are 96 heights on the Resource Sheet.
Find out how you can use the random number button on your calculator
to generate integer random numbers between 1 and 96.

8 (a) Number the heights on the Resource Sheet in some systematic way.
   (b) Use your calculator to select a random sample of 5 heights.
   (c) Use this sample to estimate the mean height of the students.
   (d) Find several more sample means.
   (e) Use these sample means to obtain an improved estimate for the
   mean height.

9 (a) Repeat Question 8 for samples of size 10.
   (b) Which estimate do you think is likely to be more accurate: one obtained
   from samples of size 5 or one obtained from samples of size 10?

10 Collect the results for Questions 8 and 9 obtained by the whole class.
   (a) Use all the means of samples of size 5 to obtain an estimate of the
   mean height.
   (b) Use all the means of samples of size 10 to obtain an estimate of the
   mean height.
   (c) What is your final estimate of the mean height of the students?
   How accurate do you think it is?

Many populations divide naturally into subgroups. For example,
populations of people can be divided into subgroups by gender and by age.
When a population is divided into subgroups which *do not overlap*, these
groups are called **strata**. The best way of dividing a population into strata
depends on the question you are researching.

One way of obtaining a representative sample of a population is to take a
separate random sample of each stratum. The size of the random sample
for each stratum needs to be proportional to the size of the stratum.
This process is called **stratified sampling**.

EXERCISE 4

1 An ice cream firm produces five different flavours of ice cream.
In one week, they produce these quantities.

Flavour	Vanilla	Mint	Strawberry	Pistachio	Lemon
Number of cartons	440	350	210	180	130

The firm needs to sample 1% of its production for quality control.
How many of each flavour should be sampled?

2 Here is some information about the number of students in a school.

Year	Number of males	Number of females	Total number of students
Y7	77	72	149
Y8	68	57	125
Y9	60	58	118
Y10	63	57	120
Y11	59	55	114
Y12	30	34	64
Y13	19	24	43
Total	376	357	733

Obtain a stratified sample of size 100 for the whole school, taking both gender and age group into account.

3 A market gardener is experimenting with three different types of strawberry. The area devoted to each type is listed here.

Type A: 150 m²
Type B: 120 m²
Type C: 90 m²

He estimates that there are about 15 strawberry plants in every square metre. To estimate some data about the whole strawberry population, he wants to select a stratified sample of 50 plants. How many of each type should he select?

Designing questionnaires

One of the most common methods used to collect data from people is the **questionnaire**. In the previous section, there was discussion about the ways of choosing a representative sample of people to give the questionnaire to, so as to minimise bias.

However, the questionnaire itself must also be carefully constructed if bias is to be avoided.

EXERCISE 5

1 A student is conducting a survey into which school subjects students think are important and which they enjoy most. She intends using a questionnaire.

(a) What is wrong with the wording of these questions?

Do you find history boring, like most students?

Do you agree that Maths is important for getting a job?

Do you like games as a break from dull classroom subjects?

(b) Suggest some better worded questions to use instead of these.

2 Sometimes it is convenient to have questions on your questionnaire which can be answered either *yes* or *no*.
Reword each of these questions so that they can be answered *yes* or *no*.
You might need to use several questions in place of one of these questions.

What sports do you like?

What do you do on Saturdays?

What are your views about smoking?

3 Sometimes it is useful to have a definite number as the answer to a question. Reword each of these questions so that the answer is a number.

Do you take a lot of subjects at school?

Is your science class a big group?

Do you come from a large family?

Do you often go for a bike ride?

4 Here are some questions that might be asked in surveys.

- Are the trains poor around here? YES/NO

- Do you agree that CDs are too expensive? YES/NO

- Do you think that children watch too much television ? YES/NO

- If there was a local election this week, for which party would you vote? ....

- Do you eat cereal for breakfast? If yes, which are your three favourites?

  1 ....   2 ....   3 ....

- How long does it take you to travel to school ? Please circle one:

  5–10 mins   11–15 mins   16–20 mins   21–25 mins   more than 25 mins

- Give these school meal items a score for flavour, texture and appearance.
  Score: 1 means poor
  　　　2 means OK
  　　　3 means good
  　　　4 means very good

Meal item	Flavour score				Texture score				Appearance score			
Pizza	1	2	3	4	1	2	3	4	1	2	3	4
Sausages	1	2	3	4	1	2	3	4	1	2	3	4
Chips	1	2	3	4	1	2	3	4	1	2	3	4
Salad	1	2	3	4	1	2	3	4	1	2	3	4
Jacket potato	1	2	3	4	1	2	3	4	1	2	3	4

Look at each question in turn.
Say how good a question you think it is.
If you think it is a good question say why.
If you think that it is *not* a good question, say how it might be improved.

Correlation and lines of best fit

DISCUSSION POINT
What do these scatter diagrams tell you?

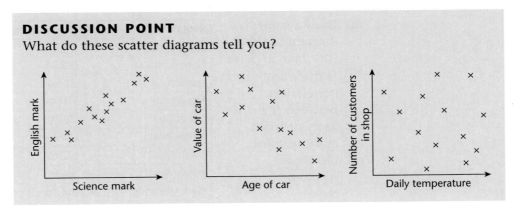

On a scatter diagram, a straight line is sometimes drawn which goes as close as possible to all or most of the points.

This line is called a **line of best fit**. It can be useful for predicting results which depend on the relationship between the two sets of data.

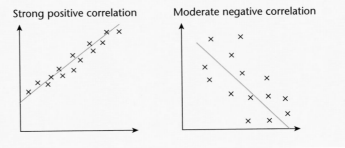

EXERCISE 6

1 Sketch scatter diagrams which could represent the relationship between each of these pairs of data.
   (a) *Ice cream sales* and *daily temperature*
   (b) The *heights of adults* and *their ages*
   (c) The *weights of pieces of cheddar cheese* and *their prices*
   (d) The *number of potatoes in a kilogram* and the *size of the potatoes*
   (e) The *number of sweaters sold* and the *daily temperature*

2 Here is some data, published in 1996, about the amount spent on lottery tickets and the grant per head received by each region.

(a) Draw a scatter diagram to show this data.

(b) Is there any correlation between the amount spent and the grant received? Are some regions significantly different to others?

Region	Spend per head (£)	Grant per head (£)
East Midlands	97.81	8.90
Eastern region	125.65	12.80
London	77.96	54.20
Merseyside	110.44	13.70
North-East	78.70	19.10
North-West	102.46	25.30
South-East	122.67	17.90
South-West	99.94	13.00
West Midlands	108.26	14.90
Yorks & Humbs	107.11	21.30
Northern Ireland	137.76	18.90
Scotland	100.36	29.10
Wales	108.35	46.10

3 This table shows the exam marks of twelve students in Science and English tests.

Student	1	2	3	4	5	6	7	8	9	10	11	12
Science mark	59	45	60	38	44	71	34	59	57	53	56	80
English mark	69	50	75	40	51	95	37	69	72	68	69	78

(a) Draw a scatter diagram for the English and Science marks. Draw in a line of best fit.

(b) Describe the relationship between the performance of students in Science and in English.

(c) Another student scored 65 in the Science test but missed the English test. What mark would you expect this student to score on the English test?

4 This table shows the hand spans and English shoe sizes of twenty Y10 students.

(a) Draw a scatter diagram of shoe size against hand span.

(b) Draw a line of best fit.

(c) Use your line of best fit to predict the shoe size for someone with a hand span of 260 mm.

(d) Use your line of best fit to predict the hand span for someone with a shoe size of 2.

Hand span (mm)	English shoe size	Hand span (mm)	English shoe size
170	4	195	6
180	6	200	6
210	6	230	10
205	7	215	9
180	$4\frac{1}{2}$	170	$5\frac{1}{2}$
235	10	210	7
230	9	225	8
235	8	230	$8\frac{1}{2}$
205	$8\frac{1}{2}$	190	$5\frac{1}{2}$
200	7	215	$8\frac{1}{2}$

5 This table shows the heights and arm spans of 15 students.

Height	Arm span
6ft 2ins	187 cm
6ft 0ins	182 cm
5ft 4ins	163 cm
5ft 5ins	165 cm
5ft 6ins	167 cm
5ft 3ins	160 cm
5ft 5ins	164 cm
5ft 6ins	167 cm
5ft 2ins	156 cm
5ft 6ins	168 cm
5ft 7ins	169 cm
5ft 5ins	165 cm
5ft 6ins	168 cm
5ft 10ins	177 cm
6ft 0ins	183 cm

(a) Draw a scatter diagram of height against arm span.

(b) Work out the mean height and the mean arm span.
Plot the point representing the means on your scatter diagram.

(c) Draw a line of best fit which passes through the points representing the means.

(d) Use your line to estimate
  (i)   the height of a student whose arm span is 180 cm
  (ii) the arm span of a student whose height is 5ft 8ins

6 These are the weekly takings and weekly profit of five branches of a chain of shops.

Shop	A	B	C	D	E
Takings (£)	6400	9920	5760	8160	8000
Profit (£)	640	1760	720	1200	1280

(a) Draw a scatter diagram of profit against takings.

(b) Work out the mean takings and mean profit.

(c) Draw a line of best fit passing through the point representing the means.

(d) Use your line to estimate
  (i)   the takings of a branch making a profit of £1000 per week
  (ii) the profit of a branch taking £10 000 per week

7 The total termly absences for students in a particular tutor group were recorded over a period of five years.

	Y7	Y8	Y9	Y10	Y11
Autumn term	19	21	28	22	25
Spring term	63	50	135	62	69
Summer term	34	30	41	55	97

(**a**) Plot these points on a graph, using axes like these.

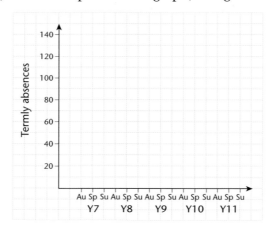

A line of best fit is often called a **trend line,** when data collected over a period of time is being graphed.

(**b**) Give possible reasons for
   (**i**)   the higher numbers in the Spring Term
   (**ii**) the high number of 135
   (**iii**) the high number of 97
(**c**) Draw a **trend line** through your points.
(**d**) What conclusion does your trend line suggest?

8 This table shows the number of people employed by a small but expanding firm over a period of one year.

Month	Jan	Feb	Mar	Apr	May	Jun	Jul	Aug	Sep	Oct	Nov	Dec
Number of employees	50	59	61	67	71	72	75	82	88	91	94	95

(**a**) Plot these points on a graph.
(**b**) Draw a trend line through your points.
(**c**) If the firm continued to expand at the same rate, estimate the number of employees there will be six months later in June.

9 This table shows the growth in the total population of the UK this century.

Year	1900	1910	1920	1930	1940	1950	1960	1970	1975	1980	1985	1990	1995
Total population (millions)	38.2	42.1	44.0	46.0	50.2	52.7	54.5	55.8	56.4	56.5	56.8	57.6	58.9

(a) Plot these results on a graph.

(b) Use your graph to predict the UK population in 2025.

(c) Suggest a better way of predicting the UK population in 2025.

Standard deviation

DISCUSSION POINT

In Chapter 4 of *Book 1*, these instructions were given for finding the standard deviation for small sets of data.

- Find the mean.
- Find the difference between each item of data and the mean.
- Square these differences.
- Add up all the squared differences.
- Divide by the number of items of data.
- Square root the answer.

GCSE formula sheets give this information about standard deviation. Standard deviation for a set of numbers $x_1, x_2, ..., x_n$ having a mean of x is given by

$$s = \sqrt{\frac{\Sigma(x - \bar{x})^2}{n}} \text{ or } s = \sqrt{\frac{\Sigma x^2}{n} - \left(\frac{\Sigma x}{n}\right)^2}$$

Make sure you understand these formulae. Why do they both give the same answer? Why might the second one sometimes be more useful?

Check that both formulae give the same answer for these ten GCSE mock exam marks obtained by a student.

63, 64, 63, 38, 64, 44, 81, 60, 44, 61

You also need to be able to find the standard deviation for frequency distributions.

Discuss how you would find an estimate for the standard deviation for this set of data, which shows the earnings of staff working at a hotel.

Wage (£w)	Frequency
$0 \leq w < 50$	18
$50 \leq w < 100$	22
$100 \leq w < 150$	28
$150 \leq w < 200$	6
$200 \leq w < 300$	2
$300 \leq w < 500$	1

1 (a) This table gives the monthly rainfall, in millimetres, for a town in the West of England in 1976 and in 1980.

	Jan	Feb	Mar	Apr	May	Jun	Jul	Aug	Sep	Oct	Nov	Dec
1976	58.5	39.8	49.6	19.7	64.0	17.5	29.8	26.5	150.3	160.1	88.0	96.9
1980	77.2	93.7	103.6	17.7	32.5	127.1	73.0	92.3	65.4	131.3	92.7	77.6

Use the data to calculate the mean and standard deviation for the monthly rainfall for each year.

(b) Compare the rainfall in these two years.

2 This table shows the number of children in each of 100 families.

Number of children in family	0	1	2	3	4	5	6
Frequency	4	26	41	20	6	2	1

Calculate the mean and standard deviation of the number of children in the families.

3 The heights of 50 Christmas trees were measured.

Height of tree (h metres)	Frequency
$0 \leq h < 1$	4
$1 \leq h < 1.5$	12
$1.5 \leq h < 2$	23
$2 \leq h < 2.5$	8
$2.5 \leq h < 3$	3

Calculate an estimate for the mean and standard deviation of the heights of the Christmas trees.

4 This table provides some data about absence from work.

No. of days absence	No. of employees
0–14	86
15–29	30
30–44	5
45–59	0
60–74	1
75–89	2

(a) Calculate an estimate for the mean and standard deviation of the number of days absence.

(b) Recalculate your estimates when you exclude the three long-term absentees from the data.

5 A group of students measured the heights of everyone in two Y10 tutor groups. Here are their results.

Height (cm)	Frequency (males)	Frequency (females)
155–159	0	1
160–164	0	8
165–169	7	12
170–174	7	2
175–179	5	4
180–184	7	0
185–189	1	0

(a) Calculate an estimate for the mean and standard deviation of the heights of
   (i)   the male students
   (ii) the female students

(b) Use your answers to compare the heights of the male and female students in the survey.

6 This table provides information about waiting times in a hospital.

Waiting time (t mins)	No. of patients (f)
$0 \leq t < 60$	15
$60 \leq t < 120$	21
$120 \leq t < 180$	5
$180 \leq t < 240$	4
$240 \leq t < 300$	2

(a) Calculate an estimate for the mean and standard deviation of the waiting time for a patient at this hospital.

(b) Over the next year, the hospital manages to reduce the waiting time for everyone by 10 minutes. Revise your estimates for the mean and the standard deviation in the light of this information.

COURSEWORK OPPORTUNITY

Rational standard deviation

The mean of the numbers 1, 2, 3, 4, 5 and 6 is 3.5. The standard deviation is 1.7078... which is an irrational number.

- How can you be sure of this?
- What happens for the numbers 1, 2, 3, 4, 5, 6 and 7?
- What is the standard deviation of the numbers 1, 2, 3, ... N?
- For which values of N is this rational?

Analysing and comparing sets of data

Exercise 8 brings together much of the knowledge and skills you have learnt. You may need to remind yourself of some of the ideas you met in Chapter 4 of *Book 1*.

Cumulative frequency diagrams are explained on page 273 in the Revision Guide.

Histograms with unequal class intervals are explained on page 267 in the Revision Guide.

EXERCISE 8

1 Look at these two distributions.

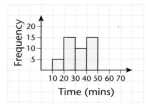 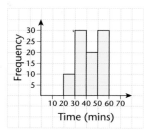

Which of these statements is true?

A: The distributions have the same mean and the same standard deviation.

B: The distributions have the same mean but different standard deviations.

C: The distributions have different means but the same standard deviation.

2 Look at these distributions.

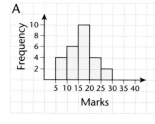 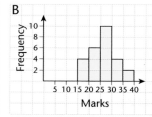 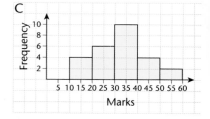

The mean of distribution A is *m* and the standard deviation is *s*.

What is the mean and standard deviation of

(a) distribution B?

(b) distribution C?

(c) distribution D?

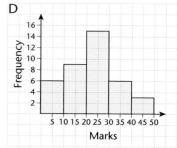

3 The marks obtained by 200 students in their GCSE mock examination have a mean of 58 and a standard deviation of 14.

(a) It is decided to add 5 to each of the marks. What is the new mean and standard deviation?

(b) The marks then have to be scaled by multiplying them all by 1.5. What is the new mean and standard deviation?

Questions 4, 5 and 6 are about designing suitable chairs for a reception class.

People's **popliteal height** tells you how high above the floor to make the seat of a chair.

4 This cumulative frequency curve shows the popliteal height for five-year-old children.

Use this curve to estimate

(a) the median popliteal height for five-year-olds

(b) the interquartile range of popliteal heights

(c) the height the seat of the chair should be so that 95% of five-year-old children's feet reach the floor when they are sitting on it

(d) the percentage of five-year-old children whose feet would reach the floor when they are sitting on a chair with a seat 300 mm above the floor

Another important measurement for chair design is people's **buttock–popliteal length**. This tells you how deep to make the chair seat.

5 This table shows how buttock–popliteal lengths for five-year-old children are distributed.

(a) Draw a cumulative frequency curve for this data.

(b) Find the median buttock–popliteal length for five-year-olds.

(c) Find the interquartile range for this data.

(d) How deep should the seat of a chair be so that 95 per cent of five-year-olds could sit back on it and still be able to bend their knees?

Buttock–popliteal length (b mm)	Percentage of five-year-olds
$230 \leq b < 240$	1
$240 \leq b < 250$	2
$250 \leq b < 260$	5
$260 \leq b < 270$	12
$270 \leq b < 280$	18
$280 \leq b < 290$	26
$290 \leq b < 300$	16
$300 \leq b < 310$	10
$310 \leq b < 320$	5
$320 \leq b < 330$	3
$330 \leq b < 340$	2

6 These are the dimensions (in millimetres) of a chair designed for infant classrooms.

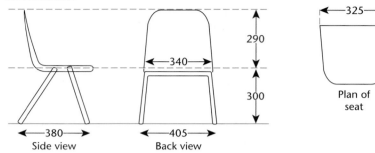

Side view   Back view   Plan of seat

(a) What percentage of five-year-olds would be able to
(i) reach the floor with their feet when sitting on this chair?
(ii) bend their knees when sitting back on this chair?
(b) Comment on your answers.

7 (a) The circumferences of 150 fir trees were measured. Here are the results.
(i) Plot a cumulative frequency curve for this data.
(ii) Estimate the median and interquartile range for the trunk circumferences.

Circumference (cm)	Frequency
45–	16
60–	31
75–	53
90–	29
105–	12
120–150	9

(b) This data is about the circumferences of 150 spruce trees.
Use it to draw a second cumulative frequency curve on your graph.
(c) Consider the circumferences of the fir trees and spruce trees.
Comment on any similarities and differences.

Minimum value	39 cm
Lower quartile	81 cm
Median	96 cm
Upper quartile	105 cm
Maximum value	126 cm

8 This table shows how the UK population in 1995 was distributed.

Age group (years)	0–19	20–34	35–49	50–64	65 and over
Number of people (millions)	14.8	13.4	12.0	9.1	9.2

(a) Draw a histogram to represent this data.
(b) Calculate an estimate for the mean age of the 1995 population.
(c) Calculate an estimate for the standard deviation of ages in 1995.
(d) This table shows the predicted UK population for 2025.

Age group (years)	0–19	20–34	35–49	50–64	65 and over
Number of people (millions)	13.4	11.0	11.3	12.8	12.5

Draw a histogram to represent the predicted population.
(e) Calculate an estimate for the mean and standard deviation for the age of the predicated population in 2025.
(f) Comment on your results.

For Question 8, part (a), you need to decide what to do about the age group '65 and over'.

9 The heights of a group of beech trees and a group of oak trees, correct to the nearest metre, are given in these tables.

Beech trees height (m)	Frequency
4	2
5	8
6	5
7	35
8	0
9	0

Oak trees height (m)	Frequency
4	0
5	4
6	6
7	12
8	17
9	1

Pearson's coefficient is a measure of the skewness (or asymmetry) of a distribution.

$$\text{Pearson's coefficient} = \frac{\text{mean} - \text{mode}}{\text{standard deviation}}$$

Calculate Pearson's coefficient for both distributions and comment on your results.

10 The design teachers in a school want to assess the spatial abilities of their Y7 classes. They devise a construction puzzle.
These were the times taken by the 75 students to complete the puzzle.

(a) Calculate estimates for the mean and standard deviation for the time taken to complete the puzzle.

(b) Draw a cumulative frequency diagram to represent this data.

(c) Estimate the median and interquartile range for the data.

Time (t secs)	Number of students
$0 < t \le 10$	1
$10 < t \le 20$	8
$20 < t \le 30$	12
$30 < t \le 40$	19
$40 < t \le 50$	13
$50 < t \le 60$	9
$60 < t \le 70$	8
$70 < t \le 80$	5

(d) One teacher suggests that these categories could be used to grade the students' spatial ability.
Good: Time taken is less than (mean – standard deviation)
Poor: Time taken is more than (mean + standard deviation)
Average: Not good or poor
Work out how many students there are in each category.

(e) Another teacher suggests that these categories could be used.
Good: The quickest 15% of students
Poor: The slowest 15% of students
Average: Not good or poor
Work out how many students there are in each category.

Using probability to analyse random events

► Calculator with a random number facility

In Question 1, you find experimental probabilities. Questions 2 to 4 are about finding theoretical probabilities in the same situation.

For Questions 2 part (b) and 4 part (c), don't forget that you can arrange the digits in any order.

1 (a) Use a calculator to pick digits at random.
Pick three digits at random (there is no assumption that they should all be different). Can you make a 3-digit number from them which is
(i) even?   **(ii)** a multiple of 3?   **(iii)** a multiple of 5?

(b) Repeat part (a) many times or collect results from a group or from the whole class.
Use your results to estimate the probability of being able to make each of the different multiples from three digits picked at random.

2 (a) Pick three digits at random. When you look at the digits, how do you decide whether an even number can be made from them?

(b) Draw a tree diagram to show the possibilities for picking three digits. The first digit picked can be odd or even, the second digit odd or even, and so on. Which branches of the tree indicate that the three digits can be used to make an even number?

(c) What is the probability that the three digits picked can form an even number?

3 (a) How many multiples of 3 are there between 0 and 999?

(b) What is the probability that a number picked at random between 0 and 999 is a multiple of 3?

(c) If three digits make a multiple of 3, does it matter how they are arranged? What is the probability that three digits picked at random make a multiple of 3?

4 (a) If a number is a multiple of 5, which digits can it end in?

(b) A digit is picked at random. What is the probability that it is a suitable digit for a multiple of 5 to end in?

(c) Copy and complete this tree diagram to show the possibilities for picking three digits. The first digit picked can be suitable for a multiple of five to end in (S) or not suitable (N).

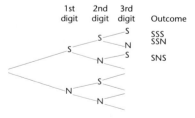

Which branches of the tree indicate that the three digits can be used to make a multiple of 5?

(d) What is the probability that the three digits picked can form a multiple of 5?

5 Three different dots from this grid are picked at random.
You are going to calculate the probability that the dots picked
lie in a straight line.

(a) How many sets of three dots are there?

(b) How many sets of three dots lie in a straight line?

(c) What is the probability that the three dots picked lie in a straight line?

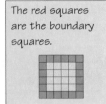

The red squares
are the boundary
squares.

6 (a) Get a calculator to pick three of these squares at random.
Three different squares must be picked.
How many of the squares picked are boundary squares?

(b) Repeat part (a) many times or collect results from a group or from the
whole class. Use your results to estimate the probability of 0, 1, 2 or 3
boundary squares being picked.

7 (a) If one of the squares on the grid in Question 6 is picked at random,
what is the probability that it is a boundary square?

(b) Draw a tree diagram to calculate the probability of 0, 1, 2 or 3
boundary squares being picked when 3 different squares are chosen.

Sampling techniques and questionnaires

When a sample is used to make statements about a population it needs to be
as **representative** as possible of that population. If it is not representative,
then it is a **biased sample**.

In **simple random sampling**, every item has the same chance of being chosen.
Each item in the population is assigned a number and these numbers are then
drawn out of a hat or selected in some other way through the use of random
numbers.

In **systematic sampling**, each item in the population is assigned a number and
then every 10th or 20th (or whatever) item is chosen.

Many populations divide naturally into subgroups. For example, populations
of people can be divided into subgroups by gender and by age. When a
population is divided into subgroups which *do not overlap*, these groups are
called **strata**. The best way of dividing a population into strata depends on
the question you are researching. One way of obtaining a representative
sample of a population is to take a separate random sample of each stratum.
The size of the random sample for each stratum needs to be proportional to
the size of the stratum. This process is called **stratified sampling**.

One of the most common methods used to collect data from people is the
questionnaire. The questionnaire given to a representative sample of people
must be carefully constructed if bias is to be avoided.

Nelson GCSE Maths   STATISTICS AND PROBABILITY (HIGHER)

Correlation and lines of best fit

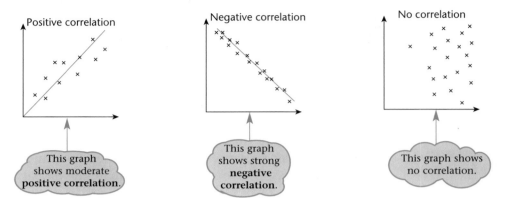

Positive correlation

This graph shows moderate positive correlation.

Negative correlation

This graph shows strong negative correlation.

No correlation

This graph shows no correlation.

Standard deviation

This measures how spread out the data is.

$$s = \sqrt{\frac{\Sigma(x - \bar{x})^2}{n}} \text{ or } s = \sqrt{\frac{\Sigma x^2}{n} - \left(\frac{\Sigma x}{n}\right)^2}$$

You can also use the statistical functions on your calculator to calculate means and standard deviations.

Any of these methods give a standard deviation of 12.1 for these ten GCSE mock exam marks obtained by a student.

63, 64, 63, 38, 64, 44, 81, 60, 44, 61

You also need to be able to find the mean and standard deviation for frequency distributions.

This shows the earnings of staff working at a hotel.

Wage (£w)	Frequency
$0 \leq w < 50$	18
$50 \leq w < 100$	22
$100 \leq w < 150$	28
$150 \leq w < 200$	6
$200 \leq w < 300$	2
$300 \leq w < 500$	1

An estimate for the mean wage is £98 and for the standard deviation is £63.

5

ALGEBRAIC MANIPULATION

This chapter is about:

- algebraic fractions
- solving equations involving fractions
- rearranging formulae
- inequalities
- solving problems involving regions given by inequalities
- using inequalities for modelling.

Nelson GCSE Maths   ALGEBRAIC MANIPULATION (HIGHER)

This first exercise is a reminder of some of the work done in Chapter 1 of Book 1.

Algebraic fractions

EXERCISE 1

1 Simplify these expressions.

(a) $\dfrac{6}{9}$ (b) $\dfrac{1200}{2000}$ (c) $\dfrac{156}{144}$ (d) $\dfrac{3a}{4a}$

(e) $\dfrac{6a}{6b}$ (f) $\dfrac{9c}{12c}$ (g) $\dfrac{3c}{6d}$ (h) $\dfrac{6a}{3b}$

2 Simplify these expressions.

(a) $\dfrac{ab}{ac}$ (b) $\dfrac{bcd}{acd}$ (c) $\dfrac{pqr}{mnp}$ (d) $\dfrac{3xy}{6xz}$

(e) $\dfrac{12pqr}{16pqs}$ (f) $\dfrac{8abc}{20cde}$

3 Simplify these expressions.

(a) $\dfrac{a^2}{ab}$ (b) $\dfrac{xy^2}{y^3}$ (c) $\dfrac{a^2b^2}{2ab}$ (d) $\dfrac{mn^3}{m^3n}$

(e) $\dfrac{8a^2b^2}{12abc^2}$ (f) $\dfrac{4ab^2c^3}{10a^3b^2c}$

4 Rewrite each of these as one fraction.

(a) $\dfrac{x}{2} + \dfrac{x}{4}$ (b) $\dfrac{a}{3} + \dfrac{a}{6}$ (c) $\dfrac{4}{n} + \dfrac{3}{n}$ (d) $\dfrac{c}{4} - \dfrac{c}{8}$

(e) $\dfrac{p}{10} - \dfrac{p}{15}$ (f) $\dfrac{7}{2x} - \dfrac{2}{x}$

5 Rewrite each of these as one fraction.

(a) $\dfrac{x}{3} + \dfrac{x+2}{6}$

(b) $\dfrac{a-1}{2} + \dfrac{a+2}{4}$

(c) $\dfrac{c+1}{5} - \dfrac{c+2}{3}$

(d) $\dfrac{a+b}{8} - \dfrac{2a-3b}{12}$

(e) $\dfrac{2(p-3q)}{7} + p + 2q$

(f) $\dfrac{a+2b}{2} + \dfrac{2a+3b}{3} - \dfrac{3a+5b}{4}$

6 Rewrite each of these as one fraction.

(a) $\dfrac{1}{a} + \dfrac{1}{b}$

(b) $\dfrac{3}{x} - \dfrac{2}{y}$

(c) $\dfrac{6}{pq} - \dfrac{2}{p}$

(d) $\dfrac{9}{x} - 5$

(e) $\dfrac{n}{3} - \dfrac{3}{n}$

(f) $\dfrac{a}{b} - \dfrac{b}{a}$

7 Rewrite each of these as one fraction.

(a) $\dfrac{x}{3} \times \dfrac{y}{2}$

(b) $\dfrac{a}{b} \times \dfrac{b}{c}$

(c) $\dfrac{p}{q} \times \dfrac{2r}{p}$

(d) $\dfrac{m}{6} \div \dfrac{m}{3}$

(e) $\dfrac{p}{2} \div \dfrac{p}{10}$

(f) $\dfrac{xy}{z} \div \dfrac{yz}{x}$

(g) $\dfrac{p^2}{q} \times \dfrac{q^2}{r} \times \dfrac{r^2}{p}$

(h) $\dfrac{w}{x} \times \dfrac{x}{y} \div \dfrac{y}{z}$

DISCUSSION POINT

Someone runs 100 metres and then walks 100 metres. The speed of running is $x\,\text{ms}^{-1}$ and the speed of walking is $y\,\text{ms}^{-1}$.

- Find the total time taken. Write the answer as one fraction.
- If the running speed is twice the walking speed, find the total time in terms of y.
- If the running speed is $3\,\text{ms}^{-1}$ faster than the walking speed, find the total time in terms of y.

Someone else jogs 500 feet at a speed of $s+1$ feet per second and then walks 500 feet at a speed of $s-1$ feet per second.

- Find the total time taken, writing the answer as one fraction.

EXERCISE 2

1 Write each of these as one fraction.

(a) $3 + \dfrac{3}{n+2}$

(b) $\dfrac{6}{y+3} - 3$

(c) $\dfrac{4}{x-1} + \dfrac{4}{x+1}$

(d) $\dfrac{2}{y-1} - \dfrac{2}{y+1}$

(e) $\dfrac{3}{c-1} - \dfrac{2}{c+5}$

(f) $\dfrac{4}{x} - \dfrac{2}{x+2}$

2 Write each of these as one fraction.

(a) $5 + \dfrac{4}{n+2} - \dfrac{3}{2(n+2)}$

(b) $\dfrac{x-3}{2} - \dfrac{2}{x-3}$

(c) $\dfrac{p}{p+q} - \dfrac{q}{p-q}$

(d) $\dfrac{x+y}{x-y} - \dfrac{x-y}{x+y}$

3 **(a)** Mary is saving for a holiday. After x weeks she has saved £60.
What is the mean amount saved each week?
(b) Ann saved £30 in $(x - 2)$ weeks.
What is the mean amount she saved each week?
(c) Write the difference between the two means as a single fraction.

4 A car travels 60 miles at an average speed of s m.p.h. On the return
journey, it travels at an average speed of $(s - 5)$ m.p.h.
Work out the difference between the times taken for the outward and
return journeys, writing your answer as a single fraction.

DISCUSSION POINT
Discuss how to simplify these fractions.

$$\frac{x^2 - 1}{x + 1} \qquad\qquad \frac{x^2 + 3x + 2}{x^2 + 2x} \qquad\qquad \frac{3x^2 - 8x - 3}{4x^2 - 17x + 15}$$

EXERCISE 3

1 Simplify each of these fractions.

(a) $\dfrac{3x + 6}{3}$ **(b)** $\dfrac{3a}{6a - 9a^2}$ **(c)** $\dfrac{x^2 + 2x + 1}{x^2 + x}$ **(d)** $\dfrac{x - 2}{x^2 - 4}$

(e) $\dfrac{x^2 - 6x + 5}{x^2 - 5x}$ **(f)** $\dfrac{x^2 - 8xy - 20y^2}{x^2 - 12xy + 20y^2}$

2 Simplify each of these fractions.

(a) $\dfrac{2a^2 + 5a + 2}{a^2 - 4}$ **(b)** $\dfrac{9z^2 - 25}{3z^2 + 7z - 20}$

(c) $\dfrac{9 - 4x^2}{9 - 12x + 4x^2}$ **(d)** $\dfrac{4p^2 + 4pq - 15q^2}{2p^2 - pq - 15q^2}$

(e) $\dfrac{4a^3 + 6a^2}{6a^2 + 25a + 24}$ **(f)** $\dfrac{4a^2 - 47ab - 12b^2}{12a^2 + 35ab + 8b^2}$

3 Write each of these as one fraction, and simplify as much as possible.

(a) $\dfrac{2x + 4}{x^2 - 1} \times \dfrac{x^2 + 2x + 1}{6}$ **(b)** $\dfrac{2x^2 - 11x - 6}{x^2 - 36} \times \dfrac{3x^2 + 14x - 24}{6x^2 - 5x - 4}$

(c) $\dfrac{x^2 + 3x + 2}{2x + 4} \div \dfrac{x^2 + 2x - 3}{x + 3}$ **(d)** $\dfrac{5x^2 - 6x}{15x^2 - 38x + 24} \div \dfrac{3x}{6x^2 + x - 12}$

⭐ **4** Write each of these as one fraction, and simplify as much as possible.

(a) $\dfrac{3}{x^2 - 2x} + \dfrac{2}{x - 2}$ **(b)** $\dfrac{1}{x - 1} - \dfrac{1}{x + 1} - \dfrac{1}{x^2 - 1}$

(c) $\dfrac{1}{x^2 - 1} + \dfrac{2}{x^2 - 2x + 1}$ **(d)** $\dfrac{5}{2x^2 - 5x - 7} - \dfrac{3}{3x^2 + 7x + 4}$

(e) $\dfrac{4 - x}{x^2 + 5x + 6} - \dfrac{5 + x}{x^2 - 2x - 8}$

Question 5 is
about doing things
backwards. You will
need to think about
how to do this.

5 (a) Write the fraction

$$\frac{5x + 7}{(x + 1)(x + 2)}$$

as the sum of two fractions

$$\frac{A}{x + 1} + \frac{B}{x + 2}$$

where A and B are numbers. Find the values of A and B.

(b) Write each of these fractions in a similar way.

(i) $\dfrac{12a}{(a + 1)(a - 1)}$ **(ii)** $\dfrac{8p - 16}{p^2 - 2p - 15}$ **(iii)** $\dfrac{x + 4}{(x + 1)^2}$

Solving equations involving algebraic fractions

DISCUSSION POINT

Discuss how to solve these equations.

$$\frac{4}{2x + 1} = \frac{5}{3x + 1} \qquad\qquad \frac{9}{x - 4} - \frac{15}{2x + 1} = 2$$

EXERCISE 4

1 Solve these equations.

(a) $9 - \dfrac{3x}{2} = 13$ **(b)** $\dfrac{3x + 5}{3} - \dfrac{5x - 1}{4} = 2$ **(c)** $\dfrac{5}{y} + 7 = 4$

(d) $\dfrac{37}{x} + 10 = \dfrac{25}{x}$ **(e)** $\dfrac{5}{3x - 1} = \dfrac{8}{5x - 3}$ **(f)** $\dfrac{7}{2x - 1} + \dfrac{5}{x + 8} = 0$

2 Solve these equations.

(a) $\dfrac{1}{x} - \dfrac{1}{x - 4} = 1$ **(b)** $\dfrac{6}{x - 1} - \dfrac{5}{x + 1} = 1$ **(c)** $\dfrac{8}{x} + \dfrac{3}{x - 3} = 1$

(d) $\dfrac{3}{x + 1} + \dfrac{7}{2x - 3} = 2$ **(e)** $\dfrac{5}{x - 3} - \dfrac{4}{x + 3} = 2$ **(f)** $\dfrac{3}{2x + 2} + \dfrac{7}{x + 7} = 1$

3 Solve these equations.

(a) $\dfrac{15}{x} + \dfrac{7}{x - 2} = 8$ **(b)** $\dfrac{3}{x + 4} + \dfrac{6}{2x - 1} = 1$ **(c)** $\dfrac{20}{x - 1} - \dfrac{4}{x + 5} = 3$

DISCUSSION POINT

A car travels at an average speed of v m.p.h. on the outward journey and at an average speed of $v + 12$ m.p.h. on the return. The distance travelled each way is 72 miles. The total time taken for both journeys is $3\frac{1}{2}$ hours.

- Find the total time taken for both journeys in terms of v.
- Show that v satisfies the quadratic equation $7v^2 - 204v - 1728 = 0$
- Solve this equation to find the value of v.

Nelson GCSE Maths   ALGEBRAIC MANIPULATION (HIGHER)

1 A rugby team scored n points in their first five matches.
  (a) What is the mean number of points per match?
  (b) In the next three matches, they scored 35 points altogether.
      The mean number of points per match rose by 0.7.
      Find n and also the mean number of points after eight matches.

2 A hockey team scores 20 goals in x matches.
  (a) What is the average (mean) number of goals per match?
  (b) In the next two matches, the team scored 3 goals altogether.
      Their goal average dropped by 0.2. Find x.

3 A cone and a cylinder have the same height, h inches.
  The radius of the cone's base is 1 inch and the radius of the cylinder's
  base is $\frac{3}{5}$ inch. The volume of the cylinder is $\frac{4}{25}\pi$ cubic inches more than
  the volume of the cone.
  Find the height of the cone and the cylinder.

4 72 people are going to be seated at identical tables for a meal.
  The tables can either hold n people or $n + 2$ people.
  (a) Show that one arrangement requires

  $$\frac{144}{n(n + 2)}$$

  more tables than the other arrangement.
  (b) If one arrangement requires 3 more tables than the other
      arrangement, find the value of n.

5 To celebrate Tom's birthday, some friends decide to go to a concert.
  They decide to share the total cost of the outing, which will be £480,
  equally between the n people going.
  They then remember that they do not want Tom to pay for the outing
  and each person's share goes up by £2.
  Find the value of n.

6 Ann cycles 6 miles per hour faster than Darren walks. Darren sets out
  from home to walk into town. Ann leaves home 18 minutes later on
  her bike. She overtakes Darren after travelling 2 miles.
  How fast does Darren walk?

7 A man jogs to a shop at $s + 1$ feet per second. He walks back at $s - 1$ feet
  per second. The distance to the shop is 800 yards. His total journey time
  (both ways) is 11 minutes 15 seconds.
  (a) Write down an equation for s, and show that it can be simplified to
      give $9s^2 - 64s - 9 = 0$
  (b) Solve the equation and hence find the time he took to jog to the
      shop, correct to the nearest second.

8 The square ABCD has sides of length s cm.
The rectangle ACEF has an area of $20\,\text{cm}^2$.
The perimeter of pentagon ABCEF is 20 cm.
  (a) Find the two possible values for s, correct to
  3 significant figures.
  (b) Find the possible areas of the pentagon, correct
  to 3 significant figures.

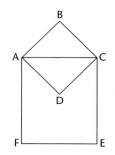

Changing the subject of a formula

EXERCISE 6

1 (a) Find x if $7 = 3x + 5$ (b) Find x if $a = bx + c$

2 (a) Find x if $16 = 4x - 7$ (b) Find x if $a = bx - c$

3 (a) Find x if $5 = 7 - 13x$ (b) Find x if $a = b - cx$

4 (a) Find x if $3x - 8 = 13x - 1$ (b) Find x if $ax - b = cx - d$

5 (a) Find x if $5x + 7 = 9 - 6x$ (b) Find x if $ax + b = c - dx$

6 (a) Find x if $3(x + 5) = 17$ (b) Find x if $a(x + b) = c$

7 (a) Find x if $\frac{x}{3} + 4 = 9$ (b) Find x if $\frac{x}{a} + b = c$

8 (a) Find x if $\frac{4}{x} + 5 = 12$ (b) Find x if $\frac{a}{x} + b = c$

9 (a) Find x if $\frac{4}{x - 7} + 2 = 9$ (b) Find x if $\frac{a}{x - b} + c = d$

Making x the subject of a formula means solving an equation for x, when
the equation involves other letters too.

EXERCISE 7

1 Make x the subject in each of these equations.

    (a) $px + q = r$
    (b) $2ax - 3b + 4c = 0$
    (c) $b^3 - a^2x = c^3$

    (d) $a(bx + c) = b(cx - d)$
    (e) $x(2a - b) = c(3x + d)$
    (f) $\frac{ax}{2} = b^2$

    (g) $\frac{2a^2}{x} = 3b$
    (h) $a^2 - 2ax = b^2 + 3bx$
    (i) $\frac{x}{a} + b = \frac{x}{c}$

    (j) $\frac{a^2}{x - b} - b = 3c$
    (k) $\frac{x - a}{x + b} = 5c$
    (l) $\frac{ax}{x - b} = c$

    (m) $\frac{x}{x + a} + \frac{b}{x + c} = 1$

2 Make b the subject of each of these equations.

(a) $A = ab$ (b) $P = 2a + 2b$

(c) $A = \dfrac{bh}{2}$ (d) $A = 2ab + 2bc + 2ca$

3 Make the letter indicated the subject of each of these.

(a) $A = 2\pi r$ (Make r the subject)

(b) $V = \pi r^2 h$ (Make h the subject)

(c) $A = 2\pi r(r + h)$ (Make h the subject)

(d) $V = \frac{1}{3}\pi r^2 h$ (Make h the subject)

(e) $P = \pi r + 2r$ (Make r the subject)

(f) $v = u + at$ (Make t the subject)

(g) $F = \frac{9}{5}C + 32$ (Make C the subject)

(h) $A = P + \dfrac{PTR}{100}$ (Make P the subject)

(i) $S = 180 - \dfrac{360}{n}$ (Make n the subject)

(j) $\dfrac{1}{u} + \dfrac{1}{v} = \dfrac{1}{f}$ (Make u the subject)

EXERCISE 8

1 (a) Find x if $x^2 = 10$ (b) Find x if $x^2 = a$

2 (a) Find x if $3x^2 = 13$ (b) Find x if $ax^2 = b$

3 (a) Find x if $\dfrac{x^2}{5} = 11$ (b) Find x if $\dfrac{x^2}{a} = b$

4 (a) Find x if $\dfrac{6}{x^2} = 7$ (b) Find x if $\dfrac{a}{x^2} = b$

5 (a) Find x if $3 + \sqrt{x} = 8$ (b) Find x if $a + \sqrt{x} = b$

6 (a) Find x if $5 = \sqrt{\dfrac{7x}{9}}$ (b) Find x if $a = \sqrt{\dfrac{bx}{c}}$

7 (a) Find x if $3 = \sqrt{\dfrac{11}{4x}}$ (b) Find x if $a = \sqrt{\dfrac{b}{cx}}$

8 (a) Find x if $\dfrac{\sqrt{2x + 3}}{5} = 7$ (b) Find x if $\dfrac{\sqrt{ax + b}}{c} = d$

EXERCISE 9

1 Make x the subject in each of these.

(a) $x^2 = 2b$ (b) $x^2 = 9c^2$ (c) $2ax^2 = 8b$ (d) $\dfrac{x^2}{3a} = 3b$

(e) $\dfrac{x^2}{5b} = 20b$ (f) $\dfrac{2p}{x^2} = 3q$ (g) $\left(\dfrac{a}{x}\right)^2 = b^2$ (h) $\sqrt{x} = 3c$

(i) $5a\sqrt{x} = 2d$ (j) $a\sqrt{\dfrac{bx}{c}} = d$ (k) $a\sqrt{x} + b = c$ (l) $a\sqrt{x} - b = c\sqrt{x} + d$

2 Make the variable specified the subject of the equation.

(a) $P = \dfrac{V^2}{R}$ (Make V the subject)

(b) $A = 4\pi r^2$ (Make r the subject)

(c) $V = \dfrac{1}{3}\pi r^2 h$ (Make r the subject)

(d) $s = \dfrac{1}{2}at^2$ (Make t the subject)

(e) $L = W - I^2 R$ (Make I the subject)

(f) $V = \dfrac{4}{3}\pi r^3$ (Make r the subject)

(g) $a = \sqrt{\dfrac{V}{6}}$ (Make V the subject)

(h) $r = \sqrt{\dfrac{V}{\pi h}}$ (Make V the subject)

(i) $T = 2\pi \sqrt{\dfrac{l}{g}}$ (Make l the subject)

(j) $25T^2 = R^3$ (Make T the subject; then make R the subject)

(k) $x^2 + y^2 = z^2$ (Make x the subject)

(l) $\dfrac{1}{f} = \dfrac{1}{u} + \dfrac{1}{v}$ (Make v the subject)

(m) $h = \dfrac{6r^2}{r^2 - 9}$ (Make r the subject)

(n) $E = \dfrac{1}{2}mv^2 + mgh$ (Make v the subject)

(o) $y = \dfrac{b}{(x + c)^2}$ (Make x the subject)

(p) $V = \dfrac{IR}{R + r}$ (Make R the subject)

Inequalities

DISCUSSION POINT

How would you use inequalities to describe the numbers on the section of this number line which is coloured red?

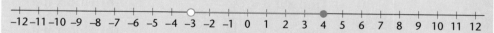

Discuss how to solve these inequalities.

- $3x + 5 > 20$
- $3(x - 10) \leq 2x$
- $-3x < 9$
- $20 - 2x \geq 5$
- $2 \leq 2x + 4 < 10$

Exercise 10

1 Use inequalities to describe the sections of the number line which are coloured red.

(a)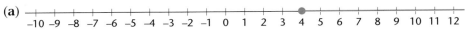

number line from −10 to 12, filled dot at 4

(b) number line from −10 to 12, open dot at −2

(c) number line from −10 to 12, filled dots at −1 and 3

(d) number line from −10 to 12, open dot at 2 and filled dot at 7

2 Solve these inequalities and illustrate the solutions on the number line.

(a) $x + 4 < 7$

(b) $x - 5 \le 1$

(c) $x + 9 < 3$

(d) $2x - 3 > -5$

(e) $2 \le 3x + 8 \le 11$

(f) $3x + 6 > 2x - 1$

(g) $2(x + 5) \le 14$

(h) $5(x + 10) > 3x$

3 Solve these inequalities.

(a) $-2x + 5 \ge 9$

(b) $6 - 5x < -14$

(c) $5(4 - x) \le 20$

(d) $3(x - 7) > 8(4 + x)$

(e) $4 - \frac{x}{2} \le \frac{x}{4} - 11$

(f) $\frac{3x}{5} + \frac{x - 1}{10} > 1$

In all the questions in Exercise 11, *n* is an integer.

Exercise 11

1 Write down all the integers n for which $0 \le n < 5$.

2 Write down all positive integers n for which $2n < 7$.

3 Write down all integers n for which

(a) $20 < 6n < 40$

(b) $0 < 3n - 5 \le 10$

(c) $0 < 7n + 16 < 30$

(d) $-1 \le \frac{n}{2} \le 1$

(e) $0 \le 4x + 20 < 10$

(f) $5 < 7x - 10 < 10$

4 Write down all integers n for which

(a) $0 < 6 - n < 4$

(b) $-3 \le 13 - 2n \le 3$

(c) $-10 < -3n < 0$

(d) $6 > \frac{1}{2} - \frac{3n}{2} > 3$

(e) $-5 > 8 - \frac{n}{3} > -8$

(f) $200 < 500 - 99n \le 500$

5 Write down all integers n for which

(a) $n^2 < 5$

(b) $3 < n^2 < 10$

(c) $-7 < n^2 < 7$

(d) $n^2 \le 9$ and $n < 1$

6 How many integers satisfy each of these?

    (a) $0 \le n \le 100$ **(b)** $0 < 3n < 100$ **(c)** $250 < 7n < 750$ **(d)** $n^2 < 1000$

DISCUSSION POINT

- For what values of x is $(x - 2)(x - 5) < 0$?
  Sketch the graph of $y = (x - 2)(x - 5)$.
- Discuss how this graph can be used to solve the inequality $(x - 2)(x - 5) < 0$.
- For what values of x is $x^2 - 5x \ge 6$?
- For what values of x is $(x - 3)^2 < 16$?

EXERCISE 12

1 Solve these inequalities.

  (a) $(x - 3)(x + 4) < 0$ **(b)** $(x - 2)(x - 6) > 0$

  (c) $x^2 + 4x + 3 \ge 0$ **(d)** $x^2 - 7x - 18 < 0$

  (e) $2x^2 - 5x + 2 \le 0$ **(f)** $5x^2 + 6x > 0$

  (g) $x^2 + 2x \le 8$ **(h)** $x(3x - 8) > 35$

2 Solve these inequalities.

  (a) $x^2 < 36$ **(b)** $x^2 \ge 100$

  (c) $x^2 + 5 > 30$ **(d)** $64 > x^2 - 36$

  (e) $3x^2 + 4 \le 23$ **(f)** $4x^2 - 3 > 1$

  (g) $(x - 4)^2 \le 9$ **(h)** $(x - 3)^2 > 49$

  (i) $x(x - 5) \ge x(5x - 9)$ **(j)** $6x(x - 2) < x - 6$

  (k) $(x - 7)^2 \ge 0$ **(l)** $(x + 5)^2 < 0$

3 Solve these inequalities.

  (a) $\frac{x^2}{2} \le 3x - 4$ **(b)** $\frac{x^2}{3} > 2x + 9$

  (c) $\frac{x^2}{5} > 4x + 25$ **(d)** $3x \ge \frac{x^2}{4}$

  (e) $x^2(x - 1)(x - 2) < 0$ **(f)** $(x - 1)(x - 2)(x - 3) \ge 0$

4 Solve these inequalities.

  (a) $(x + 1)(x - 2) \ge 4 - 2x$ **(b)** $(x - 1)(x + 5) < 2(2x^2 - 3x - 1)$

  (c) $(x + 3)(x + 7) \le (x - 5)(x - 9)$ **(d)** $(x + 3)^2 > x^2 + 2x + 7$

  (e) $(x - 2)^2 \ge x^2$ **(f)** $(x - 4)^2 < 4(x + 2)^2$

Graphs of inequalities

DISCUSSION POINT

- Sketch the graph of $y = 2x + 3$. Where on your sketch is $y > 2x + 3$?
- Sketch the graph of $3x + 4y = 12$. Where on your graph is $3x + 4y < 12$?

EXERCISE 13

1 Sketch these graphs, shading the area required.

(a) $y > 2x$ (b) $y \leq x - 5$

(c) $y - x \leq 1$ (d) $x + y < 6$

(e) $2y \geq x + 4$ (f) $y + 2x \geq 4$

(g) $2x - 5y \geq 10$ (h) $3x + 4y + 15 \leq 0$

2 The interior of a parallelogram satisfies these four inequalities.

$y < 2x$ $y > 2x - 4$ $y > 0$ $y < 3$

Sketch the parallelogram.

3 Give three inequalities to define the interior of this triangle.

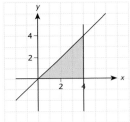

4 Give four inequalities to define the exterior of this rhombus.

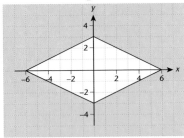

5 State four inequalities that define the interior of this isosceles trapezium.

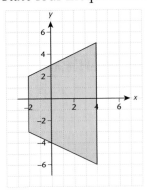

6 State four inequalities that define the interior of this kite.

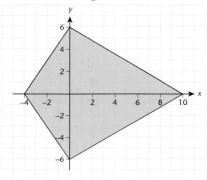

7 A triangle satisfies these three inequalities.

$y \leq 2x$ $2x + y \leq 8$ $y \geq 0$

(a) Sketch the triangle.

(b) If the value of $x + y$ is evaluated everywhere in the triangle, where is it greatest? What is this greatest value?
Where is $x + y$ least? What is this least value?

(c) Where in the triangle is $3x + y$ greatest and where is it least? What are the greatest and least values?

(d) Where in the triangle is $y - x$ greatest and where is it least? What are the greatest and least values?

8 The interior of a quadrilateral satisfies these four inequalities.

$y \leq 2x$ $2y \leq x + 10$ $y + 2x \leq 20$ $y \geq 0$

(a) Sketch the quadrilateral.

(b) Find the maximum and minimum values in the quadrilateral of
    (i) $x + y$ (ii) $x + 3y$ (iii) $y - 2x$ (iv) $2y - x$

9 The vertices of a quadrilateral are at (–5, 1), (2, 5), (5, –7) and (–2, –3).

(a) Sketch the quadrilateral.

(b) Find the maximum and minimum values in the quadrilateral of
    (i) $x + y$ (ii) $3x + y$ (iii) $x + 4y$ (iv) $2y - 3x$

Using inequalities for modelling

Inequalities can be used to model real-life situations and solve related problems.

EXERCISE 14

1 (a) In a class, the number of boys (b) is more than twice the number of girls (g).
Express this statement as an inequality.

(b) In the same class, the total number of children is less than 30.
Express this as an inequality.

2 The difference between the maximum temperature ($x°C$) and the minimum temperature ($n°C$) in a school must not be more than 5°C. Express this statement as an inequality.

3 The maximum speed allowed on the motorway is 70 m.p.h. If a car travels legally, write each of these as an inequality.
   (a) The time (t seconds) it takes to travel 50 miles down the motorway
   (b) The distance (d miles) the car travels in $1\frac{1}{2}$ hours down the motorway

4 A group of friends buy some chocolate to eat after school. Chocolate pyramids cost 27p and chocolate cones cost 34p. They have £3 to spend and they buy P pyramids and C cones. Write down an inequality satisfied by P and C.

5 At a concert the number of children (c) cannot be greater than half the number of adults (a). Write this as an inequality.

6 In a test, everyone scores at least half marks but no one scores full marks. If a student scores x% in the test write down inequalities for x.

7 The area of a car park is 2400 m². Buses take up 30 m² each and cars take up 6 m² each. If there are b buses and c cars in the car park, write down an inequality involving b and c.

8 In a zoo, there are e elephants and s storks. The total number of legs of the elephants and storks is less than 100. The number of elephant legs is at least four more than the number of stork legs. Express this information as inequalities.

▶ Graph paper

DISCUSSION POINT

A group of students is setting up a mini-enterprise project. The students have decided to market Christmas cards and gift tags. It costs them £1.50 to produce each pack of cards and 75p for each pack of tags. They must not exceed their budget of £60. They want to produce at least twice as many packs of cards as tags, as they think the cards will be more popular. Their teacher has stipulated that, to make the enterprise worthwhile, they must produce at least 40 packs of items altogether to sell.

• How many packs of cards and packs of tags should they produce to satisfy all the constraints?

• If they sell packs of cards for £1.95 and packs of tags for £1, how many of each should they produce to maximise their profit?

Set up a suitable mathematical model of this situation.

• What are the variables?

• What are the constraints?

Draw a diagram to find the best solution for the students.

EXERCISE 15

1 Jill is making cakes for Shula to sell at the village fête.

Fruit cakes need 200 g of flour and 50 g of margarine. Sponge cakes require 100 g of each.

Jill has 2 kg of flour and 800 g of margarine. She wants to make as many cakes as possible. How many of each type should she make?

2 A school is planning its annual music concert. There are 150 seats available. It is decided that at least one-third of the people attending the concert must be students. The concert will be cancelled if less than 60 parents buy tickets. The price is £3 for parents and £2 for students. The school wants to raise at least £300 to cover the costs of the production.

(a) Draw a diagram to show all the ways in which tickets can be sold for the concert to go ahead.

(b) What is the least total number of tickets that can be sold for the concert to go ahead?

3 A university student has two part-time jobs to help to pay for her fees. One job is serving in a cafe, for which she gets paid £4 per hour. She has to work at least 12 hours a week to keep this job, and they never need her for more than 15 hours work. She also takes in ironing from other students for which she charges £2.50 per hour.

She wants to earn at least £60 a week but does not want to work for more than 20 hours per week.

What choices are open to her? What is the most she can earn?

4 A teacher is planning his 50-minute French lesson. The students need to spend some time on speaking and listening, and some time on reading and writing.

He knows that the students will not be able to concentrate on a speaking and listening session of more than 15 minutes. If the reading and writing session is more than three times longer than the speaking and listening session the students will become bored.

He wants to spend at least 10 minutes on speaking and listening, and at least 30 minutes on reading and writing.

How can he plan his lesson?

5 Peter and Paul are employed to make articles on a certain machine, which requires one person to operate it. Peter can make 10 articles per hour. Paul can make 15 articles per hour, but union regulations state there must not be a difference of more than 2 hours in the time people work.

The machine must not be used for more than 12 hours a day and at least 120 articles have to be produced. Peter is paid £5 per hour and Paul is paid £7 per hour.

How should the company plan the working hours for Peter and Paul to minimise the wage bill but meet the other constraints?

Algebraic fractions

These can often be simplified by factorising.

$$\frac{x^2 - 1}{x + 1} = \frac{(x - 1)(x + 1)}{x + 1} = x - 1$$ Cancel the $(x + 1)$.

Use the same rules for combining algebraic fractions as you use for numerical fractions.

$$\frac{2}{y - 1} - \frac{2}{y + 1} = \frac{2(y + 1)}{(y - 1)(y + 1)} - \frac{2(y + 1)}{(y - 1)(y + 1)}$$

$$= \frac{2(y + 1) - 2(y - 1)}{(y + 1)(y - 1)}$$

$$= \frac{2y + 2 - 2y + 2}{(y - 1)(y + 1)}$$

$$= \frac{4}{(y - 1)(y + 1)}$$

$$\frac{2x + 4}{x^2 - 1} \times \frac{x^2 + 2x + 1}{6} = \frac{2(x + 2)}{(x - 1)(x + 1)} \times \frac{(x + 1)(x + 1)}{6}$$

$$= \frac{(x + 2)(x + 1)}{3(x - 1)}$$ Cancel the $2(x + 1)$.

Solving equations involving algebraic fractions

$$\frac{4}{2x + 1} = \frac{5}{3x + 1}$$ Multiply through by $(2x + 1)(3x + 1)$.

$\Rightarrow \qquad 4(3x + 1) = 5(2x + 1)$

$\Rightarrow \qquad\qquad 2x = 1$

$\Rightarrow \qquad\qquad x = \frac{1}{2}$

$$\frac{9}{x - 4} - \frac{15}{2x + 1} = 2$$ Multiply through by $(x - 4)(2x + 1)$.

$\Rightarrow \quad 9(2x + 1) - 15(x - 4) = 2(x - 4)(2x + 1)$

$\Rightarrow \qquad\qquad 4x^2 - 17x - 77 = 0$

$\Rightarrow \qquad\qquad (x - 7)(4x + 11) = 0$

$\Rightarrow \qquad\qquad\qquad x = 7$

$\qquad\qquad\qquad\qquad \text{or } x = -2\frac{3}{4}$

Nelson GCSE Maths   ALGEBRAIC MANIPULATION (HIGHER)

Changing the subject of a formula

These examples cover most of the different types you are likely to meet.

Make T the subject in $A = P + \dfrac{PRT}{100}$.

Multiply by 100: $\hspace{4cm} 100A = 100P + PRT$

Rearrange terms: $\hspace{4cm} PRT = 100A - 100P$

Divide by PR: $\hspace{4.5cm} T = \dfrac{100A - 100P}{PR}$

Make I the subject in $L = W - I^2R$.

Rearrange terms: $\hspace{4cm} I^2R = W - L$

Divide by R: $\hspace{4.5cm} I^2 = \dfrac{W - L}{R}$

Take the square root: $\hspace{4cm} I = \sqrt{\dfrac{W - L}{R}}$

Make l the subject in $T = 2\pi\sqrt{\dfrac{l}{g}}$.

Rearrange terms: $\hspace{4cm} \dfrac{T}{2\pi} = \sqrt{\dfrac{l}{g}}$

Square both sides: $\hspace{4cm} \dfrac{T^2}{4\pi^2} = \dfrac{l}{g}$

Multiply by $4\pi^2 g$: $\hspace{4cm} T^2g = 4\pi^2 l$

Divide by $4\pi^2$: $\hspace{4.5cm} l = \dfrac{T^2g}{4\pi^2}$

Make n the subject in $S = 180 - \dfrac{360}{n}$.

Multiply by n: $\hspace{4cm} Sn = 180n - 360$

Rearrange terms: $\hspace{3.5cm} 180n - Sn = 360$

Factorise: $\hspace{4cm} n(180 - S) = 360$

Divide by bracket: $\hspace{4.5cm} n = \dfrac{360}{180 - S}$

Make R the subject in $V = \dfrac{12R}{r + R}$.

Multiply by $(r + R)$: $\hspace{3cm} V(r + R) = 12R$

Multiply out bracket: $\hspace{3cm} Vr + VR = 12R$

Rearrange terms: $\hspace{3cm} 12R - VR = Vr$

Factorise: $\hspace{3.5cm} R(12 - V) = Vr$

Divide by bracket: $\hspace{4cm} R = \dfrac{Vr}{12 - V}$

Make v the subject in $\dfrac{1}{f} = \dfrac{1}{u} + \dfrac{1}{v}$.

Rearrange terms: $\hspace{4cm} \dfrac{1}{v} = \dfrac{1}{f} - \dfrac{1}{u}$

Write as one fraction: $\hspace{4cm} \dfrac{1}{v} = \dfrac{u - f}{uf}$

Invert both sides: $\hspace{4.5cm} v = \dfrac{uf}{u - f}$

Inequalities

Inequalities use the symbols $<$, $\leq$, $>$ and $\geq$.
They show the range of values for which a statement is true.

$$2x - 5 \leq 7$$
$$\Rightarrow \quad 2x \leq 12$$
$$\Rightarrow \quad x \leq 6$$

$$6 - x < 5$$
$$\Rightarrow \quad 6 < 5 + x$$
$$\Rightarrow \quad 1 < x$$

They can be shown on a number line.

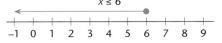

Quadratic inequalities

Example
$(x - 2)(x - 5) < 0$
The solution to this is $2 < x < 5$.
You can see this from this graph.

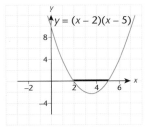

Or, you can think about the sign of each bracket.
In this case, the brackets need to have opposite
signs so that their product is negative.
Hence $2 < x < 5$.

Example
$(x - 3)^2 < 16$
$\Rightarrow \quad -4 < x - 3 < 4$
$\Rightarrow \quad -1 < x < 7$

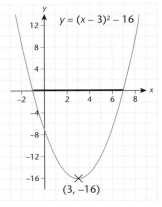

Regions

Inequalities are used to describe **regions** on a graph.

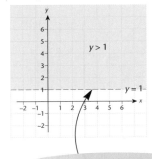

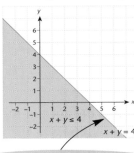

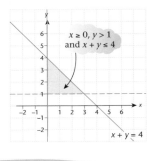

The dotted line means that the points on the boundary line are not included in
the region. The solid line means that they are.

This technique can be used to solve real-life problems: see Exercise 15 on
page 94.

6 FURTHER TRIGONOMETRY

- Pythagoras' theorem and trigonometry in three dimensions
- areas and volumes of plane and solid shapes
- the sine rule and cosine rule for a triangle
- the formula $\frac{1}{2}ab\sin C$ for the area of a triangle
- problems involving upper and lower bounds
- sines, cosines and tangents for angles of any size
- graphs of trigonometric functions
- solving trigonometric equations
- trigonometry without a calculator
- rational and irrational values of trigonometric functions.

Pythagoras' theorem and trigonometry in three dimensions

DISCUSSION POINT

A square-based pyramid rests on a horizontal table. The square base has four edges of length 5 cm, and the four slant edges are of length 6 cm.

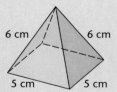

- How high is the apex of the pyramid above the table?
- What is the volume of the pyramid?
- What angle does one of the slant edges of the pyramid make with the table?
- What angle does one of the slanting faces make with the base of the pyramid?

1 The square base of this pyramid has edges of length 8 cm.
The four slant edges are of length 10 cm.

(a) Find the distance between the apex
of the pyramid and the centre of
the square base.

(b) Find the volume of the pyramid.

(c) Find the angle between one of
the slanting faces and the base
of the pyramid.

(d) Find the angle between one of the slant
edges and the base of the pyramid.

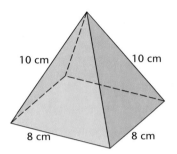

2 This cuboid has base edges of lengths 3 cm and 4 cm and a height of 5 cm.

(a) Find the length of the diagonal AC of the base.

(b) The diagonal AC meets three edges of the cuboid
at each of its ends.
Find the angle between this diagonal
and each of the three edges
it meets at one of its ends.

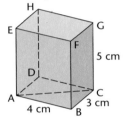

3 This cuboid has edges of length
5 cm, 7 cm and 9 cm.

(a) Find the length of the
diagonal AG.

(b) The diagonal AG meets three
other edges of the cuboid at A.
Find the angle between AG and
each of these three edges.

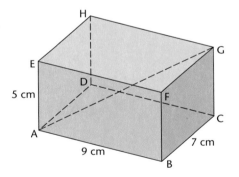

4 This pyramid has a square base with edges of length 10 cm.
Another edge of the pyramid is
perpendicular to the base and the
length of this edge is 8 cm.

Find the length of each of the
remaining three edges and the angle
each of these edges makes with the
base of the pyramid.

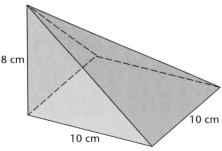

Nelson GCSE Maths FURTHER TRIGONOMETRY (HIGHER)

5 All eight edges of this square-based pyramid are of length 15 cm.

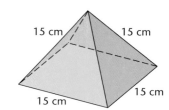

(a) Find the distance of the apex of the pyramid from its square base.

(b) Find the angle each of the slant edges makes with the base of the pyramid.

(c) Find the angle each of the slanting faces make with each other.

(d) Find the angle between two of the adjacent slanting faces.

6 The side of this hill is an inclined plane. A straight path PQ directly up this hill has a gradient of 1 in 3.

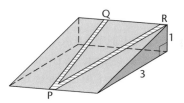

Another straight path PR up the hill starts from the same point and makes an angle of 60° with the direct path.
What is its gradient?

7 This picture shows the shape of the roof of a house. The horizontal base of the roof is 12 m by 8 m. The horizontal ridge at the top of the roof is 8 metres long and is 2 m above the base of the roof. The four slanting edges of the roof are all the same length.

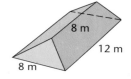

(a) Calculate the pitch of each of the plane faces of the roof (i.e. the angle the face makes with the horizontal).

(b) Calculate the length of the slanting edges of the roof.

8 A is the apex of a cone. O is the centre of the base and AO is perpendicular to the base. B is a point on the circumference of the circular base of the cone. The base of the cone has radius 10 cm.
The volume of the cone is 500 cm².

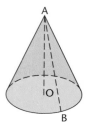
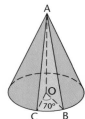

(a) Find the distance between A and the base of the cone.

(b) Find the length of AB.

(c) Find the angle AB makes with the base of the cone.

(d) C is a point on the circumference of the cone and ∠BOC is 70°.
Find the angle between the lines AB and AC.

9 A regular tetrahedron has four equilateral triangular faces.
The edges of this regular tetrahedron are all of length 12 cm.

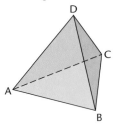 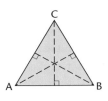

(a) Look at the face ABC.
Find the distance of the centre of this face from one of its corners.

(b) Find the distance of the vertex D from the face ABC.

(c) Find the volume of the tetrahedron.

(d) Find the angle one edge makes with an adjacent face (e.g. the angle between edge AD and face ABC).

(e) Find the angle between two of the faces of the tetrahedron.

10 A cube is dissected into six identical square-based pyramids. The cube has edges of length 1 m. Consider one of the six square-based pyramids into which this cube has been divided.

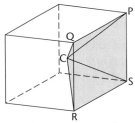 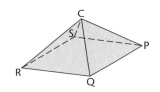

(a) Find the volume of this pyramid.

(b) Find all edge lengths of this pyramid.

(c) Find the angle between one of the triangular faces and the square face of this pyramid.

11 A regular octahedron consists of two square-based pyramids stuck together at their bases. All the edges of the octahedron are the same length.
Suppose the edges of the octahedron are all of length 6 cm.

(a) Find the volume of the octahedron.

(b) Find the angle that the longest diagonal of the octahedron makes with each of the faces it meets.

(c) Choose an edge of the octahedron. It meets six other edges of the octahedron. Find the angle the chosen edge makes with each of these edges.

(d) Is your answer to part (c) changed if you choose a different edge of the octahedron?

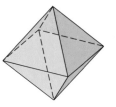

12 A cube has sides of length 1 unit. Four of the vertices of the cube are
selected so that they are the vertices of a regular tetrahedron.
The tetrahedron is obtained by cutting off the other four corners of the cube.

(a) Draw a sketch of one of the cut off corners.

(b) What fraction of the volume of the cube is the volume of each
of these pieces?

(c) What fraction of the volume of the cube is the volume of
the tetrahedron?

(d) Find the exact value of the edge lengths of this regular tetrahedron.

(e) Find the exact value of the surface area of this regular tetrahedron.

The sine rule

DISCUSSION POINT

Draw several different triangles and label their sides and angles
as in this diagram.

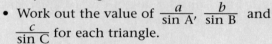

- Measure the sides and angles of each
  of your triangles.

- Work out the value of $\dfrac{a}{\sin A}$, $\dfrac{b}{\sin B}$ and
  $\dfrac{c}{\sin C}$ for each triangle.

- What do you notice?

Use what you noticed to calculate   Use what you noticed to calculate
side b in this triangle.   the angle at C in this triangle.

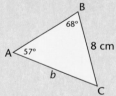   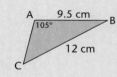

The sine rule

This rule – called the **sine rule** – applies to any triangle and can be used to
calculate a side or an angle.

$$\frac{a}{\sin A} = \frac{b}{\sin B} = \frac{c}{\sin C}$$

You can use the sine rule

- *either* if you know two sides of a triangle and the angle opposite one of
  them, and want to find the other angles of the triangle

- *or* if you know all three angles and one of the sides and want to find one
  or both of the other sides.

For an explanation of why this formula works, see Question 8 of Exercise 2.

1 Find the lengths of the two unmarked sides in these triangles.

(a)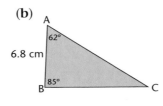

(b)

(c)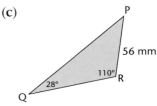

2 Find the sizes of the two unmarked angles in these acute-angled triangles.

(a)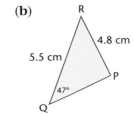

(b)

(c)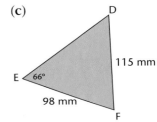

3 Find the perimeter of this triangle.

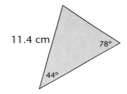

4 Find the perimeter of this obtuse-angled triangle.

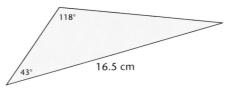

5 A vertical flagpole has its base at B. A person stands at point A and another person stands at point C, 100 metres from A. ABC is a straight line.

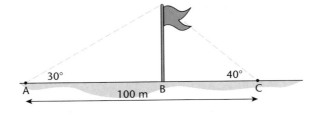

The angle of elevation of the top of the flagpole from A is 30° and from B it is 40°.
Find the height of the flagpole.

6 The sides of an equiangular octagon, ABCDEFGH, are alternately of length 3 cm and x cm.

The area of the square ACEG is 16 cm².
Find x.

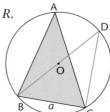

7 The sine rule is

$$\frac{a}{\sin A} = \frac{b}{\sin B} = \frac{c}{\sin C}$$

Explain what happens to the sine rule when the angle A is a right angle.

8 ABC is a triangle. The length of BC is a.
O is the centre of the circle through A, B and C.
BD is a diameter of the circle. The radius of the circle is R.
(a) What type of triangle is triangle BDC?
(b) Find sin D in terms of R and a.
(c) Find sin A in terms of R and a.
(d) Use your answer to part (c) to prove
    the sine rule.

Providing a
mathematically
rigorous
justification

9 Use the result of Question 8 part (c) to find the radius of the circle through the vertices of this triangle.

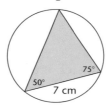

10 The radius of a circle is 10 cm. ABC is an equilateral triangle with vertices on the circle. Find the length of one side of the triangle.

DISCUSSION POINT
Find the angle marked ? in each of these triangles.

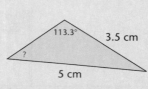

Can you explain your answers?

The cosine rule

DISCUSSION POINT

The cosine rule

This rule – the **cosine rule** – applies to any triangle and can be used to calculate a side or an angle.

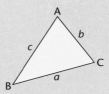

$$c^2 = a^2 + b^2 - 2ab\cos C$$

- What happens to the rule when the angle at C is 90°?
- Compare c^2 with $a^2 + b^2$ when the angle at C is less than 90°.
- What happens when the angle at C is greater than 90°?
- Check that the cosine rule gives the correct answer for these two triangles.

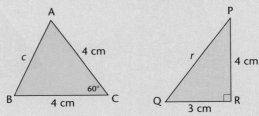

You can use the cosine rule

- *either* if you know two sides of a triangle and the angle between them and want to find the third side
- *or* if you know all three sides and want to find one or more of the angles.

Use the cosine rule to find *b* in this triangle.

Use the cosine rule to find angles D, E and F.

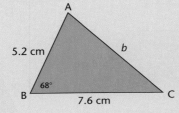

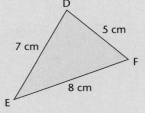

For an explanation of why the cosine rule works, see Question 7 of Exercise 3.

EXERCISE 3

1 Find the length of the unmarked side in each of these triangles.

(a)

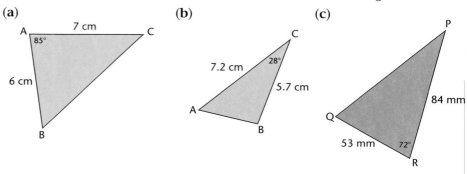

(b)

(c)

2 Find all three angles of each of these triangles.

(a)

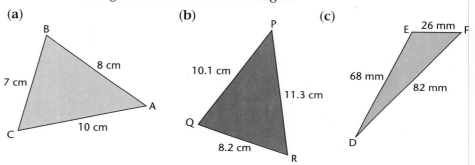

(b)

(c)

3 In which of these triangles is one angle exactly 120°?

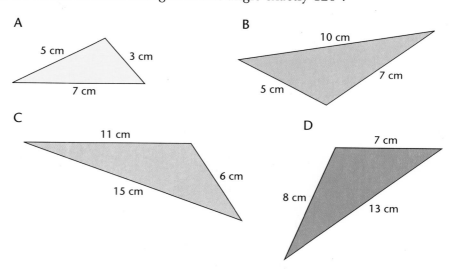

4 In which of these triangles is the perimeter a whole number of centimetres?

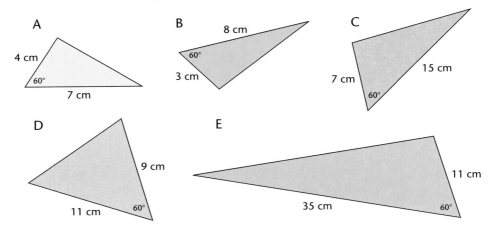

5 The sides of a regular pentagon are of length 4 cm.
Use the cosine rule to find the length of each of the diagonals.

6 The sides of an equiangular octagon, ABCDEFGH, are alternately of length 2 cm and 3 cm.

Find the area of the square ACEG.

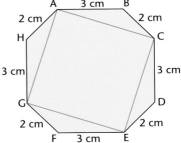

Providing a
mathematically
rigorous
justification

7 ABC is a triangle. A perpendicular is drawn from A to meet BC at D.

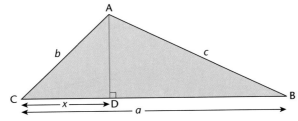

a, b, c and x are the lengths of BC, AC, AB and CD respectively.
(a) Write x in terms of b and $\cos C$.
(b) Use Pythagoras' theorem to find two different expressions for the square of the length of AD.
(c) Hence show that $b^2 = c^2 - a^2 + 2ax$
(d) Use parts (a) and (c) to complete the proof of the cosine rule.

The formula $\frac{1}{2}ab\sin C$

This rule applies to any triangle.

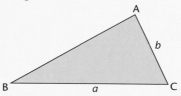

The area of triangle ABC is $\frac{1}{2}ab\sin C$.

You can use this rule to find the area of a triangle if you know two sides of a triangle and the angle between them.

Providing a
mathematically
rigorous
justification

DISCUSSION POINT

Use this diagram to prove the formula $\frac{1}{2}ab\sin C$ for the area of a triangle, when the angle at corner C is an acute angle.

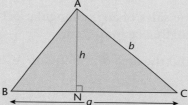

Draw a suitable diagram and prove the formula when the angle C is an obtuse angle.

Explain what happens to the rule $\frac{1}{2}ab\sin C$ when C is a right angle.

EXERCISE 4

1 Find the area of each of these triangles.

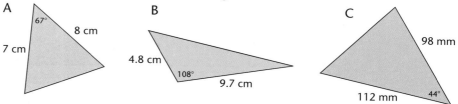

2 Each of these triangles has an area of $10\,\text{cm}^2$. Find the angle marked x in each triangle.

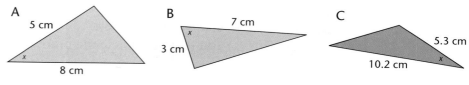

3 Find the area of an equilateral triangle with sides of length 6 cm.

4 Find the area of a rhombus in which each side is 4 cm long and one of the angles is 30°.

5 Two of the sides of a triangle are 8 cm and 6 cm.
   (a) What should the angle between these sides be, if the area of the triangle is to be as large as possible?
   (b) What should the angle between these sides be, if the area of the triangle is to be half the largest possible area?

6 An equiangular hexagon, ABCDEF, has sides alternately of length 2 cm and 3 cm.
   (a) Prove that triangle ACE is equilateral.
   (b) Find the length of AC.
   (c) Find the area of triangle ACE.
   (d) Find the area of the hexagon ABCDEF.

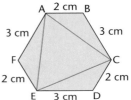

Applications of the sine and cosine rules

EXERCISE 5

1 The sides of a hexagon, ABCDEF, are all 5 cm long. The angles at A, C and E are each 140° and at B, D and F are each 100°.
   (a) Find the length of BD.
   (b) Find the length of BE.

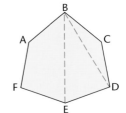

2 Two ships leave a port, P, at the same time. One of them is travelling at an average speed of 11.5 km/h on a bearing of 295°. The other travels South-West at an average speed of 14 km/h.

How far are the ships apart after two hours?

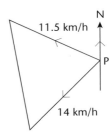

3 A straight coastline runs North–South. In a lookout station on the coast, Jim notices a ship on a bearing of 122°. In a lookout station 15.7 km south on the same coast, Fred notices the same ship on a bearing of 053°.
   (a) Is the ship nearer to Jim or to Fred?
   (b) How far is the ship from Jim?
   (c) How far is the ship from the coast?

4 A woman walks for 5 km on a bearing of
160° and then for 7 km on a bearing of 235°.

(a) How far is she from her starting point?

(b) If she wants to return to her starting
point by walking in a straight line, on
what bearing should she walk?

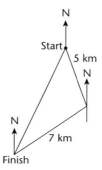

5 Anne knows that two villages, Ayford and Beasby, are 5 miles apart and
that Beasby is due West of Ayford. On a walk in the country one day, she
notices that the church in Ayford is on a bearing of 160° and the church
in Beasby is on a bearing of 230°. Calculate her distance from Ayford.

6 Anne and Mary are on the horizontal floor of a valley and decide to find
the height of a hill. They measure out 200 metres. Anne stands at one end
of the 200 metres. The angle of elevation of the top of the hill H is 27°.
Mary stands at the other end of the 200 metres. She notices that Anne
and the top of the hill are in the same direction. The angle of elevation of
the top of the hill from Mary is 18°.

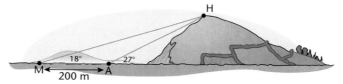

(a) Calculate the distance of the top of the hill from Mary.

(b) Calculate the height of the hill above the valley.

7 Bob and Andy are in two villages which are 12 km apart and at the same
altitude. Andy's village is due East of Bob's. Bob notices a church on a
hillside at an angle of elevation of 5° and on a bearing of 082°.
Andy notices the same church on a bearing of 281°.

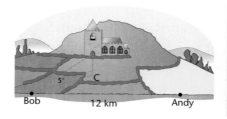
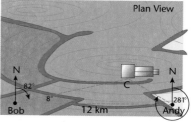

(a) Who is nearer to the church, Bob or Andy?

(b) If the villages are 75 m above sea level, what is the altitude of the
church above sea level?

8 From the top of a cliff 40 m high, a coastguard notices two canoes.
One is on a bearing of 273° and at an
angle of depression of 18°.
The other is on a bearing of 302° and
at an angle of depression of 11°.
How far apart are the canoes?

coastguard

40 m

9 Anne stands on horizontal ground and measures the angle of elevation of
the top of a tower as 37°, correct to the nearest degree. She takes the
measurement 1.6 m above the ground, correct to the nearest 0.1 m.
She then measures her distance from the bottom of the tower as 33 m
correct to the nearest metre.
   (a) Use her measurements to calculate the height of the tower.
   (b) Using the accuracy given, calculate the greatest and least values for
   the height of the tower.

10 In triangle DEF, ∠DEF is 72° measured correct to the nearest degree.
The length of DE is 3.5 cm and of EF is 4.2 cm, each measured correct to
the nearest 0.1 cm.
   (a) Find the upper and lower bounds for the length of DF.
   (b) Find upper and lower bounds for the area of the triangle.

Spreadsheet

11 In the triangle ABC, the distance from A to B is 13 km and from A to C is
18 km. The bearing of C from A is 235° and the bearing
of B from A is 020°.
The distances are measured correct to the nearest km and the
bearings correct to the nearest 5 degrees.
Find upper and lower bounds for the distance of B from C.

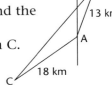
N B

13 km

A

C

18 km

12 A stretch of river has straight parallel banks. There is a notice board N on
one bank of the river. On the opposite bank Andy and Brian are standing
120 m apart. Andy measures the angle between the notice board and the
bank as 27°. Brian measures it as 17°.
   (a) Calculate the width of the river.
   (b) Suppose that the angles are
   correct to ±2° and the distance
   is correct to ±1 m. Calculate the
   maximum and minimum
   widths the river could be.

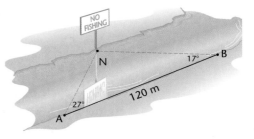
NO
FISHING

N   17° B

120 m

27°

A

Sines, cosines and tangents for angles of any size

The sine and cosine of any angle
This is a reminder of the definitions given in Chapter 9 of *Book 1*.

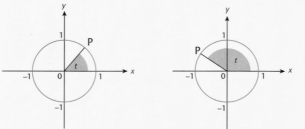

When *t* is any angle, not necessarily between 0° and 90°, these definitions
can be made.

$\cos t$ is the *x*-coordinate of point P

$\sin t$ is the *y*-coordinate of point P

EXERCISE 6

1 These pictures show unit circles with angles of 125°, 160°, 230° and 310°

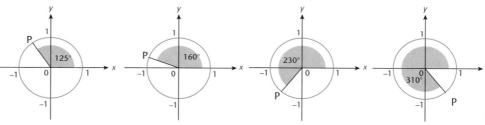

Find each of these, correct to 2 decimal places.

(**a**) cos 125°   (**b**) sin 125°   (**c**) cos 160°   (**d**) sin 160°
(**e**) cos 230°   (**f**) sin 230°   (**g**) cos 310°   (**h**) sin 310°

2 These pictures show unit circles with angles of −60°, −155°, 400° and 500°.

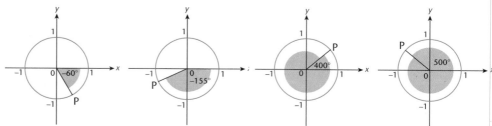

Find each of these, correct to 2 decimal places.

(**a**) cos −60°   (**b**) sin −60°   (**c**) cos −155°   (**d**) sin −155°
(**e**) cos 400°   (**f**) sin 400°   (**g**) cos 500°   (**h**) sin 00°

Use this data for
Questions 1 and 2.

Angle	Cosine	Sine
20°	0.94	0.34
25°	0.91	0.42
40°	0.77	0.64
50°	0.64	0.77
55°	0.57	0.82
60°	0.5	0.87

3 (a) Use a calculator to find these, correct to 3 decimal places.

    (i) cos 210°   **(ii)** sin 300°   **(iii)** sin 100°

    (iv) cos –100°   **(v)** cos 430°   **(vi)** sin 600°

  (b) Which of your answers in part **(a)** are positive? Which are negative? Draw sketches to explain why.

The tangent of any angle

This is a reminder of the definition given in Chapter 9 of *Book 1*.

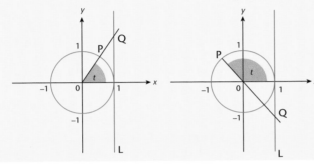

When t is any angle, not necessarily between 0° and 90°, this definition can be made:

tan t is the y-coordinate of point Q

EXERCISE 7

1 These pictures show unit circles with angles of 125°, 160°, 230°, 310°.

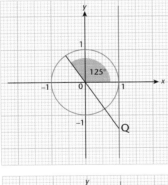

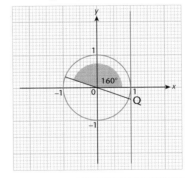

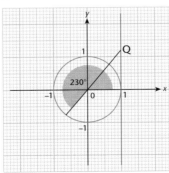

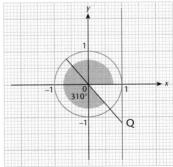

  (a) Use the pictures to estimate the tangents of the four angles.

  (b) Using your calculator, write down the tangents of these angles, correct to 3 decimal places.

2 These pictures show unit circles with angles of −60°, −155°, 400° and 500°.

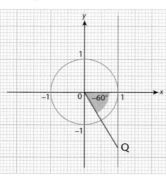 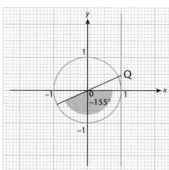

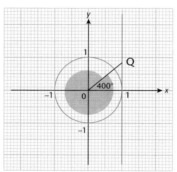 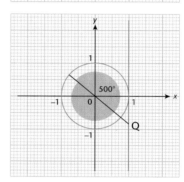

(a) Use the pictures to estimate the tangents of the four angles.

(b) Using your calculator, write down the tangents of these angles, correct to 3 decimal places.

3 (a) Use a calculator to find each of these, correct to 3 decimal places.

(i) tan 220°	(ii) tan 300°	(iii) tan 100°
(iv) tan −100°	(v) tan 445°	(vi) tan 600°

(b) Which of your answers in part (a) are positive? Which are negative? Draw sketches to explain why.

Exercise 8

1 Find the values of these.

(a) cos 180°	(b) sin 360°	(c) tan 180°
(d) sin 90°	(e) cos −90°	(f) sin 540°
(g) cos −450°	(h) tan 135°	(i) tan −135°

Use this triangle to help you to answer Question 2(a).

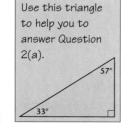

2 Use the fact that cos 57° = 0.545 correct to 3 decimal places.

(a) Write down sin 33°, correct to 3 decimal places.

(b) Write down these, correct to 3 decimal places.

(i) cos −57°	(ii) sin 147°	(iii) cos 303°
(iv) sin −213°		

3 Use the fact that tan 22.62° is $\frac{5}{12}$ to write these as fractions.

   (**a**) sin 22.62°   (**b**) cos 22.62°

   (**c**) tan 67.38°   (**d**) sin –22.62°

   (**e**) cos –202.62°   (**f**) tan –247.38°

   (**g**) tan 337.38°

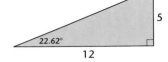

Trigonometric equations

EXERCISE 9

1 (**a**) Draw a graph of $y = \sin x$ for values of x between 0° and 360°.

   (**b**) Use your calculator to find the value of x between 0° and 90° for which $\sin x = 0.4$. Give your answer correct to 1 decimal place.

   (**c**) Use your graph and your answer to part (**b**) to help you to find the other value of x between 0° and 360° for which $\sin x = 0.4$.

2 Here is the graph of $y = \cos x$ for values of x between –180° and 180°.

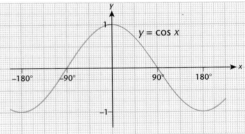

   (**a**) $\cos p = \cos 110°$ and p is an angle between –180° and 180° but *not* equal to 110°. Find the value of p.

   (**b**) $\cos q = -\cos 35°$ and q is an angle between –180° and 180°. Find all possible values of q.

3 Here is the graph of $y = \tan x$ for values of x between –90° and 450°.

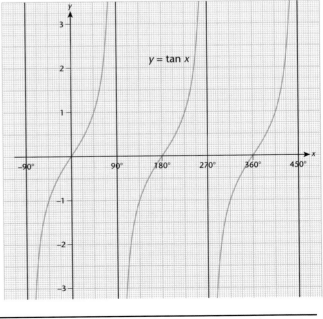

   (**a**) $-90° < p < 450°$ and $\tan p = 1$. Find all possible values of p.

   (**b**) $-90° < q < 450°$ and $\tan q = -1$. Find all possible values of q.

   (**c**) $-90° < r < 450°$ and $\tan r = \tan 317°$. Find all possible values of r.

4 (a) Find the values of θ between 0° and 360° for which $\sin\theta = 0.3$.

  (b) Find the values of θ between 0° and 360° for which $\tan\theta = -2$.

5 (a) Find the values of θ between −90° and 450° for which $\cos\theta = 0.4$.

  (b) Find the values of θ between −90° and 450° for which $\sin\theta = -0.4$.

6 t lies between 0° and 360° and $\sin t = \cos 310°$.
Find all possible values of t.

7 (a) t lies between −360° and 360° and $\tan t \times \tan 50° = 1$.
Find all possible values of t.

  (b) u lies between −360° and 360° and $\tan u \times \tan 215° = -1$.
Find all possible values of u.

8 t lies between 0° and 360° and $\cos t = 0.6$.
Find the possible values for $\sin t$.

9 t lies between 90° and 360° and $\sin t = 0.6$.
Find $\cos t$.

10 (a) For which values of x is $\sin x$ the same as $\sin 70°$?

  (b) For which values of x is $\sin x$ the same as $\sin 200°$?

11 A trundle wheel moves one metre forward each time it makes a complete turn. In the diagram, P is the point of contact between the trundle wheel and the ground. There is a clicker C, which makes a click sound each time it comes to the bottom of the trundle wheel. The trundle wheel is being used on horizontal ground.

  (a) Find the radius of the trundle wheel.

  (b) Explain why the height, h cm, of C above the ground is $15.9(1 - \cos\theta)$ cm, where θ denotes the angle POC.

  (c) Find two values of θ for which $h = 24$.

  (d) How far does the trundle wheel travel when θ increases from 0° to 205°?

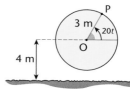

12 The circle shown in this diagram has a radius of 3 m and its centre is fixed 4 metres above the ground. The circle is fixed in a vertical plane.

The point P moves round the circle.
The point P starts from a position where OP is horizontal. After a time t seconds, the height, h metres, of P above the ground is given by
$h = 4 + 3\sin(20t)°$.

  (a) What is the maximum value of h?

  (b) What are the first two values of t for which this maximum height occurs?

  (c) What are the first two values of t for which $h = 5$?

13 t hours after midnight, the depth of water in metres at the end of a pier is approximately $5 + 3\sin(30t)°$. Find the depth of water.
   (a) at midnight   **(b)** at 2 a.m.   **(c)** at 3 a.m.   **(d)** at 5 a.m.

14 t hours after midday, the depth of water in metres at some quay steps is approximately $5 + 4\cos(30t)°$.
   (a) Find the depth of water at 3 p.m.
   (b) Find the depth of water at 5.30 p.m.
   (c) A ship needs at least 7 metres of water to berth at these quay steps. Until what time in the afternoon can the ship safely berth at the steps?

Rationals and irrationals

EXERCISE 10

1 The two equal sides of this triangle are each 1 unit long.
   (a) What is the exact length of the hypotenuse of this triangle?
   (b) What are the exact values of
      (i) $\tan 45°$?   **(ii)** $\cos 45°$?
      (iii) $\sin 45°$?

2 This picture shows an equilateral triangle divided into two triangles. Each side of the equilateral triangle is 2 units long.
   (a) Find the lengths of BD and AD.
   (b) What are the exact values of
      (i) $\sin 60°$?   **(ii)** $\cos 60°$?
      (iii) $\tan 60°$?   **(iv)** $\sin 30°$?
      (v) $\cos 30°$?   **(vi)** $\tan 30°$?

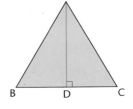

3 Copy and complete this table to show which numbers are rational and which are irrational.

	sin	cos	tan
0°	rational		
30°			
45°			
60°			irrational
90°			

4 A nonagon is inscribed in a circle of radius 8 cm.
   (a) Explain why angle AOD is 120°.
   (b) Find the exact length of the diagonal AD.

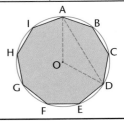

Nelson GCSE Maths FURTHER TRIGONOMETRY (HIGHER)

5 Look at this diagram. Rectangle ABCD has sides of lengths 5 units and 3 units. Rectangle EFGC has sides of lengths 4 units and 3 units. Rectangle EFGC is rotated clockwise about vertex C.

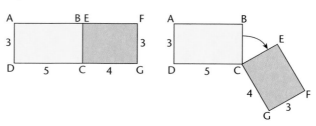

(a) Is the distance BE a rational or an irrational number of units after rectangle EFGC has rotated through
(i) 60°?　　　　(ii) 90°?　　　　(iii) 120°?　　　　(iv) 180°?

(b) Is the distance BG a rational or an irrational number of units after rectangle EFGC has rotated through
(i) 90°?　　　　(ii) 180°?

(c) Is the distance DE a rational or an irrational number of units after rectangle EFGC has rotated through
(i) 90°?　　　　(ii) 180°?

For Question 6, you might find it helpful to draw sketches of the triangles.

6 (a) In this triangle, $\sin x = \frac{3}{5}$.
Find the *exact* value of $\cos x$ and of $\tan x$.

(b) In a triangle, $\cos y = \frac{8}{17}$.
Find the *exact* value of $\sin y$ and of $\tan y$.

(c) In a triangle, $\tan z = \frac{21}{20}$. Find the *exact* value of $\sin z$ and of $\cos z$.

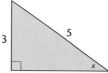

7 (a) $\sin p = \frac{12}{13}$. How many different possible values are there for $\cos p$? Are these values rational or irrational?

(b) $\cos q = -\frac{13}{15}$. How many different possible values are there for $\sin q$? Are these values rational or irrational?

(c) $\sin r = \frac{2}{\sqrt{13}}$. How many different possible values are there for $\tan r$? Are these values rational or irrational?

(d) $\tan s = -1\frac{1}{3}$. How many different possible values are there for $\cos s$? Are these values rational or irrational?

8 Which of these are possible? Which are impossible? For each statement, find an example to show it is possible or explain why it is not possible.

A: There is an angle x for which $\sin x$, $\cos x$ and $\tan x$ are all rational.

B: There is an angle x for which $\sin x$, $\cos x$ and $\tan x$ are all irrational.

C: There is an angle x for which $\tan x$ is rational, but $\cos x$ and $\sin x$ are irrational.

D: There is an angle x for which $\sin x$ is rational, but $\cos x$ and $\tan x$ are irrational.

E: There is an angle x for which $\sin x$ and $\tan x$ are rational, but $\cos x$ is irrational.

9 A, B, C are adjacent vertices on a regular octagon centre O. AO = 10 cm.

(a) Show that AC = 10√2 cm.

(b) AC and OB intersect at D.
Find the exact length of BD and hence the length of each side of the octagon.

(c) Find the exact values of tan 22.5°, sin 22.5° and cos 22.5°.

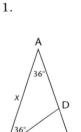

(d) Show that tan 67.5° + tan 22.5° = 2√2.

(e) Find the exact value of each of these, and say whether it is rational or irrational

    (i)   tan 67.5° − tan 22.5°

    (ii)   tan 67.5° × tan 22.5°

    (iii)   tan 67.5° ÷ tan 22.5°

10 Starting with a regular dodecagon, use a method similar to that outlined in Question 9 to find the values of tan 75° and tan 15°.

11 In triangle ABC, the length of AB is x and the length of BC is 1.
∠BAC = 36°. ∠ABC = ∠ACB = 72°. BD bisects angle ABC.

(a) Show that triangle ABC is similar to triangle BCD.

(b) Use part (a) to find the length of CD in terms of x.

(c) What type of triangles are BCD and ABD?

(d) Use parts (b) and (c) to show that the length of AC is $1 + \dfrac{1}{x}$.

(e) Use the fact that triangle ABC is isosceles to write down an equation for x.
Solve this equation to find x.

(f) Find the exact values of cos 72° and cos 36°.

(g) Find the exact value of each of these, and say whether it is rational or irrational.

    (i)   cos 36° + cos 72°

    (ii)   cos 36° − cos 72°

    (iii)   cos 36° × cos 72°

    (iv)   cos 36° ÷ cos 72°

12 Here is a regular pentagon with its diagonals.

Find the exact ratio of the sides of the larger and smaller regular pentagons in this diagram.

Using Pythagoras' theorem in three dimensions

Applying Pythagoras' theorem to triangle PQR gives
$PR = \sqrt{a^2 + b^2}$.
Applying Pythagoras' theorem to triangle PSR gives
$PS = \sqrt{a^2 + b^2 + c^2}$.

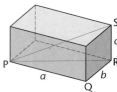

Trigonometry in three dimensions

The angle between an edge and a face
The angle between the edge CP and the base PQRS
is ∠CPN. If lengths are known this angle can be
calculated using trigonometry in triangle CPN.

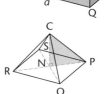

The angle between two faces
The angle between the face PQC and the base PQRS is
∠CMN. Note that both CM and NM are at right angles
to the edge PQ where the faces meet. The angle can be
calculated using trigonometry in triangle CMN.

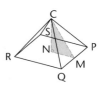

The sine rule
$$\frac{a}{\sin A} = \frac{b}{\sin B} = \frac{c}{\sin C}$$

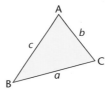

The cosine rule
$$c^2 = a^2 + b^2 - 2ab\cos C$$

You can use the sine rule

- *either* if you know two sides of a triangle and the angle opposite one of
  them and want to find the other angles of the triangle
- *or* if you know all three angles and one of the sides, and want to find one
  or both of the other sides.

You can use the cosine rule

- *either* if you know two sides of a triangle and the angle between them and
  want to find the third side
- *or* if you know all three sides, and want to find one or more of the angles.

Using the cosine rule to find an angle
To find angle D

$$8^2 = 7^2 + 5^2 - 2 \times 7 \times 5 \times \cos D$$
$$\Rightarrow \quad 64 = 74 - 70\cos D$$
$$\Rightarrow \quad 70\cos D = 10$$
$$\Rightarrow \quad \cos D = \tfrac{1}{7}$$
$$\Rightarrow \quad D = 81.8° \text{ approximately.}$$

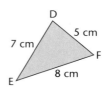

Area of a triangle

The area of triangle ABC is $\frac{1}{2}ab\sin C$.

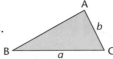

Trigonometric equations

To solve trigonometric equations, you need to be familiar with the graphs of sine, cosine and tangent for angles of any size.

Example

Find the values of x between $0°$ and $360°$ for which $\sin x = 0.4$.

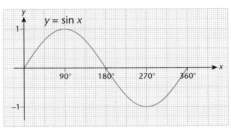

From the graph, it can be seen where approximate solutions occur.
Using a calculator you can discover that one of the solutions is $23.6°$.
So the other solution is
$180 - 23.6° = 156.4°$.
Some equations are more complicated.

Example

When $h = 5$, find the first four positive solutions for t to the equation

$$h = 4 + 3\sin(10t)°$$
$$5 = 4 + 3\sin(10t)°$$
$$\Rightarrow \quad 3\sin(10t)° = 1$$
$$\Rightarrow \quad \sin(10t)° = \tfrac{1}{3}$$
$$\Rightarrow \quad 10t = 19.47, \ 160.53, \ 360 + 19.47, \ 360 + 160.53, \ ...$$

So, the first 4 positive solutions are $t = 1.95$, $t = 16.1$, $t = 37.9$ and $t = 52.1$

Trigonometry without a calculator

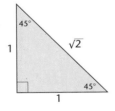

$\sin 45° = \frac{1}{\sqrt{2}}$, $\cos 45° = \frac{1}{\sqrt{2}}$, $\tan 45° = 1$

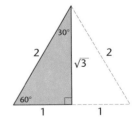

$\sin 30° = \frac{1}{2}$, $\cos 30° = \frac{\sqrt{3}}{2}$, $\tan 30° = \frac{1}{\sqrt{3}}$

$\sin 60° = \frac{\sqrt{3}}{2}$, $\cos 60° = \frac{1}{2}$, $\tan 60° = \sqrt{3}$

If you know, for example, that $\cos y = \frac{15}{17}$, then you can calculate $\sin y$ and $\tan y$ by using Pythagoras' theorem to find the third side of the appropriate right-angled triangle.

$\sin y = \frac{8}{17}$, $\tan y = \frac{8}{15}$

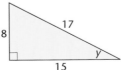

Nelson GCSE Maths FURTHER TRIGONOMETRY (HIGHER)

USING GRAPHS TO SOLVE PROBLEMS

This chapter is about:

- transformations of functions and their graphs
- graphs of trigonometric functions
- solving equations from intersecting graphs
- using graphs to solve inequalities
- finding and using the approximate area under a curve
- finding and using tangents to a curve.

Revisiting quadratic graphs

There was work on
drawing quadratic
functions in
Chapter 11 of Book
1, and in Chapter 3
of this book.
Exercise 1 is a
reminder.

EXERCISE 1

1 (a) Sketch the graph of $y = x^2$.
 (b) On the same axes, sketch the graphs of $y = x^2 + 2$, $y = x^2 + 4$, $y = x^2 - 2$ and $y = x^2 - 4$. Clearly label which is which.
 (c) What transformation maps $y = x^2$ on to $y = x^2 + 4$?
 (d) What transformation maps $y = x^2$ on to $y = x^2 + c$?

2 (a) Sketch the graph of $y = x^2$.
 (b) Sketch the graphs of $y = (x - 1)^2$, $y = (x - 2)^2$, $y = (x + 1)^2$ and $y = (x + 2)^2$. Clearly label which is which.
 (c) What transformation maps $y = x^2$ on to $y = (x + 2)^2$?
 (d) What transformation maps $y = x^2$ on to $y = (x + b)^2$?

3 (a) Sketch the graph of $y = (x - 2)^2 - 3$.
 (b) Sketch the graph of $y = (x + 1)^2 + 2$.
 (c) What transformation maps the first of these graphs on to the second?

4 Sketch the graphs of $y = x^2$, $y = 2x^2$ and $y = \frac{1}{2}x^2$.
 Clearly label which is which.

5 (a) Sketch these graphs.
   A: $y = x^2$ B: $y = -x^2$ C: $y = x^2 + 4$ D: $y = 4 - x^2$
 (b) What transformation maps
   (i) A on to B?   (ii) B on to C?   (iii) C on to D?   (iv) B on to D?

6 Each of these quadratic graphs shows the coordinates of the maximum and minimum points. Each graph is a translation of either $y = x^2$ or $y = -x^2$. Write down the equation of each graph.

A

B
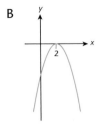

C
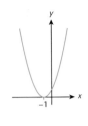

D

E
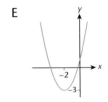

F

7 Consider this graph. A: $y = x^2 - 4x + 3$.
   (a) Sketch the graph A. Where does it cross the x-axis?
   (b) What is the equation of the result if the graph A is
      (i) reflected in the x-axis?
      (ii) reflected in the y-axis?
      (iii) reflected in the line $y = 2$?
      (iv) translated by the vector $\binom{0}{-3}$?
      (v) translated by the vector $\binom{3}{0}$?

8 This design is made from parts of quadratic graphs.
   One of the graphs has equation $y = x^2 - 4$.

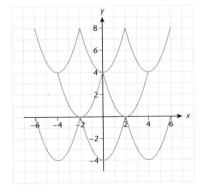

   (a) At what points does the graph $y = x^2 - 4$ cross the axes?
   (b) Find the equations of the other graphs shown.

Transforming graphs

EXERCISE 2

1 Sketch on the same axes, $y = x^3$ and $y = 2x^3$. Label clearly which is which.

2 Match these equations with these graphs.

$y = x^3 - 2$ $y = (x - 2)^3$ $y = 2 - x^3$

$y = (2 - x)^3$ $y = 2x^3$ $y = -(x + 2)^3$

A 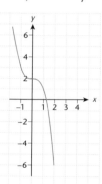 B 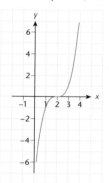 C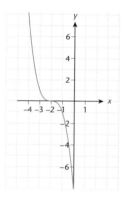

D 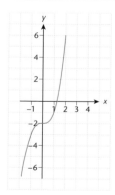 E 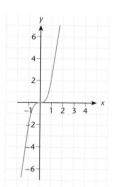 F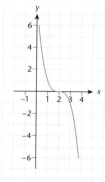

3 Describe precisely the symmetry of each of the graphs in Question 2.

4 (a) Sketch the graph of

   (i) $y = \frac{1}{x}$ **(ii)** $y = -\frac{1}{x}$ **(iii)** $y = \frac{1}{x} + 2$ **(iv)** $y = \frac{1}{x + 2}$

   (b) Describe precisely the symmetry of each of the graphs in part (a).

DISCUSSION POINT

The same principles of transformation apply, whatever type of graph you are sketching.

In these graphs, $f(x)$ means an expression involving x.

This is the graph $y = f(x)$.

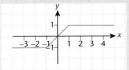

What do these graphs look like?

- $y = f(x) - 2$
- $y = f(x - 2)$
- $y = f(2x)$
- $y = 2f(x)$
- $y = -f(x)$
- $y = f(-x)$
- $y = f\left(\dfrac{x}{2}\right)$

EXERCISE 3

1 This is the graph of $y = f(x)$.

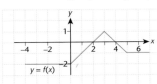

Sketch these graphs.

(**a**) $y = f(x) + 2$ (**b**) $y = -f(x)$ (**c**) $y = 2f(x)$
(**d**) $y = f(x + 3)$ (**e**) $y = f(2x)$ (**f**) $y = f(-x)$

2 This is the graph of $y = f(x)$ with its maximum point A marked.
Sketch these graphs, giving the coordinates of the minimum or
maximum point corresponding to A.

(**a**) $y = f(x) - 3$
(**b**) $y = -2f(x)$
(**c**) $y = 4 - f(x)$
(**d**) $y = f(x - 2)$
(**e**) $y = f(x + 2) + 2$
(**f**) $y = 3f(x - 1) - 4$
(**g**) $y = f(-x)$
(**h**) $y = -f(-x)$

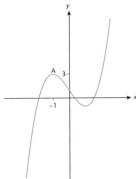

3 This is the graph of $y = f(x)$.
Write down, in terms of f, the equation of the graph you obtain if the graph $y = f(x)$ is
  (a) reflected in the x-axis
  (b) reflected in the line $y = 6$
  (c) reflected in the y-axis
  (d) translated by the vector $\binom{0}{-4}$
  (e) translated by the vector $\binom{3}{-4}$
  (f) rotated by half a turn about the origin

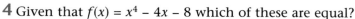

4 Given that $f(x) = x^4 - 4x - 8$ which of these are equal?

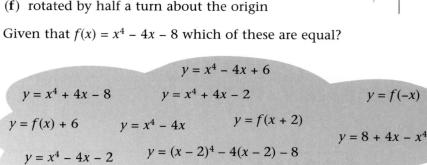

$y = x^4 - 4x + 6$

$y = x^4 + 4x - 8$ $y = x^4 + 4x - 2$ $y = f(-x)$

$y = f(x) + 6$ $y = x^4 - 4x$ $y = f(x + 2)$

$y = 8 + 4x - x^4$

$y = x^4 - 4x - 2$ $y = (x - 2)^4 - 4(x - 2) - 8$

$y = f(x) + 8$

$y = (x + 2)^4 - 4(x + 2) - 8$

$y = -f(x)$

5 This is the graph of $y = f(x)$. It crosses the x-axis at $(-2,0)$ and $(3,0)$, it crosses the y-axis at $(0,2)$ and it has a maximum point at $(-1,3)$.

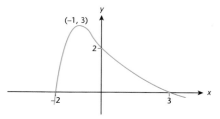

For each of these transformations of $y = f(x)$, state the coordinates of the maximum point and of the points at which it crosses the axes where these can be deduced.

  (a) $y = f(x) + 2$ **(b)** $y = f(x) - 5$
  (c) $y = f(x - 3)$ **(d)** $y = 2f(x)$
  (e) $y = f(-x)$ **(f)** $y = f(2x)$

6 This shows the graph of $y = f(x)$, where $f(x) = x^2 - 4x$.

(a) Make a sketch of this graph and add to your sketch the graph of $y = f(x - 3)$. What is the x-coordinate of the point where these graphs meet?

(b) Describe the transformation which maps the graph $y = f(x)$ to the graph $y = f(x - a)$.

(c) The graphs $y = f(x)$ and $y = f(x - a)$ meet at the point P. Find the x-coordinate of P.

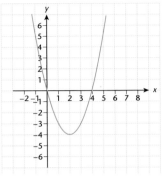

Graphs of trigonometric functions

EXERCISE 4

1 (a) Copy these axes, and on them sketch the graph of $y = \sin x$ for values of x between $0°$ and $360°$.

(b) Using your graph, together with your calculator, find all the solutions to the equation $\sin x = -0.35$, in the range $0°$ to $360°$, giving your answers to 2 decimal places.

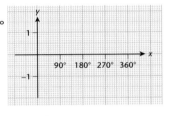

2 This is the graph of $y = \sin x$.

(a) Make a rough copy of this graph.

(b) On the same axes, sketch $y = \cos x$.

(c) On the same axes, sketch $y = 2\sin x$.

(d) On the same axes, sketch $y = \sin x + 1$.

(e) On the same axes, sketch $y = \sin 2x$.

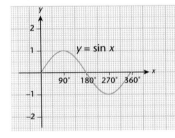

3 (a) Copy these axes, and on them sketch the graph of $y = \cos x$.

(b) On the same axes, sketch the graph of $2\cos x$.

(c) Use your graph to find what approximate values of x between $0°$ and $360°$ are solutions to the equation $2\cos x = 1.2$.

(d) Use your calculator to work out the solutions for part (c) correct to the nearest degree.

(e) Use your graph to find what approximate values of x between $0°$ and $360°$ are solutions to the equation $4\cos x = -1.2$.

(f) Use your calculator to work out the solutions for part (e) correct to the nearest degree.

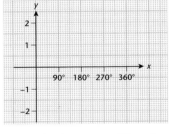

4 (a) Using the axes given in Question 3, sketch the graphs of $y = \cos x$ and $y = 2\sin x$.

(b) Use your graphs to find the approximate solutions to the equation $\cos x = 2\sin x$ for values of x between $0°$ and $360°$.

(c) Use trial and improvement to find these solutions, correct to the nearest degree.

5 (a) Using the axes given in Question 3, sketch graphs of $y = \sin x$ and $y = \sin 2x$.

(b) Use your graphs to find approximate solutions to the equation $\sin x = \sin 2x$ for values of x between $0°$ and $360°$.

(c) Use a calculator to check your solutions.

6 (a) Sketch the graphs of $y = \cos x$ and $y = \dfrac{x}{300}$ on the same axes, for values of x between $-360°$ and $360°$.

(b) How many solutions are there to this equation?

$$\cos x = \frac{x}{300}$$

(c) Use trial and improvement to find these solutions, correct to the nearest degree.

7 (a) Draw the graph of $y = 2 + 3\sin x$ for values of x from $0°$ to $360°$.

(b) Use your graph to find the approximate values of x between $0°$ and $360°$ where the graph crosses the x-axis.

(c) Using your calculator, work out these values correct to 2 decimal places.

8 (a) Copy these axes.

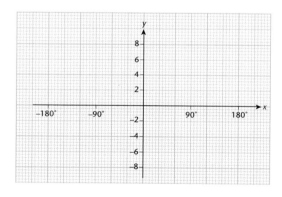

(b) On your axes, draw the graphs of $y = \tan x$ and $y = \tan 2x$.

9 (a) Copy these axes.

(b) On your axes, draw the graphs of
$y = \tan x$ and $y = 5 - \tan x$.

(c) From your graph, find the approximate
solution to the equation $\tan x = 5 - \tan x$
which lies between $0°$ and $180°$.

(d) Use your calculator to find this solution,
correct to 2 decimal places.

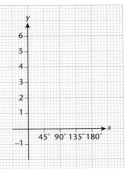

10 Ann is pushing her daughter on a swing. Here is an approximate formula
for the distance, in metres, of her daughter from Ann's hands after
t seconds.

$d = 2 - 2\cos(120t)°$

(a) Plot d against t for values of t from 0 to 6.

(b) How far is the daughter from Ann's hands after
(i) 1.5 seconds? **(ii)** 2.25 seconds?

(c) At how many times during the first 6 seconds is the daughter 1.5
metres from Ann?
Estimate, from the graph, the times when this occurs.

Graphs of various functions

EXERCISE 5

1 (a) Copy these axes and, on them, draw the graph of $y = 2^x$.

(b) Use your graph to estimate the value of x for which
$y = 5$.

(c) Use your graph to estimate
(i) $\sqrt{2}$ **(ii)** $\sqrt{8}$

2 (a) Copy these axes.

(b) On your axes draw these graphs.

A: $y = 2^x$ B: $y = 2^{x-1}$

C: $y = 2^{-x}$ D: $y = -2^x$

(c) Graphs B and C intersect at point P.
Calculate the x-coordinate of P.

Show that the y-coordinate of P is $\dfrac{\sqrt{2}}{2}$.

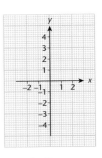

(d) How many other points of intersection are there of the graphs?
State the coordinates of the points of intersection.

3 Draw these graphs for x between -3 and 3.

    (a) $y = \left(\frac{1}{2}\right)^x$ **(b)** $y = 4 - \left(\frac{1}{2}\right)^x$ **(c)** $y = \left(\frac{1}{2}\right)^{2-x}$ **(d)** $y = 2 - \left(\frac{1}{2}\right)^{2-x}$

4 (a) The relationship between x and y is that y decreases by $\frac{1}{5}$ each time x increases by 10. Copy and complete this table.

x	0	10	20	30	40
y	100				40.96

    (b) Draw a graph of y plotted against x for values of x from 0 to 40.

    (c) Estimate the value of y when $x = 35$.

    (d) The relationship between x and y is given by this equation.

    $y = 100a^{\frac{x}{b}}$

    What are the values of a and b?

    (e) Use the equation to find the value for y when $x = 35$, correct to 1 decimal place.

5 (a) Sketch the graphs of $y = 3^x$ and $y = 9 \times 3^x$.

    (b) The transformation which maps $y = 3^x$ to $y = 9 \times 3^x$ is one of these. Which one is it?

    A: A translation with vector $\binom{0}{9}$

    B: An enlargement with scale factor 9

    C: An enlargement with scale factor $\frac{1}{9}$

    D: A translation with vector $\binom{3}{0}$

    E: A translation with vector $\binom{-3}{0}$

    F: A reflection in the line $x = 4.5$

    G: A translation with vector $\binom{-2}{0}$

    H: A translation with vector $\binom{2}{0}$

EXERCISE 6

1 Draw the graph of $y = \frac{1}{x^2}$ for x between -2 and 2.

2 Use your answer to Question 1 to help you to sketch these graphs.

    (a) $y = \frac{2}{x^2}$ **(b)** $y = -\frac{1}{x^2}$

    (c) $y = \frac{1}{x^2} + 2$ **(d)** $y = \frac{1}{(x-1)^2}$

3 (a) Sketch these graphs on the same drawing.

    $y = x$ $y = x^2$ $y = x^3$ $y = x^4$

    (b) What are the meeting points of these graphs?

    (c) Describe the symmetry of the graph of $y = x^n$ for different values of n, where n is a positive integer.

4 Match these equations with these graphs.
a, b, c, d, e, f and *K, L, M, N, P, Q* are numbers.

$$y = \frac{M}{x + c} \qquad y = L(x + b)^3 \qquad y = Q\tan(x + f)°$$

$$y = N2^{dx} \qquad y = K(x - a)^2 \qquad y = \frac{P}{(x + e)^2}$$

A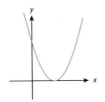

B

C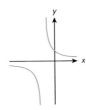

D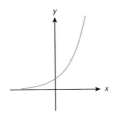

E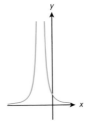

F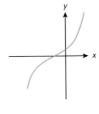

COURSEWORK OPPORTUNITY

Graph
Plotter

Exploring abs(*x*) and int(*x*)

abs(*x*) means the **absolute value**, or *size*, of the number *x*.
This is the graph of *y* = abs(*x*).

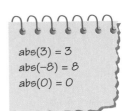

abs(3) = 3
abs(−8) = 8
abs(0) = 0

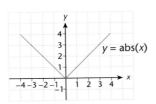

Work out how to draw these:

♦ A V shape with its bottom point at any specified point on the graph
♦ A V shape with sides of any steepness
♦ An upside down V shape
♦ Shapes like this:

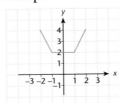

Find the equations needed to draw each of these graphs.

A 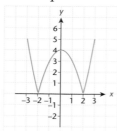 B 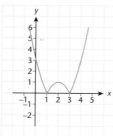 C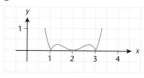

Experiment with other shapes you can make using the abs function and provide a comprehensive guide to these.

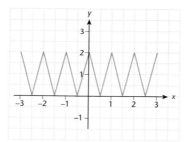

int(3.4) = 3
int(7.9) = 7
int(6) = 6

int(*x*) means the **integer part** of *x*.
Graphical calculators and graph plotters have different interpretations for int(*x*) when *x* is negative.
On some, int(−2.4) = −3.
On others, int(−2.4) = −2.
♦ Work out what the graph of *y* = int(*x*) looks like.
♦ Use int on its own, or with abs to produce a variety of graphs.
   Provide a comprehensive guide to these.
   For example, this graph can be produced using abs and int.

Solving equations from intersecting graphs

In Chapter 13 of Book 1, there were questions about solving quadratic equations by drawing graphs. Exercise 7 extends these ideas.

Exercise 7

1 Look at this graph of $y = x^3 - 3x^2$.

   Use this graph to estimate the solutions
   to this equation.

   $x^3 - 3x^2 + 3 = 0$

   Then use trial and improvement to find the solutions
   correct to 2 decimal places.

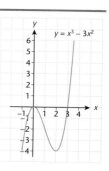

2 (a) Draw the graph of $y = x^2 - 4x - 5$ for values of x from -2 to 6.

(b) Use the graph to solve these equations. In some cases, you will need to draw straight lines on the graph.

    (i) $x^2 - 4x - 5 = 0$ **(ii)** $x^2 - 4x - 4 = 0$ **(iii)** $x^2 = 5x + 7$

    (iv) $2x^2 - 8x - 3 = 0$ **(v)** $2x^2 - 7x - 8 = 0$

3 (a) Draw the graphs of $y = x^3 - 3$ and $y = 2x^2 + 2x - 5$ on the same axes, for values of x between -2 and 3.

(b) Use your graphs to find approximate solutions to these equations.

    (i) $x^3 - 3 = 4$ **(ii)** $2x^2 + 2x - 5 = 0$ **(iii)** $x^3 - 2x^2 - 2x + 2 = 0$

(c) Draw a straight-line graph on the same axes, which can be used with the other graphs to find approximate solutions to these equations.

    (i) $x^3 - 3x - 1 = 0$ **(ii)** $2x^2 - x - 3 = 0$

(d) Check your answer to part (c)(ii) by solving the quadratic equation using a different method.

4 (a) Draw a graph of $y = x^3 - 4x$, for values of x from -3 to 3.

(b) Use the graph to find approximate solutions to this equation.

    $x^3 - 4x = -2$

    Use your calculator to obtain a better estimate.

(c) The graph is now to be used to solve this equation.

    $x^3 - 6x - 1 = 0$

    To solve this equation, what other line must be drawn on the axes?

(d) Draw the line and find approximate solutions to the equation. Use your calculator to obtain a better estimate.

5 This is a graph of $y = x^4$ and a quadratic graph.

(a) What is the equation of the quadratic graph?

(b) The points where the graphs intersect give the real solutions of this equation.

    $x^4 + bx^2 + cx = 0$

    State the values of b and c.

(c) Use trial and improvement to find these solutions, correct to 2 decimal places.

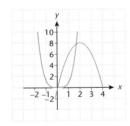

6 Draw the graphs of $y = x$, $y = x^2$ and $y = \frac{6}{x}$ on the same axes, using values of x from -3 to 3.

(a) From the graph write down, approximately where necessary, the coordinates of the points where the graphs intersect.

(b) The coordinates of all except one of the points of intersection can be written in the form $(6^p, 6^q)$ for suitable values of p and q.

    State which point is the exception.

    Express each of the other points in the form $(6^p, 6^q)$.

Using graphs to solve inequalities

EXERCISE 8

1 This is the graph of $y = x^2 - 5$.
Use this graph to solve these
inequalities, correct to 1 decimal
place.

(a) $x^2 < 10$

(b) $3 < x^2 < 8$

(c) $x^2 > 5$

(d) $x^2 > -8$

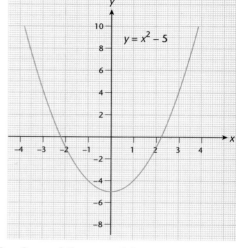

2 These are the graphs of $y = 2x$, $y = 10 - 3x$ and $2y = x - 16$.

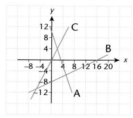

(a) Which graph is which?

(b) Draw the graphs accurately and use them to solve these inequalities,
correct to 1 decimal place.

(i) $2x > 10 - 3x$ (ii) $10 - 3x > \frac{x}{2} - 8$

(iii) $x - 16 < 4x < 20 - 6x$ (iv) $4x > 20 - 6x > x - 16$

3 These are the graphs of $y = x^4$ and $y = 4x - x^2$.
For what values of x

(a) is $x^4 < 8$?

(b) is $4x - x^2 > 3$?

(c) is $x^4 > 4x - x^2$?

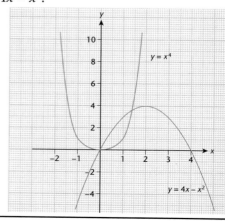

The area under a curve

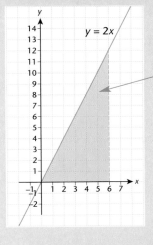

The shaded area under this straight line graph is 36 square units. How do you know?

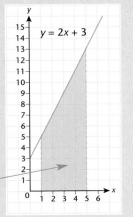

What is the shaded area under this graph?

This graph is a curve and so it is harder to find the area under it.

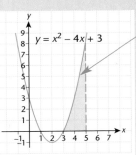

You estimate the area by dividing it into strips.

Think of each strip as an approximate trapezium.

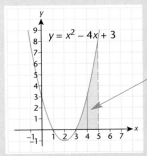

Here is the same area divided into two strips. Estimate its area.

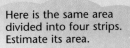

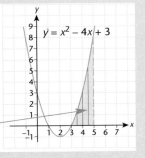

Here is the same area divided into four strips. Estimate its area.

- Which approximation is likely to be more accurate?
- Do your approximations underestimate or overestimate the area?

This method for finding the area under a curve is called the **trapezium rule**.

1 Draw the graph of $y = 6x - x^2$ for values of x between -2 and 8.
Estimate the area between the graph and the x-axis, using the trapezium rule with four strips.
Does your answer underestimate or overestimate the area?

2 (a) Sketch the graph of $y = 2x^2 + 4$ for values of x between -2 and 6.
Shade the area bounded by the graph and by the lines $x = -2$, $x = 6$ and $y = 0$.

(b) Use the trapezium rule with eight strips to estimate the shaded area.
Does your answer overestimate or underestimate the area?

3 Here is the graph of $y = x^3 - 9x$.

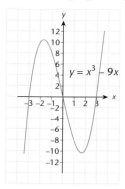

Use the trapezium rule to estimate the *total* area between the graph and the x-axis.

4 Some students want to determine the area of cross-section of a small river.

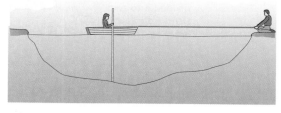

The depth of the river is measured at different distances from the bank. These are the results.

Distance from bank (m)	0	1	2	3	4	5	6	7	8
Depth (m)	0	1.2	2.1	2.7	2.8	2.4	1.8	0.7	0

(a) Use this data to draw the cross-section of the river.
(b) Estimate the cross-sectional area.

DISCUSSION POINT

This is the speed–time graph for a car travelling at 80 feet per second.

- How far does the car travel in 8 seconds?
- What is the shaded area under the graph?

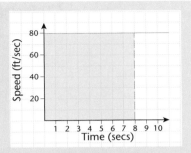

This is the speed–time graph for a car accelerating uniformly from 0 to 80 feet per second in 10 seconds.

- What is the average (mean) speed of the car during these 10 seconds?
- Use the average speed to work out how far the car travels during these 10 seconds.
- What is the shaded area under the graph?

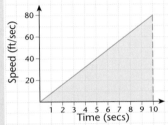

In view of the above results, it may seem reasonable to believe that the area under a speed–time graph always gives the distance travelled.
Discuss this, so that you understand it as clearly as possible.

This graph shows the speed of a car during 10 seconds.

- Use the trapezium rule to estimate the total distance travelled by the car.

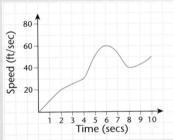

EXERCISE 10

1 This graph shows the journey of an underground train between two stations.

(a) Estimate the distance between the stations.

(b) Estimate the time at which the train is half way between the stations.

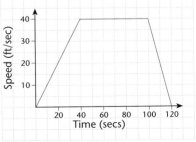

2 This graph shows the journey of a cyclist.

Estimate the distance the cyclist travelled.

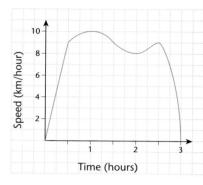

3 This table describes the first ten seconds of a car's journey as it accelerates from rest.

    (**a**) Draw the graph of v against t.

Time (t secs)	0	2	4	6	8	10
Speed (v m/s)	0	10	18	22.5	27.5	31

  (**b**) Use the graph to estimate the distance travelled by the car during the first ten seconds of its journey.

4 A car is initially stationary. During the first 8 seconds of its journey, it accelerates steadily until it is travelling at 20 m/s. For the next 10 seconds, it travels at 20 m/s. It then decelerates steadily, stopping after it has travelled a further 100 m.

  (**a**) Draw a speed–time graph for this journey.

  (**b**) What is the total time of the journey?

  (**c**) What is the total distance travelled by the car?

DISCUSSION POINT

Speed can be thought of as the rate of change of distance over time. Sometimes graphs show other rates.

This graph shows the rate at which a test car consumed petrol while it was driven at gradually increasing speed around a 6-km circuit.

Find an estimate for the number of litres of petrol used by the car during the test run.

In other situations, a rate of change might be plotted against distance instead of time.

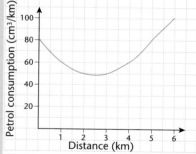

To find the volume of a small tree trunk, its circumference at different heights is measured.

From this, the cross-sectional area at each height is calculated. How?

This table shows the cross-sectional areas for a tree trunk 6 m high.

Height above ground (m)	0	1	2	3	4	5	6
Cross-sectional area (cm²)	240	190	150	100	80	60	50

Plot a graph and use it to estimate the volume of the tree trunk.

EXERCISE 11

1 When speed in m/s is plotted against time in seconds, the area under the curve is a measure of distance in metres.
What does the area under the curve measure for each of these?
   (a) Speed of a car in m.p.h. plotted against time in hours
   (b) Area of cross-section of a 3D shape in cm² plotted against length in centimetres
   (c) Acceleration of a train in m/s² plotted against time in seconds
   (d) Rate of flow of water into a tank in litres per minute plotted against time in minutes
   (e) Pulse rate per minute against minutes doing exercise.

2 A water tank used for watering the garden is fed by rainwater running from a roof. Here is a graph showing the rate at which water flows into a tank during a rainy afternoon.
   (a) Estimate the volume of water flowing into the tank during the afternoon.
   (b) The tank is a cylinder with diameter 0.6 m. Estimate the rise in water level in the tank during the afternoon.

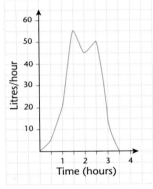

3 The graph below shows the pulse rate of an athlete taking exercise. This table gives his pulse rate (beats per minute) after each minute.

Time (mins)	0	1	2	3	4	5	6	7	8	9	10
Pulse rate	70	105	130	155	170	120	110	115	130	120	90

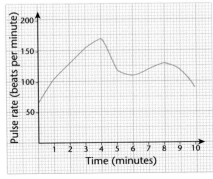

How many times did the athlete's heart beat during the exercise?

4 Look at this cone.

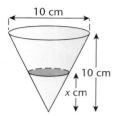

10 cm

10 cm

x cm

(a) Show that the cross-sectional area of the cone at height x cm above the vertex is $\frac{1}{4}\pi x^2$ cm^2.

(b) Draw a graph of cross-sectional area against height, plotting points for x values of 0, 2, 4, 6, 8 and 10.

(c) Use the trapezium rule to estimate the area under the graph, and hence the volume of the cone.

(d) Check the accuracy of your answer to part (c) by using the formula for the volume of a cone.

5 The base of this pyramid is a square with sides of length 4 cm. The height of the pyramid is 8 cm.

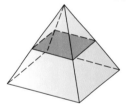

(a) Show that the area of the cross-section of the pyramid at a height of x cm above the base is $(4 - \frac{1}{2}x)^2$.

(b) Draw a graph of cross-sectional area against height, plotting points for x values of 0, 2, 4, 6, and 8.

(c) Estimate the area under the graph and hence the volume of the pyramid.

(d) Check the accuracy of your answer to part (c) by using the formula for the volume of a pyramid.

6 This hemisphere has a radius of 10 cm.

(a) Show that the area of the circular cross-section of the hemisphere at a distance of x cm from the plane face is $\pi(100 - x^2)$.

(b) Draw a graph of cross-sectional area against height.

(c) Estimate the area under the graph, and hence, the volume of the hemisphere.

(d) Check the accuracy of your answer to part (c) by using the formula for the volume of a sphere.

Tangents to graphs

These are the graphs of $y = x^2$ and $y = 3x$.

$y = 3x$ is a straight line. Its gradient is 3.

$y = x^2$ is a parabola. Its gradient is different at different points of the graph.

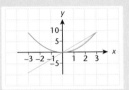

- At what point of the graph is its gradient zero?

- At what points of the graph is the gradient positive?

- At what points of the graph is the gradient negative?

One way of defining the gradient of the graph is to draw the tangent.

The gradient of a graph at a point is the gradient of its tangent at that point.

This shows $y = x^2$ and two of its tangents.

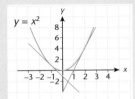

- What is the gradient of the tangent to $y = x^2$ through the point (2, 4)?

- What is the gradient of the tangent to $y = x^2$ through the point (–1, 1)?

- At what point on the graph is the gradient of the tangent zero?

EXERCISE 12

1 This is the graph of $y = 4x - x^2$. Two tangents to the graph have been drawn.

(a) What is the gradient of the tangent to the graph at (0, 0)?

(b) What is the gradient of the tangent at (3, 3)?

(c) At what point on the graph is the gradient of the tangent zero?

(d) At what point on the graph is the gradient of the tangent equal to –4?

(e) For which values of x is the gradient of the tangent negative?

2 (a) Draw the graph of $y = \frac{1}{2}x^2 - 2x$ for values of x between –2 and 6.

(b) Describe the symmetry of this graph.

(c) The gradient of the tangent to the graph through the point $(3, -1\frac{1}{2})$ is m. Draw the tangent and estimate the value of m.

(d) At what point on the graph is the gradient of the tangent $-m$?

(e) The gradient of the tangent to the graph through the point (–2, 6) is n. Draw the tangent and estimate the value of n.

(f) At what point on the graph is the gradient of the tangent $-n$?

(g) At what point on the graph is the gradient of the tangent zero?

3 Draw the graph of $y = x^2 + 3x - 1$ for values of x from -4 to 2.

    (a) Use your graph to estimate the gradient of the curve when $x = 1$ and when $x = -2$.

    (b) For what values of x is the gradient of the curve negative?

4 Draw the graph of $y = x^3$ for values of x from -3 to 3.

    (a) Use your graph to estimate the gradient of the curve when $x = 1$ and when $x = -2$.

    (b) For what values of x is the gradient of the curve negative?

5 This is the graph of $y = x^3 - 4x$. One of the tangents to the graph is drawn.

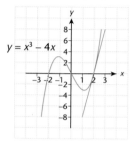

    (a) Describe the symmetry of the graph.

    (b) What is the gradient of the tangent at the point $(2, 0)$?

    (c) At what other point on the graph does the tangent have the same gradient as at $(2, 0)$?

    (d) At what points on the graph is the gradient of the tangent zero?

    (e) At what point on the graph is the gradient of the tangent equal to the gradient of the tangent at $(-1, 3)$?

    (f) For what values of x is the gradient positive?

6 Here is the graph of $y = x^2$ with one of its tangents drawn.

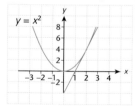

The gradient of the tangent at $(2, 4)$ is 4.

    (a) Draw a *sketch* of $y = x^2 + 3$.
        At what point on this graph is the gradient of the tangent equal to 4?

    (b) Draw a *sketch* of $y = (x - 2)^2$.
        At what point on this graph is the gradient of the tangent equal to 4?

    (c) Draw a *sketch* of $y = -x^2$.
        At what point on this graph is the gradient of the tangent equal to 4?

    (d) Draw a *sketch* of $y = 2x^2$.
        At what point on this graph is the gradient of the tangent equal to 4?

DISCUSSION POINT

This graph shows the motion of a plane down a runway before taking off.

- What is the speed of the plane after 15 seconds?
- Is the plane travelling faster after 20 seconds? Or slower?

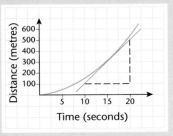

This graph shows the speed of a car as it speeds up on joining a motorway.

- What is the car's approximate acceleration after 30 seconds?
- When is the car neither accelerating nor decelerating?

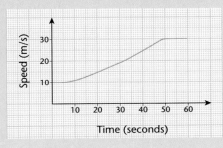

▶ Resource Sheet G
Distance–time graphs
▶ Resource Sheet H:
Speed–time graphs

EXERCISE 13

1 When speed in m/s is plotted against time in seconds the gradient of the curve measures acceleration in m/s². What does the gradient of the curve measure for each of these?

(a) The speed of a car in feet per second plotted against time in seconds

(b) The distance in kilometres travelled by a cyclist plotted against time in hours

(c) The volume of water in a tank in litres plotted against time in seconds

(d) The temperature of a cooling liquid in °C plotted against time in minutes

For Questions 2 and 3, you need a copy of Resource Sheet G: Distance–time graphs.

In Question 2, give the speeds in miles per hour. There are 1760 yards in a mile.

2 Jason is late for school.
This graph shows his journey from home to school.

(a) At what time is Jason's speed fastest? Estimate this speed.

(b) At what time is Jason's speed slowest? Estimate this speed.

(c) What is Jason's average speed from home to school?

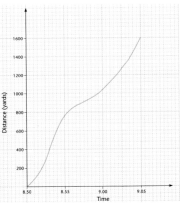

3 A ball is thrown up into the air.
This graph shows its distance above
the ground plotted against the time
it has been in the air.

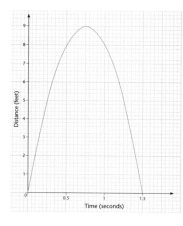

  (a) Estimate the ball's speed after
  half a second.
  (b) Estimate the ball's speed after
  $1\frac{1}{4}$ seconds.
  (c) How long does the ball take to
  reach its highest point?
  (d) What is the average speed of the
  ball on its upward journey?

4 At a village fête, there was a race for adults.
This graph shows the performance of the winner throughout the race.

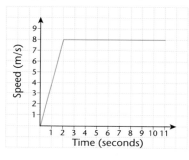

  (a) How long was the race?
  (b) What was the acceleration of the winner at the beginning of the race?

5 This graph shows a train's journey between stations.

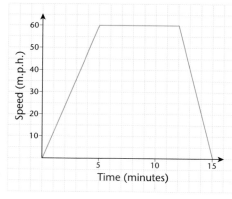

  (a) What is the speed of the train after 5 minutes?
  (b) What is the speed of the train after 15 minutes?
  (c) Between which times is the train slowing down?
  (d) Estimate the distance between the stations.

For Questions 6 and 7, you need the Resource Sheet H: *Speed–time graphs*.

6 On Resource Sheet H, look at the graph which shows the movement of a bus after leaving a bus stop.

    (a) What was the acceleration of the bus after 5 seconds?

    (b) What was the acceleration of the bus after 10 seconds?

    (c) How far did the bus travel in the first 12 seconds?

    (d) What was the average speed of the bus during the first 12 seconds?

7 On Resource Sheet H, look at the graph which shows the performance of the winner of a cycle sprint race.

    (a) How fast was the cyclist travelling at the end of the race?

    (b) Apart from the first 5 seconds of the race, what was the cyclist's slowest speed during the race?

    (c) Over what distance was the race?

    (d) By drawing a tangent to the graph, find the cyclist's acceleration 130 seconds after the race started.

    (e) What was the cyclist's deceleration 60 seconds after the race started?

8 This table shows the speed, v metres per second, of a cyclist, t seconds after she applies the brakes.

t	0	0.5	1	1.5	2	2.5	3	3.5	4
v	8	7.9	7.5	6.9	6	4.9	3.5	1.9	0

    (a) Draw a speed–time graph to show how the speed of the cyclist varies with time.

    (b) From your graph, estimate the acceleration of the cyclist after 2 seconds.

    (c) Estimate after how many seconds the acceleration of the cyclist is $-3 \, \text{m/s}^2$.

    (d) Find the area under the graph and hence estimate the total distance travelled by the cyclist before stopping.

9 A jogger goes out for a run. Her run is shown in this speed–time graph.

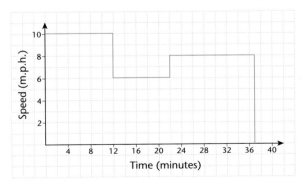

    (a) How far did the jogger run?

    (b) Draw a distance–time graph for the jogger's run.

10 A ball is rolled down a slope. The time is measured at different points of the slope. These are the results.

Distance down the slope (cm)	10	20	30	40	50	60	70	80	90	100
Time from start (sec)	0.91	1.29	1.58	1.83	2.04	2.24	2.42	2.58	2.74	2.89

(a) Draw a distance–time graph.

(b) Use your distance–time graph to estimate the speed of the ball after 0, 0.5, 1, 1.5, 2, and 2.5 seconds.

(c) Draw a speed-time graph.

(d) What can you say about the acceleration of the ball?

CHAPTER SUMMARY

Transforming graphs

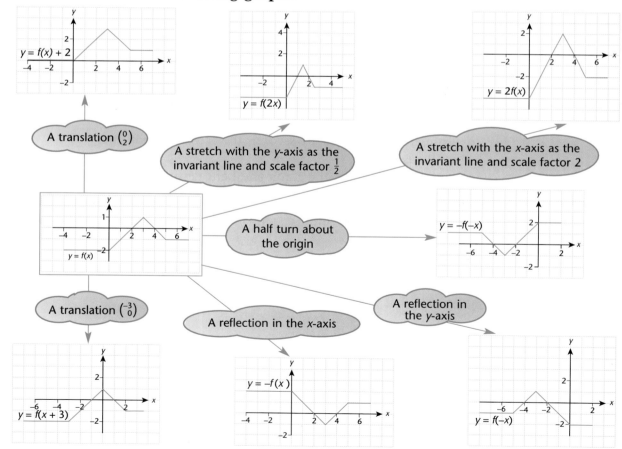

Graphs of the form $y = a^x$

These all pass through the point $(1, 0)$ (because $a^0 = 1$)
and are entirely above the x-axis if $a > 0$.

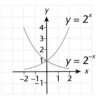

Area under a curve

This can be estimated by splitting the area into strips which are
approximately trapezia.

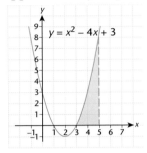 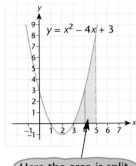 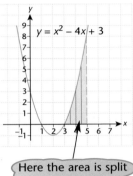

Here the area is split
into two strips.

Here the area is split
into four strips.

The more strips used, the more accurate is the estimate.

Applications

- Finding area of cross sections (Exercise 9, Question 4)
- Finding the distance travelled from a speed–time graph (Exercise 10)
- Finding volumes (Exercise 11)

Tangents to graphs

The gradient of a graph at a point is the gradient of its tangent at that point.
This shows $y = x^2$ and two of its tangents.

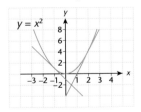

It can be seen that the gradient of the tangent to $y = x^2$ at $(2, 4)$ is 4, and the
gradient of the tangent to $y = x^2$ at $(-1, 1)$ is -2. The gradient of the tangent at
the origin is zero.

Applications

- Finding speed from a distance–time graph
- Finding acceleration from a speed–time graph

CIRCLES AND VECTORS

This chapter is about:

- using congruent triangles in proofs
- chords and tangents of circles
- revisiting some circle theorems
- the equal tangents theorem
- the alternate segment theorem
- the intersecting chords theorem
- ruler and compass constructions
- loci
- ratios in polygons and circles
- vector geometry
- equations of circles.

Chords and tangents and circles

This exercise is about radius-chord properties of circles.

EXERCISE 1

1 A circle has a radius of 5 cm.
What is the length of the longest chord in this circle?

2 This diagram shows a circle with a chord AB and a radius OP.
The chord and the radius intersect at M, the mid-point of AB.

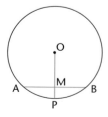

Providing a mathematical justification

(a) Draw a sketch of this diagram. Draw the lines OA and OB.
(b) Prove that triangles OAM and OBM are congruent.
(c) Deduce that OP is perpendicular to AB.

3 A circle has a radius of 5 cm. A chord of 6 cm is drawn in the circle.
Find the perpendicular distance of the chord from the centre.

4 When a chord of length 10 cm is drawn in a circle, its perpendicular
distance from the centre of the circle is 12 cm. Find the radius of the circle.

5 In a circle of radius 12 cm, a diameter and a chord are perpendicular.
Their point of intersection divides the diameter in the ratio 3:5.
Find the length of the chord. Give your answer in surd form.

6 In a circle, a diameter and a chord are perpendicular.
Find the length of the diameter
  (a) if the length of the chord is 24 cm and the point of intersection of the
  diameter and the chord divides the diameter in the ratio 4:1
  (b) if the length of the chord is $10\sqrt{3}$ cm and the point of intersection of
  the diameter and the chord divides the diameter in the ratio 3:1

DISCUSSION POINT

A tangent to a circle is a line which touches the circle at one point;
it does not cut into the interior of the circle.

This diagram consists of a circle, one of its diameters and the tangent to
the circle at one end of the diameter.

Discuss how you can provide a justification for the theorem that the
tangent is perpendicular to the diameter.

Providing a mathematical justification

This exercise is about tangent properties of circles.

EXERCISE 2

1 A circle and one of its diameters are drawn.
Prove that the two tangents to the circle at the ends of the diameter
are parallel.

2 A circle and two of its diameters are drawn. The tangents to the circles at
the ends of the diameters are also drawn.
  (a) Prove that the four tangents form a parallelogram.
  (b) By drawing in a line of symmetry, prove that the parallelogram is a
  rhombus.

3 A circle has centre O and radius 8 cm. The length of OP is 17 cm. The tangent to the circle from P touches the circle at T.

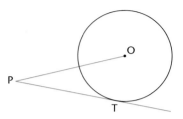

Find the length of PT.

4 PT and PU are two tangents to a circle with centre O and radius 4 cm, touching the circle at T and U respectively.

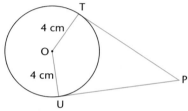

(a) Explain why PT and PU are the same length.
(b) The kite OTPU has a perimeter of 20 cm. Find the distance of P from O. Give your answer in surd form.

5 P is a point outside a circle with centre O and radius 7 cm. OP is 10 cm. Tangents from P meet the circle at T and U.
(a) Calculate angle TPU.
(b) Calculate the length of the arc of the circle between T and U and nearest to P.

DISCUSSION POINT
Question 4 in Exercise 2 can be generalised to this important theorem about tangents.

The two tangents from a point to a circle are equal in length.

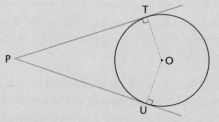

In other words, PT = PU. Prove this theorem.

Providing a
mathematical
justification

Revisiting some circle theorems

Providing a
mathematical
justification

DISCUSSION POINT

All these theorems were given in Chapter 14 of *Book 1*.

> **The angle in a semicircle is a right angle.**
>
>

Discuss how you can prove this theorem using congruent triangles.

> **The angle at the centre of a circle is twice the angle at the circumference.**
>
>
>
> $\angle AOB = 2\angle APB$ Reflex $\angle AOB = 2\angle APB$

Discuss how you can prove this theorem by using the exterior angle theorem with two isosceles triangles.

> **Angles in the same segment are equal.**
>
>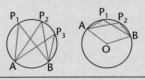

Discuss how you can deduce this theorem from the previous one.

> **The opposite angles of a cyclic quadrilateral add to 180°.**
>
>

Discuss how you can prove this theorem using the angle at the centre theorem.

> **The exterior angle of a cyclic quadrilateral is equal to the interior opposite angle.**
>
>

How can this theorem be deduced from the previous one?

Most of these theorems have a converse which is also true. For example, the converse of the first theorem can be expressed like this:

A right-angled triangle can be inscribed in a circle with the hypotenuse as diameter.

Discuss the converses of other theorems.

Nelson GCSE Maths   CIRCLES AND VECTORS (HIGHER)

EXERCISE 3

1 AC and BD are two diameters of a circle.
   (a) Prove that ABCD is a rectangle.
   (b) How must the diameters be drawn for ABCD to be a square?

2 P is a point outside a circle with centre O.
   Tangents from P meet the circle at T and U.
   (a) Prove that TOUP is a cyclic quadrilateral.
   (b) Where is the diameter of the circle in which TOUP is inscribed?

3 TU is a tangent to the circle and O is its centre.
   What size are angles x and y?

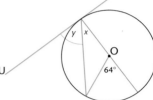

4 The line PAQ is a tangent to the circle.
   The line PB passes
   through the centre O.
   Find ∠BAQ.

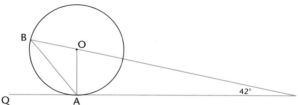

5 Triangle EFG is inscribed in a circle with centre O.
   ∠OEG = 18° and ∠FOG = 70°.
   (a) Find ∠EOG.
   (b) Find ∠EGF.
   (c) Find ∠EFG.

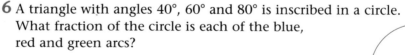

6 A triangle with angles 40°, 60° and 80° is inscribed in a circle.
   What fraction of the circle is each of the blue,
   red and green arcs?

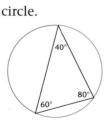

7 The centre D of the smaller circle lies on the circumference of the larger
   circle with centre C.
   The circles intersect at A and B. ∠ACB = x.
   Find the size of ∠ADC in terms of x.

8 ABCD is a quadrilateral inscribed in a circle with centre O. Sides AB and DC are produced to meet at P. Angle BOD is x and angle ABC is y. Find angle APD in terms of x and y.

9 ABCDEFG is a regular heptagon. Its symmetry ensures that it can be inscribed in a circle. Angle A has been divided into five angles by diagonals. What can you say about the sizes of these five angles? Justify your answer.

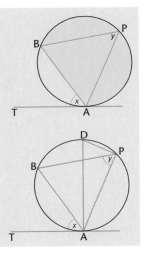

The alternate segment theorem and other theorems

Dynamic Geometry

DISCUSSION POINT

In this diagram, AT is a tangent to the circle.
AB is a chord. The alternate segment theorem is this:
The angle between a chord and a tangent is equal to an angle in the alternate segment.
In other words: $x = y$

Discuss the meaning of the words in the statement of the theorem.

The theorem can be proved by introducing an additional point D so that AD is a diameter of the circle.

Providing a mathematical justification

Prove the theorem.

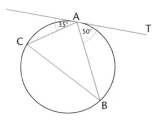

EXERCISE 4

1 In this diagram, AT is a tangent to the circle.
Find all three angles of triangle ABC.

2 In this diagram, TA and TB are tangents to the circle. ∠ATB = 50°.
Find ∠ACB.

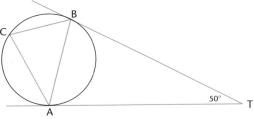

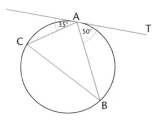

3 In this diagram, TA and TB are tangents to the circle. AC is parallel to TB. Find angles ACB and CBT.

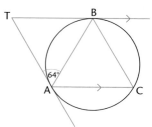

4 ABC is a triangle inscribed in a circle. AC = BC and ∠ABC = 70°. AT is a tangent to the circle and ∠TAB is an acute angle.
Find ∠TAB.

5 ABC is a triangle inscribed in a circle. The tangent at B is parallel to AC. Prove that the triangle is isosceles.

6 In this diagram, AT is a tangent to the circle and O is its centre. Find ∠OBC.

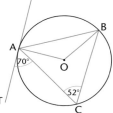

7 AT is a tangent to the circle and O is the centre. Find angle ODA.

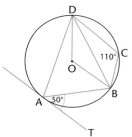

DISCUSSION POINT

In this diagram, AB and CD are chords of the circle which intersect at P. Explain why triangles ACP and DBP are similar.
Hence, prove that AP × PB = CP × PD.
This is called the **intersecting chords theorem.**

Providing a mathematical justification

EXERCISE 5

1 Use the intersecting chords theorem to find x in each of these.

(a)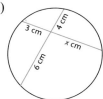
(b)
(c)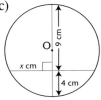
(d)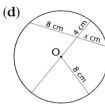

In Question 2, leave your answers in surd form.

2 This circle has a diameter, L, of 10 cm. O is the centre of the circle.

(a) Point A is on L and 3 cm from O.
Find the length of the chord through
A perpendicular to L.

(b) Point B is on L and 4 cm from O.
Find the length of the chord through
B perpendicular to L.

(c) Point C is on L and 2 cm from O.
Find the length of the chord through C perpendicular to L.

(d) Point D is on L and $2\frac{1}{2}$ cm from O.
Find the length of the chord through D perpendicular to L.

(e) Find the length of the chord through O and perpendicular to L.

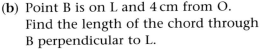
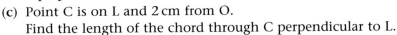

3 A circle has a diameter of 8 cm. Where could a chord be drawn so that its length is

(a) $2\sqrt{7}$ cm?   (b) $\sqrt{60}$ cm?   (c) $\sqrt{55}$ cm?

4 In this diagram, P is a point outside a circle and lines through P cut the circle at A and B, and C and D respectively.

(a) Prove that triangles PAC and PDB
are similar.

(b) Deduce that PA × PB = PC × PD.

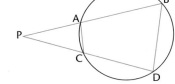

5 In this diagram. P is a point outside a circle, a line through P cuts the circle at A and B, and PT is a tangent.

(a) Prove that triangles PTA and PBT
are similar.

(b) Deduce a result similar to that in
Question 4 part (b).

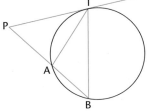

6 ABCD is a cyclic quadrilateral.
The point P is chosen on diagonal BD so that $\angle DAP = \angle CAB$.

(a) Prove that triangles ABC and APD are similar.

(b) Deduce that $AD \times BC = AC \times DP$.

(c) Prove that triangles ACD and ABP are similar.

(d) Deduce that $AB \times CD = AC \times BP$.

(e) Use parts (b) and (d) to prove this result for a cyclic quadrilateral.
$AD \times BC + AB \times CD = AC \times BD$
This result is know as **Ptolomy's theorem**.

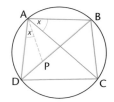

Providing a mathematical justification

7 ABC is an equilateral triangle inscribed in a circle.
P is a point on the minor arc BC.
Use Ptolomy's theorem to prove that $AP = BP + CP$.

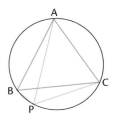

Vector geometry

Vectors were introduced in Chapter 2. Vectors can be used to prove geometrical results.

In this diagram, $\mathbf{u} = \overrightarrow{AB}$ and $\mathbf{v} = \overrightarrow{AC}$.

If two lines are equal and parallel, they have the same vector.

In parallelogram EFGH, $\overrightarrow{EF} = \overrightarrow{HG} = \mathbf{x}$.

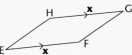

It can be useful to describe the vector which translates from A to B as $\overrightarrow{AB}$.

DISCUSSION POINT
Look at this diagram. $\overrightarrow{OA} = \mathbf{a}$, $\overrightarrow{OB} = \mathbf{b}$.

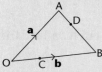

- What is AB in terms of **a** and **b**?
- C is a point one-third of the way along OB. What is $\overrightarrow{OC}$ in terms of **b**?
- D is a point one-third of the way along AB. What is $\overrightarrow{AD}$ in terms of **a** and **b**?
- What is $\overrightarrow{OD}$ in terms of **a** and **b**?
- Explain why $\overrightarrow{CD} = \frac{2}{3}\mathbf{a}$.
- What does this tell you geometrically about the lines OA and CD?

EXERCISE 6

1 In this diagram, $\overrightarrow{DE} = \mathbf{u}$, $\overrightarrow{EB} = 3\mathbf{u}$, $\overrightarrow{EC} = \mathbf{v}$ and $\overrightarrow{AE} = 3\mathbf{v}$.

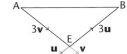

   (a) Express $\overrightarrow{AB}$ and $\overrightarrow{DC}$ in terms of $\mathbf{u}$ and $\mathbf{v}$.
   (b) How are $\overrightarrow{AB}$ and $\overrightarrow{DC}$ related geometrically?

2 In this diagram, $\overrightarrow{LX} = \frac{1}{4}\overrightarrow{LM}$, $\overrightarrow{NL} = \mathbf{u}$, $\overrightarrow{MN} = \mathbf{v}$.

   (a) Express $\overrightarrow{ML}$, $\overrightarrow{XL}$ and $\overrightarrow{MX}$ in terms of $\mathbf{u}$ and $\mathbf{v}$.
   (b) Show that $\overrightarrow{NX} = \frac{1}{4}(3\mathbf{u} - \mathbf{v})$.

3 In this triangle, $\overrightarrow{AB} = \mathbf{u}$ and $\overrightarrow{AC} = \mathbf{v}$. M and N are the mid-points of AB and AC respectively.

   (a) Express $\overrightarrow{BC}$ in terms of $\mathbf{u}$ and $\mathbf{v}$.
   (b) Express $\overrightarrow{AM}$ in terms of $\mathbf{u}$.
   (c) Express $\overrightarrow{AN}$ in terms of $\mathbf{v}$.
   (d) Express $\overrightarrow{MN}$ in terms of $\mathbf{u}$ and $\mathbf{v}$.
   (e) What do your answers to parts (a) and (d) tell you about the lines BC and MN?

4 ABCD is a parallelogram. E and F are points on the diagonal AC such that AE = EF = FC. $\overrightarrow{AB} = \mathbf{u}$ and $\overrightarrow{AD} = \mathbf{v}$.

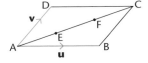

   (a) Express $\overrightarrow{AC}$ in terms of $\mathbf{u}$ and $\mathbf{v}$.
   (b) Express $\overrightarrow{AE}$ and $\overrightarrow{AF}$ in terms of $\mathbf{u}$ and $\mathbf{v}$
   (c) Express $\overrightarrow{ED}$ and $\overrightarrow{FB}$ in terms of $\mathbf{u}$ and $\mathbf{v}$.
   (d) Use your answers to explain why BEDF is a parallelogram.

5 In this diagram, $\overrightarrow{OA} = \mathbf{a}$, $\overrightarrow{OC} = 2\mathbf{a}$, $\overrightarrow{OD} = 4\mathbf{a}$, $\overrightarrow{OB} = \mathbf{b}$, $\overrightarrow{OE} = 4\mathbf{b}$, $\overrightarrow{OF} = 6\mathbf{b}$ and G is the mid-point of CF.

   (a) Express each of these in terms of $\mathbf{a}$ and $\mathbf{b}$:
      $\overrightarrow{CF}$, $\overrightarrow{CG}$, $\overrightarrow{DG}$, and $\overrightarrow{DE}$.
   (b) What can you say about the points D, G and E?

6 ABCD is a parallelogram and E is the mid-point of side BC and F is a point two-thirds of the way along diagonal AC.
$\overrightarrow{AB} = \mathbf{p}$ and $\overrightarrow{AD} = \mathbf{q}$.

   (a) Express each of these in terms of $\mathbf{p}$ and $\mathbf{q}$:
      $\overrightarrow{AE}$, $\overrightarrow{AC}$, $\overrightarrow{AF}$, $\overrightarrow{DF}$ and $\overrightarrow{DE}$.
   (b) What do your answers to part (a) tell you about the points D, E and F?

7 In this diagram, $\overrightarrow{OC} = 3\mathbf{a}$, $\overrightarrow{OD} = 4\mathbf{a}$, $\overrightarrow{OE} = 2\mathbf{b}$ and $\overrightarrow{OF} = 3\mathbf{b}$.
ODGE is a parallelogram. H is the mid-point of OG.

   (a) Express each of these in terms of $\mathbf{a}$ and $\mathbf{b}$:
      $\overrightarrow{OH}$, $\overrightarrow{CH}$ and $\overrightarrow{CF}$.
   (b) What can you conclude about the points C, H and F?

8 ABCDEF is a regular hexagon with centre O. $\overrightarrow{AB}$ = **p** and $\overrightarrow{AF}$ = **q**.
K is a point one-third of the way along FB.

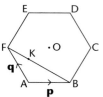

(a) Express each of these in terms of **p** and **q**:
$\overrightarrow{AO}$, $\overrightarrow{AD}$, $\overrightarrow{AC}$, $\overrightarrow{AE}$, $\overrightarrow{FB}$ and $\overrightarrow{AK}$.

(b) What can you conclude from your answers to part (a) about the points A, K and E?

9 ABC is a triangle. $\overrightarrow{AB}$ = **b** and $\overrightarrow{AC}$ = **c**. P is a point one-third of the way along AC, Q is the mid-point of BC and R is the mid-point of AQ. Use vector geometry to prove that P, R and B lie in a straight line and find the ratio in which R divides PB.

10 ABC is a triangle. D is the mid-point of BC, E is the mid-point of AC and F is the mid-point of AB. G is a point two-thirds of the way along AD. $\overrightarrow{AB}$ = **b** and $\overrightarrow{AC}$ = **c**.

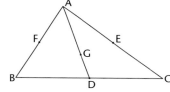

(a) Use vector methods to prove that F, G and C lie in a straight line. Where is G on the line CF?

(b) Prove that E, G and B lie in a straight line. Where is G on the line BE?

(c) AD, BE and CF are called the medians of the triangle. State, in words, the theorem you have just proved about the medians of a triangle.

11 ABCD is a parallelogram. P is the mid-point of AD and Q is the mid-point of CD. BP and AQ meet at X. $\overrightarrow{AB}$ = **b** and $\overrightarrow{AD}$ = **d**.

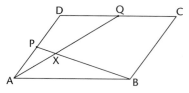

(a) Express $\overrightarrow{AQ}$ and $\overrightarrow{BP}$ in terms of **b** and **d**.

(b) $\overrightarrow{BX}$ can be written as $\lambda\overrightarrow{BP}$ for some number λ. $\overrightarrow{AX}$ can be written as $\mu\overrightarrow{AQ}$ for some number μ.

Use the fact that $\overrightarrow{AX} = \overrightarrow{AB} + \overrightarrow{BX}$ to find the values of λ and μ.

(c) What fraction of the area of parallelogram ABCD is triangle AXB?

Ruler and compass constructions and loci

DISCUSSION POINT

P is a point on the perpendicular bisector of AB.

- Use congruent triangles to prove that P is the same distance from A as it is from B.
- How does this provide the construction for the perpendicular bisector, using ruler and compasses?

P is a point on the angle bisector of angle ABC.

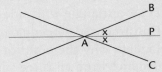

- Use congruent triangles to prove that P is the same (perpendicular) distance from BA as it is from CA.

The normal construction for drawing an angle bisector with ruler and compasses is shown in this diagram.

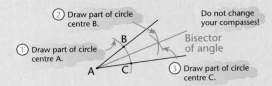

- Explain why this construction works.

This diagram shows the normal method for dropping a perpendicular from a point on to a line with ruler and compasses.

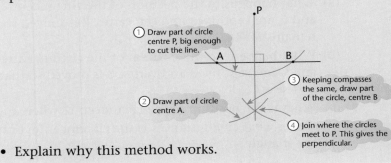

- Explain why this method works.

EXERCISE 7

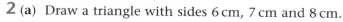

1 Use a ruler and compasses to construct each of these loci on a copy of Resource Sheet I.

    (a) Shade the points of triangle ABC which lie inside the triangle and are nearer to A than to B

    (b) Shade the points of triangle DEF which lie inside the triangle and whose distance from D is greater than the length of DE.

    (c) Shade the points in triangle GHI which lie inside the triangle and are nearer to G than to H and nearer to HI than to HG.

    (d) Shade the points in triangle JKL which are more than 5 cm from J and nearer to K than to L.

    (e) Shade the points in triangle MNO which are less than 4 cm from M and nearer to NO than to NM.

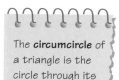

The **circumcircle** of a triangle is the circle through its three vertices.

2 (a) Draw a triangle with sides 6 cm, 7 cm and 8 cm.

    (b) Construct the perpendicular bisectors of two of the sides of the triangle.

    (c) Explain why the point of intersection of these bisectors is the same distance from all three vertices of the triangle.

    (d) Draw the circumcircle of the triangle.

    (e) Construct the perpendicular bisector of the third side of the triangle. Explain why the three perpendicular bisectors of the sides of a triangle are concurrent (i.e. all pass through a particular point).

3 This picture shows a triangle with its circumcircle and circumcentre O. Angle ABC is 50°.

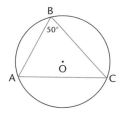

    (a) What happens to the position of the circumcentre O if the vertices A and C are kept fixed and the vertex B is moved so that angle ABC remains 50°?

    (b) What happens to the position of the circumcentre O if the vertices A and C are kept fixed and vertex B is moved so that the angle ABC increases?

    (c) What is the position of the circumcentre when angle ABC is 90°?

    (d) Under what circumstances is the circumcentre of triangle ABC outside the triangle?

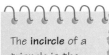

The **incircle** of a triangle is the circle touching its three sides.

4 (a) Draw a triangle with sides 6 cm, 7 cm and 8 cm.

(b) Draw the angle bisectors of two of the angles of the triangle.

(c) Explain why the point of intersection of these bisectors is the same distance from all three sides of the triangle.

(d) Draw the incircle of the triangle.

(e) Construct the angle bisector of the third angle of the triangle. Explain why the three angle bisectors of the angles of a triangle are concurrent.

5 A square has sides of length 6 cm.

(a) Draw a sketch to show the locus of points that are 2 cm from the perimeter of the square. Points can be both inside and outside the square.

(b) Calculate the total length of this locus. Leave your answer in terms of π.

6 A shape is formed by joining a square with sides of 6 cm and a semicircle, as shown.

(a) Draw a sketch to show the locus of points that are 2 cm from the perimeter of the shape.
Points can be both inside and outside the shape.

(b) Calculate the total length of the locus. Leave your answer in terms of π.

7 A shape is formed by joining an isosceles triangle and a semicircle, as shown.

(a) Sketch the shape and then sketch the locus of points which are *outside* the shape and are 3 cm from the perimeter of the shape.

(b) Calculate the total length of the locus.

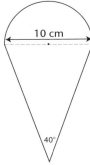

8 The length of each side of an equilateral triangle is 10 cm.

(a) Draw a sketch to show the locus of points which are *inside* the triangle and a distance 2 cm from the perimeter.

(b) Find the length of the locus.

9 Answer Question 10 for an isosceles right-angled triangle with a hypotenuse of length 12 cm.

DISCUSSION POINT

To construct a common tangent to two circles

Mark two points, A and B, 12 cm apart. Draw a circle with centre A and radius 5 cm. Draw another circle with centre B and radius 3 cm.

To construct common tangents to both circles, one circle can be regarded as an enlargement of the other. You need to find the centre of enlargement. This is how you can do this.

• The centre of enlargement lies on AB, and so draw line AB and extend it.

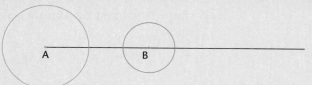

• Now draw any radius in the circle with centre A and a parallel radius in the circle with centre B. Join the ends of the radii with a line.
  The point where this line meets the line AB is the centre of enlargement. Label this point C.

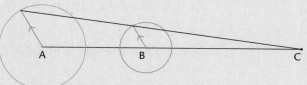

• To complete the construction, draw a circle with diameter CB.
  How does this help to draw the common tangents?

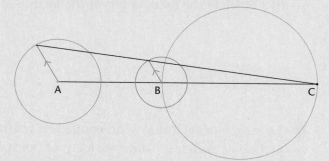

There are two more common tangents to these circles.
• Where are they?
• How can you adapt the method given above to construct them?

Rational and irrational ratios in polygons and circles

EXERCISE 8

1 In this diagram, the vertices of the inner square are the mid-points of the sides of the outer square.

   (a) What is the ratio of the areas of the squares?
Is this ratio rational? Or, is it irrational?

   (b) What is the ratio of the perimeters of the squares?
Is this rational? Or, is it irrational?

2 In this diagram, the vertices of the inner square divide the sides of the outer square in the ratio 3:4. Answer Question 1 for these squares.

3 In this diagram, the circle touches the four sides of the outer square. The vertices of the inner square lie on the circle.

   (a) Find the ratio of the perimeters and the ratio of the areas of the two squares.
Which are rational? Which are irrational?

   (b) Find the ratio of the area of the circle to the area of the outer square.
Is it rational? Or, is it irrational?

4 In this diagram, the ratio of the diameters of the two inner circles is $x:1$.

   (a) For what values of x is the ratio of the perimeter of the blue region to the perimeter of the outer circle rational?

   (b) Find the ratio of the blue area to the area of the outer circle in terms of x.

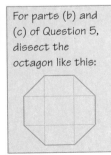

5 (a) Find the ratio of the areas of the two pieces into which one of the longest diagonals divides a regular octagon. Is it rational? Or, is it irrational?

   (b) Answer part (a) for a second longest diagonal.

   (c) Answer part (a) for one of the shortest diagonals.

6 In this diagram, the red triangle is inscribed in a semicircle.

The perimeter of the blue shape consists of a semicircle and a quarter circle.
Is the ratio of the red area to the blue area rational? Or, is it irrational?

7 In this diagram of a trapezium, the ratio of the longer to the shorter parallel sides is x:1.

    (a) What is the ratio of the areas of the red triangles?

    (b) What is the ratio of the perimeters and the ratio of the areas of the blue triangles?

        For what values of x are these ratios rational?

For part (b), let AO be 2 units.

8 ABC is an equilateral triangle and O is the centre of symmetry.

    (a) What is the exact value of cos 30°?

    (b) What is the ratio of AO to AB?

        Is it rational? Or, is it irrational?

For Question 9, use the answer to Question 8.

9 An equilateral triangle is inscribed in a circle. Find the ratio of the diameter of the circle to the perimeter of the triangle. Is it rational? Or, is it irrational?

10 This diagram shows three equal circles inscribed in a circle and touching one another. Find the ratio of the blue area to the red area. Is this rational? Or, is it irrational?

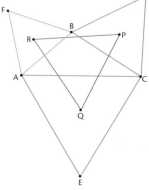

This remarkable result is supposed to have been discovered by Napoleon and is called **Napoleon's theorem**.

11 ABC is any triangle. Equilateral triangles BCD, CAE and ABF are drawn on its sides. P, Q and R are the centres of symmetry of these triangles.

    (a) Prove that triangles BPR and BDA are similar.
        What is the scale factor?
        (The answer to Question 8 will help here.)

    (b) Prove that triangles CPQ and CDA are similar.
        Prove that the scale factor is the same.

    (c) Deduce that PR = PQ.

    (d) What type of triangle is triangle PQR?

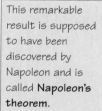

Gradients of perpendicular lines and equations of circles and their tangents

DISCUSSION POINT

These two lines are perpendicular. What is the gradient of each of the lines?

- Draw pairs of perpendicular lines on squared paper and find their gradients.

- Find a general rule connecting the gradients of perpendicular lines.

- Find a way of justifying your rule. (You might find it helpful to think about what happens when you rotate your paper by a quarter turn.)

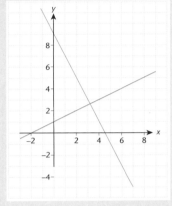

Providing a mathematical justification

DISCUSSION POINT

This circle has radius 5 and centre at the origin.

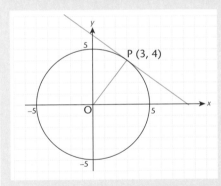

- Explain why its equation is $x^2 + y^2 = 25$.
- What is the gradient of the line OP?
- A tangent is drawn to the circle at P. What is the gradient of this tangent?
- What is the equation of the tangent?

EXERCISE 9

1 The centre of a circle is at the origin and its radius is 4. What is its equation?

2 The centre of a circle is at the point (0, 2) and its radius is 3. What is its equation?

3 Find the equations of each of these circles.

(a)

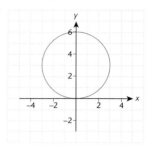

(b)

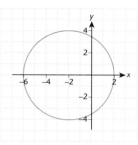

(c)

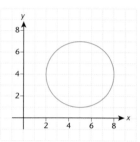

(d)

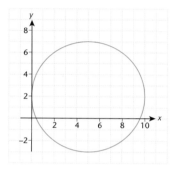

4 The centre of a circle is at the origin, O, and its radius is 10.

(a) What is the equation of the circle?

(b) The point A is at (8, 6).
What is the gradient of OA?
What is the gradient of the tangent at A?
What is the equation of the tangent at A?

(c) The point B is at (–6, 8).
What is the equation of the tangent at B?

(d) The point C is at (0, –10).
What is the equation of the tangent at C?

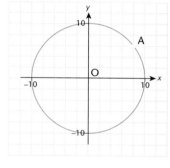

5 The radius of this circle is 4.

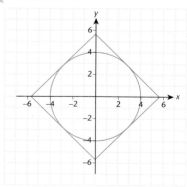

What are the equations of the tangents shown?
Leave your answers in surd form.

The circle $x^2 + y^2 = 25$ is intersected
by the line $y = 2x$.

How can you find the points of intersection?

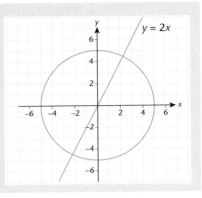

EXERCISE 10

1 Find the points of intersection of the circle $x^2 + y^2 = 16$ and the line $y = x$.

2 Find the points of intersection of the circle $x^2 + y^2 = 25$ and the line $4y = 3x$.

3 Find the points of intersection of the circle $(x - 2)^2 + y^2 = 9$ and the
line $y = x + 1$.

4 Find the points of intersection of the circle $(x - 6)^2 + (y + 2)^2 = 16$ and the
line $y = x - 4$.

5 A circle has equation $x^2 + y^2 = 64$. A chord to the circle is part of the line
$x = 5$. Find the length of the chord.

6 Which of these lines is a diameter of the circle $(x - 2)^2 + (y - 3)^2 = 49$?
  A: $y = 4x - 3$ B: $y = 2x$ C: $y = 2x - 1$ D: $y = -x$

CHAPTER SUMMARY

Chords and tangents to circles

AB is a chord. Centre O
lies on the perpendicular
bisector of AB.

A tangent to a circle is
perpendicular to
the diameter.

The two tangents from
a point to a circle
are equal in length.

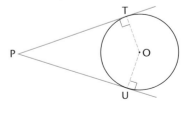

Angle properties of circles

The angle in a semicircle is a right angle.

The angle at the centre of a circle is twice the angle at the circumference.

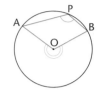

$\angle AOB = 2\angle APB$ Reflex $\angle AOB = 2\angle APB$

Angles in the same segment are equal.

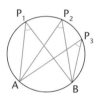
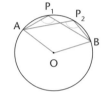

The opposite angles of a cyclic quadrilateral add to 180°.

The exterior angle of a cyclic quadrilateral is equal to the interior opposite angle.

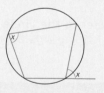

The angle between a chord and a tangent is equal to an angle in the alternate segment.

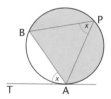

Vector geometry

$\overrightarrow{OA} = \mathbf{a}$, $\overrightarrow{OB} = \mathbf{b}$.

$\overrightarrow{AB} = \mathbf{b} - \mathbf{a}$

C is a point one-third of the way along OB. So $\overrightarrow{OC} = \frac{1}{3}\mathbf{b}$.

D is a point one-third of the way along AB. So, $\overrightarrow{AD} = \frac{1}{3}\overrightarrow{AB} = \frac{1}{3}(\mathbf{b} - \mathbf{a})$.

$\overrightarrow{OD} = \overrightarrow{OA} + \overrightarrow{AD} = \mathbf{a} + \frac{1}{3}(\mathbf{b} - \mathbf{a}) = \frac{2}{3}\mathbf{a} + \frac{1}{3}\mathbf{b}$

$\overrightarrow{CD} = \overrightarrow{CO} + \overrightarrow{OA} + \overrightarrow{AD} = -\frac{1}{3}\mathbf{b} + \mathbf{a} + \frac{1}{3}(\mathbf{b} - \mathbf{a}) = \frac{2}{3}\mathbf{a}$

This tells you that CD is parallel to OA and $\frac{2}{3}$ of its length.

REVISION EXERCISES

1: EXTENDING NUMBER SYSTEMS

Do not use a calculator for this exercise.

1 Evaluate these expressions.
 (a) 5^{-3} (b) $(\frac{1}{2})^4$ (c) $(\frac{1}{2})^{-4}$ (d) 7^0

2 Solve these equations.
 (a) $3^x = \frac{1}{9}$ (b) $8^t = \frac{1}{2}$ (c) $25^y = 125$

3 Find n in each of these.

 (a) $4^n = (4^5)^{-2} \times 4^7$ (b) $x^n = \dfrac{(\sqrt{x})^3}{x^{-2}}$

 (c) $3^n = \dfrac{(3^5)^{\frac{1}{2}}}{9}$ (d) $x^n = x^7 \div \dfrac{x^{-4}}{x^2}$

4 Work out each of these, giving your answers in standard form.
 (a) $(3 \times 10^5) \times (4 \times 10^3)$
 (b) $(1.8 \times 10^8) \div (2 \times 10^{-2})$
 (c) $(3 \times 10^{11}) + (4 \times 10^{10})$
 (d) $\sqrt{(1.6 \times 10^7) \div (4 \times 10^{-4})}$

5 Three of these expressions are equal. Which three?
 $\dfrac{2\sqrt{3}}{3}$ $\dfrac{3\sqrt{2}}{\sqrt{3}}$ $\dfrac{2}{\sqrt{3}}$ $\sqrt{6}$ $\dfrac{2\sqrt{3}}{2}$ $\sqrt{3} - \dfrac{1}{\sqrt{3}}$

6 Simplify these expressions.
 (a) $\dfrac{\sqrt{8}}{2}$ (b) $\dfrac{\sqrt{50} - \sqrt{32}}{\sqrt{2}}$

 (c) $(2 + 7\sqrt{3})(3 - 2\sqrt{3})$ (d) $\dfrac{\sqrt{2} + 1}{\sqrt{2} - 1}$

7 Convert each of these to a rational number.
 (a) 0.075 (b) $0.0\dot{7}\dot{5}$

8 Find, in surd form, the area of an equilateral triangle of side 8 cm.

9 (a) Write the following rational number as a fraction in its simplest form.
  $3.27\dot{2}7\dot{2}7$
 (b) Copy and complete this table for the sum $x + y$, where x and y are any two numbers. Use a tick (✔) if TRUE and a cross (✘) if FALSE.

$x + y$	Always irrational	Always rational	Sometimes rational and sometimes irrational
x rational} y rational∫			
x irrational} y rational∫			
x irrational} y irrational∫			

SEG 1996

10 The contents of books and newspapers can be stored on microfilm.
 $ABCD$ is one rectangular frame of this microfilm.
 $AB = 4.5 \times 10^{-3}$ centimetres and
 $BC = 6.2 \times 10^{-4}$ centimetres.

 (a) Calculate the area of the rectangle. Give your answer in standard form. Remember to state the units in your answer.
 (b) Calculate the perimeter of the rectangle. Give your answer in standard form. Remember to state the units in your answer.

NEAB 1997

2: TRANFORMATIONS AND VECTORS

1 (a) The translation $\binom{1}{2}$ maps $(1, 4)$ on to the point P. Find the coordinates of P.
 (b) Find the vector for the translation which maps $(0, 4)$ on to $(1, 3)$.

2 Work out the coordinates of the image of the point $(3, 8)$ after
 (a) reflection in the line $y = x$
 (b) rotation 90° clockwise about $(0, 2)$

3 In this diagram, the triangle ABC is transformed to the triangle A′B′C′.

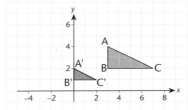

Describe this transformation fully.

4 If $\mathbf{u} = \binom{4}{-3}$ and $\mathbf{v} = \binom{-3}{-2}$, solve these equations for $\mathbf{x}$.
 (a) $\mathbf{x} + \mathbf{u} = \mathbf{v}$ (b) $\mathbf{u} - 2\mathbf{x} = 2\mathbf{v} + \mathbf{x}$

5 The blue square is translated, so that it is next to the green square to form a rectangle. Find vectors for all the translations which could be used.

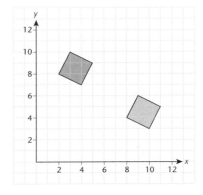

6 Lines AB and CD intersect at X.
AC is parallel to DB.

(a) Explain why triangles ACX and BDX are similar.

(b) AC = 4 cm, BD = 6 cm and CD = 12 cm. Find DX.

(c) Triangle ACX is the image of triangle BDX under an enlargement. State the centre and scale factor of the enlargement.

7 Copy this diagram.

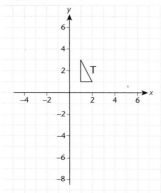

(a) Triangle T is enlarged to triangle T′ with scale factor –2 and centre the origin. Draw T′.

(b) Triangle T is enlarged to triangle T″ with scale factor 3 and centre (0, 5). What transformation will map triangle T″ to triangle T′?

8 (a) Find the image of the point (–3, 1) under this combination of transformations.

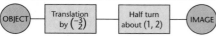

(b) Find the image of the same point if the transformations in part (a) are done in the reverse order.

(c) Find the image of (2, –1) under this combination of transformations.

(d) Is the same image obtained if the transformations in part (c) are done in the reverse order?

9 The flag B is the image of the flag A after a rotation about O followed by a translation.

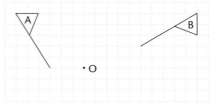

Find
(a) the angle of rotation
(b) the column vector for the translation
(c) the *single* transformation that would map A to B

10 A model power boat can travel at 0.75 m/s in still water.
It is released from a point P on the bank of a river which flows at 0.4 m/s.
The river is 15 m wide.
The boat is aimed continually in a direction perpendicular to the flow of the river, as shown in the diagram.

(a) By scale drawing or by calculation, find
  (i) the resultant speed of the boat;
  (ii) the direction in which the boat actually travels across the river.

(b) (i) How far downstream from P does the boat land on the opposite bank?
  (ii) How long does the boat take to cross the river?

NEAB 1995

1 Factorise each of these expressions completely.
(a) $10x^2y + 15xy^2$ (b) $uv - uw + xw - xv$
(c) $x^2 - 5x + 6$ (d) $x^2 - 5x - 6$

2 Factorise each of these expressions completely.
(a) $x^2 - 6x + 9$ (b) $x^2 + 6xy + 8y^2$
(c) $4x^2 - 9y^2$ (d) $6x^2 - 13x + 6$

3 Solve each of these quadratic equations by factorising.
(a) $x^2 - 5x + 4 = 0$ (b) $x^2 + 9x = 0$
(c) $x^2 + 8x + 16 = 0$ (d) $3x^2 - 10x + 3 = 0$

4 In each of these, p and q stand for numbers. Find the values of p and q for each expression.
(a) $x^2 + 4x + 5 = (x + p)^2 + q$
(b) $x^2 + 8x = (x + p)^2 + q$
(c) $x^2 - 6x + 6 = (x + p)^2 + q$
(d) $x^2 - 3x + 5 = (x + p)^2 + q$

5 Complete the square for each of these expressions. Then state the least value of the expression and the value of x which gives this least value.
  (a) $x^2 - 2x + 3$ (b) $x^2 + 10x$
  (c) $x^2 + 6x + 4$ (d) $x^2 - 10x + 25$

6 Draw a *sketch* graph for each of these, showing clearly the coordinates of the minimum point and the point of intersection with the y-axis.
  (a) $y = x^2 + 5$ (b) $y = (x - 2)^2 - 3$
  (c) $y = (x + 3)^2 + 2$ (d) $y = 2(x + 1)^2$

7 Solve each of these equations, either by completing the square or by using the formula. Give your answers correct to 2 decimal places.
  (a) $x^2 + 7x + 5 = 0$ (b) $x(2x - 11) + 4 = 0$
  (c) $x(4x - 5) = 8$

8 The length of a rectangle is 2 cm more than its width. The area of the rectangle is 20 cm².
  (a) Let w cm be the width and write down a quadratic equation satisfied by w.
  (b) Solve the equation, correct to 2 decimal places.
  (c) Calculate the perimeter of the rectangle, correct to 1 decimal place.

9 This right-angled triangle has sides of the lengths shown.

(2x + 3) cm, x cm, (x + 4) cm

  (a) Find a quadratic equation satisfied by x.
  (b) Solve the equation, leaving your answer in surd form.
  (c) Show that the perimeter of the rectangle is $6\sqrt{2} + 3$ cm.

10 Cylinder A has radius y and height $2x$. Sphere B has radius x.

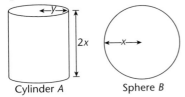

Cylinder A   Sphere B

  (a) The total surface area of cylinder A is given by the expression $2\pi y^2 + 4\pi xy$. Factorise this expression completely.
  (b) Cylinder A has the same surface area as sphere B. Show that $y^2 = 2x(x - y)$.
  (c) Calculate the value of x when $y = 3$. Give your answer to an accuracy of 1 decimal place.

SEG 1998

1 Fiona, Raiza and Simon conduct a survey on the way pupils travel to their school. To do this they each decide to take a 10% sample. The school has 800 pupils.
  (a) Give one advantage and one disadvantage of using a sample to obtain the data.
  (b) Fiona decides to go outside the school gate at 8.45 am and ask the first 80 pupils who arrive. Give one reason why this is not a good way to obtain the sample.
  (c) Raiza decides to take a simple random sample of 10% of the pupils. Describe a way in which Raiza might select her random sample.
  (d) Simon decides to take a stratified random sample. Give one advantage this may have over a simple random sample and suggest possible strata.

MEG 1998

2 Fruit and vegetables which have been grown without the use of chemicals for fertilizers and pest control are called organic. Some of the fruit and vegetables sold in a supermarket are organic, but they are usually more expensive. The management of the supermarket are conducting a survey to find out the opinions of their customers on organically grown fruit and vegetables.
  (a) Suggest **two** factors which should be considered in order to obtain a stratified sample of the customer population for this survey, explaining clearly why you consider these factors to be important.
  (b) The survey is actually conducted by questioning every twentieth customer entering the supermarket on a Monday morning. Give **one** reason why this method of sampling might produce misleading results.

WJEC 1998

3 This table contains information about the monthly rainfall (mm) and hours of sunshine at a seaside resort throughout one year.

Month	Jan	Feb	Mar	Apr	May	Jun	Jul	Aug	Sep	Oct	Nov	Dec
Rainfall (mm)	82	57	53	47	55	45	58	61	59	81	93	82
Sunshine (hrs)	53	89	138	212	178	219	196	181	167	142	70	41

  (a) Draw a scatter diagram to show this data.
  (b) Describe any correlation between the rainfall and the sunshine.

4 A researcher asks people how far they live from the city. She also asks them how many visits they have made to the city during the last three months. This table shows her results.

Distance (km)	5	8	3	9	7	1	3	4	Mean	5
Visits to city	10	5	13	2	6	16	15	11	Mean	9.75

(a) Draw a scatter diagram to show her results, using axes with 0–11 km on the horizontal axis, and 0–20 visits on the vertical axis.
(b) Draw a line of best fit on your scatter diagram
(c) Approximately how many visits would you expect a person who lives 2 km from the city to have made during the last three months?
WJEC 1998

5 These were the temperatures recorded on ten consecutive days at midday during Winter.

–1 °C, –1 °C, –2 °C, 3 °C, 4 °C, –3 °C, 0 °C, –1 °C, 1°C, 2°C

(a) Find the mean of these temperatures.
(b) Find the standard deviation of these temperatures.
(c) The temperatures are converted to °F, by first multiplying by 1.8 and then adding 32.
  (i) What is the mean of the temperatures in °F?
  (ii) What is the standard deviation of the temperatures in °F?

6 The ages of 50 teenagers at a discotheque are summarised in the table below.

Age, x years	Age mid-point	Number of pupils
$14 \leq x < 15$	14.5	4
$15 \leq x < 16$	15.5	8
$16 \leq x < 17$	16.5	11
$17 \leq x < 18$	17.5	17
$18 \leq x < 19$	18.5	6
$19 \leq x < 20$	19.5	4

(a) Find estimates for the mean and the standard deviation of the ages of the teenagers at the discotheque, giving your answers correct to one decimal place.
(b) Without further calculation, write down estimates for the mean and the standard deviation of the ages of the same people in three years time.
WJEC 1998

7 Gary found the playing time of each track in his CD collection.
The table shows the grouped distribution of times.

Time (t minutes)	$1 < t \leq 2$	$2 < t \leq 3$	$3 < t \leq 4$	$4 < t \leq 5$	$5 < t \leq 6$	$6 < t \leq 7$
Number of tracks (frequency)	5	25	45	82	33	10

(a) Calculate an estimate of the mean playing time of a CD track.
(b) (i) Copy and complete this cumulative frequency table.

Time (t minutes)	$t \leq 1$	$t \leq 2$	$t \leq 3$	$t \leq 4$	$t \leq 5$	$t \leq 6$	$t \leq 7$
Number of tracks	0	5					200

  (ii) Draw the cumulative frequency curve showing the playing times of the CD tracks.
(c) Use the cumulative frequency curve to estimate
  (i) the median playing time of a CD track,
  (ii) the probability that a randomly chosen track plays for longer than 3.7 minutes.
MEG 1998

8 This histogram shows the age distribution of the population of a town.

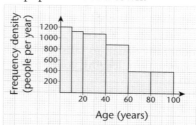

(a) How many people between the ages of 20 and 40 live in the town?
This table shows the number of patients of different ages in the town hospital on a particular day.

age (a) (years)	$0 \leq a < 10$	$10 \leq a < 20$	$20 \leq a < 40$	$40 \leq a < 60$	$60 \leq a < 100$
frequency	24	12	15	26	48

(b) Construct a histogram to illustrate these data.
(c) A journalist says
  'young people are more likely to be in hospital than old people'.
  State whether he is justified in making this claim, explaining how the histograms support your answer.

(d) Estimate the standard deviation of the ages of the patients in the town hospital.

(e) State how you would expect the standard deviation of the ages of the whole population of the town to differ from that of the hospital patients, giving a brief reason for your answer.

MEG 1998

9 Year 11 students in a school chose 3 subjects at GCSE level. They selected either Double Award Science or Single Award Science, either French or German, and either Geography or History.

$\frac{2}{3}$ of the students chose Double Award Science.

$\frac{3}{4}$ of the students who chose Double Award Science also selected French.

$\frac{1}{3}$ of the students who chose Single Award Science also selected German.

For each subject combination, $\frac{7}{10}$ of the students chose Geography.
A student is chosen at random.

(a) Copy and complete this tree diagram.
(b) What is the most popular combination

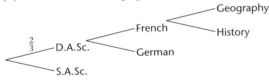

of subjects?
(c) Using the tree diagram or otherwise, calculate the probability that the student picked at random chose
   (i) Double Award Science, German and History.
   (ii) Single Award Science, German and Geography.
(d) There are 270 students in year 11.
   (i) How many students in year 11 chose Single Award Science, French and History?
   (ii) How many students in year 11 chose German?

CCEA 1998

10 In a lottery game, a computer selects, independently and at random, three numbers between 1 and 5 (inclusive). Because the numbers are chosen independently, repetitions are possible: for instance, the computer could select 1, 1, 4 or 1, 1, 1.
A player wins a prize by guessing correctly all three numbers selected by the computer, in the correct order.

(a) State the probability that a player
   (i) wins a prize,
   (ii) does not win a prize.
(b) Four players each play the game, independently.
   Calculate the probability that
   (i) none of them wins a prize,
   (ii) at least one of them wins a prize.
(c) The lottery game is changed so that the computer chooses b numbers between 1 and n (inclusive). Obtain an expression for the probability that none of a group of p players wins a prize.

MEG 1998

5: ALGEBRAIC MANIPULATION

1 Simplify these algebraic fractions.
   (a) $\dfrac{x^2 - 1}{x + 1}$
   (b) $\dfrac{a^2 + 5a + 4}{a^2 - 3a - 4}$
   (c) $\dfrac{4p^2 - 7pq + 3q^2}{p^2 - 7pq + 6q^2}$
   (d) $\dfrac{a^2 - 2a - 3ab + 6b}{a^2 - 4}$

2 Write each of these as one fraction in its simplest form.
   (a) $\dfrac{1}{m - 2} - \dfrac{1}{m}$
   (b) $\dfrac{a}{b + c} + \dfrac{a}{b - c}$
   (c) $\dfrac{y}{x^2 + xy} - \dfrac{x}{xy + y^2}$
   (d) $\dfrac{1}{x^2 - 4} - \dfrac{1}{x^2 - x - 6}$

3 At 80 kilometres per hour (kph), the 1998 model of a car travels 4 more kilometres per litre of petrol than the 1997 model.
Let the 1997 model travel x kilometres per litre of petrol at 80 kph.
   (a) Write down an expression in terms of x for the amount of petrol used in one hour at 80 kph by
      (i) the 1997 model,
      (ii) the 1998 model.
In a one hour trial, at 80 kph, the 1998 model used 1 litre of petrol less than the 1997 model.
   (b) Write down an equation satisfied by x and show that it simplifies to
   $x^2 + 4x - 320 = 0$.
   (c) Solve this equation and hence find how far the 1997 and 1998 models travel on one litre of petrol.

MEG 1998

4 Make u the subject of each of these formulae.
   (a) $s = \frac{1}{2}(u + v)t$
   (b) $v^2 - u^2 = 2as$

5 The surface area, A, of a solid cylinder can be expressed in terms of its radius r, its height h, and its volume V, by this formula:
$$A = \frac{2v}{h} + \frac{2V}{r}$$
   (a) Rewrite this formula so that V is the subject.
   (b) Rewrite this formula so that h is the subject.
   (c) Rewrite this formula so that r is the subject.

6 What is the *least* whole number n, satisfying each of these inequalities?
   (a) $4n - 3 > 14$ (b) $3n - 5 < 5n - 1$
   (c) $n^2 < 169$

7 Solve each of these inequalities.
   (a) $3x - 5 \le 19$ (b) $6x - 9 \ge 14 + 11x$
   (c) $(x - 1)(x - 7) > 0$

8 Draw the region satisfying all these inequalities.
   $y \ge 0$ $x + 2 \ge 2y$ $x \ge 3$ $x + y \le 7$

9 The interior of an isosceles trapezium is defined by four inequalities.
   Here are three of them.
   $x + y > 0$ $x + y < 4$ $y < 3x - 8$
   Give a fourth inequality that could define the trapezium.

10 Workers in a cottage industry plan to make a batch of hand-knitted jumpers and cardigans.
   A jumper takes $7\frac{1}{2}$ hours to complete and a cardigan $13\frac{1}{2}$ hours.
   The workers, between them, can work a maximum of 135 hours.
   Let x equal the number of jumpers and y the number of cardigans in the batch.
   (a) Show that this time restriction can be written as $5x + 9y \le 90$.
   Each jumper requires 800 grammes of wool and each cardigan 1000 grammes.
   The maximum amount of wool available is 12 000 grammes.
   (b) Write down an inequality in terms of x and y for this restriction.
   The batch must include at least 3 cardigans.
   (c) Write down an inequality for this restriction.
   (d) Illustrate the three inequalities on graph paper with axes $0 \le x \le 18$, and $0 \le y \le 18$. Indicate clearly the region containing the points which satisfy all the inequalities.
   The profit from each jumper is £6 and the profit from each cardigan is £8.
   (e) Find the number of jumpers and the number of cardigans which should be made to give a maximum profit.

CCEA 1998

6: FURTHER TRIGONOMETRY

1 Two ships leave a port P. One sails on a bearing of 130° for 5.4 nautical miles to A.
   The other sails on a bearing of 255° for 6.8 nautical miles to position B.
   (a) How far apart are the ships?
   (b) What is the bearing of B from A?

2 Find the unmarked sides and angles in triangle ABC.

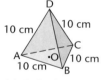

3 In an acute-angled triangle EFG, EF = 9 cm and FG = 12 cm. The area of triangle EFG is 42 cm².
   (a) Find the size of ∠EFG.
   (b) Find the length of EG.

4 A kite has sides of length 11.3 cm and 14.1 cm, and two angles of 102°.
   (a) Calculate the area of the kite.
   (b) Calculate the sizes of the other two angles of the kite.

5 The edges of a regular tetrahedron ABCD are each of length 10 cm.

   (a) Calculate the surface area of the tetrahedron.
   (b) The lines of symmetry of face ABC meet at O. Calculate the distance AO.
   (c) Calculate the angle between edge AD and face ABC.
   (d) Calculate the length of DO.
   (e) Calculate the angle between the faces ABD and ABC.

6 The base ABCD of pyramid ABCDE is a square with sides of length 8 cm. The other four edges of the pyramid each have a length of 13 cm.
   (a) O is the centre of the square base. Calculate the lengths AO and EO.
   (b) Calculate the angle between edge EA and the base of the pyramid.
   (c) Calculate the angle between edges EA and EC.
   (d) Calculate the surface area of the pyramid.

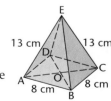

7 The diagram shows a pair of compasses positioned to draw a circle of radius 10 cm. The pencil makes an angle of 79° to the horizontal. Calculate the angle A at which the compasses are set.

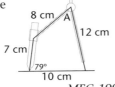

8 cm A
12 cm
7 cm
79°
10 cm

MEG 1998

8 A woman stands 115 m from the base of a tower on level ground and measures the angle of elevation of the top of the tower as 27° from a point 1 metre above the ground. If the distance is measured correct to the nearest metre and the angle correct to the nearest degree, find upper and lower bounds for the height of the tower.

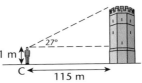

27°
1 m
C
115 m

9 (a) Sketch the graph of $y = \cos x$ for values of x between 0° and 360°.
   (b) Find all the solutions to the equation $7\cos x + 4 = 0$, between 0° and 360°.

10 (a) Use this equilateral triangle to write down the exact values of sin 30° and cos 30°, without using a calculator.

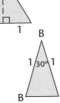

2   2
1   1 B

   (b) In this isosceles triangle, $AB = AC = 1$ and $\angle BAC = 30°$. Find the area of triangle ABC.

1 /30°\ 1
B   C

   (c) Show that BC = $\sqrt{2 - \sqrt{3}}$

7: USING GRAPHS TO SOLVE PROBLEMS

1 This is the graph of $y = x^3 - 4x$.
   (a) Using the graph, write down an approximate value for each of the solutions to the equation $x^3 - 4x = 2$.
   (b) Use trial and improvement to find the smallest solution, correct to 2 decimal places.

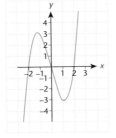

2 (a) Copy and complete this table of values for $y = x^3 - 6x^2 + 5x + 12$.

x	−1	0	1	2	3	4
y		12			0	

(b) Use this table to draw the graph of $y = x^3 - 6x^2 + 5x + 12$.
(c) Estimate the gradient of the tangent to the curve when $x = 2$.
(d) Use your graph to estimate the maximum and minimum values of y in the range $0 < x < 4$. For what values of x do these occur?
(e) Draw an appropriate straight line on the graph to solve the equation $x^3 - 6x^2 + 8x + 7 = 0$. Estimate all the solutions of the equation, correct to 1 decimal place.

3 This is the graph of $y = \cos x$ for values of x between 0° and 360°. Sketch these graphs for values of x between 0° and 360°. Label each graph clearly.
   (a) $y = \cos x - 1$
   (b) $y = \cos 2x$
   (c) $y = 2\cos x$
   (d) $y = \cos (x - 45°)$

$y = \cos x$
2
1
90° 180° 270° 360°
−1
−2

4 One cold morning, when the temperature outside was 0 °C, Kevin investigated how quickly a saucepan of hot water cooled when placed outside. Kevin brought the saucepan of water to the boil and carried it out to the garden. The initial temperature reading of the water was 96°C when Kevin started taking temperature readings at regular intervals.
He found that during each successive period of 10 minutes, the temperature reading, T°C, fell by one-quarter of its value at the start of that period.
   (a) Copy and complete this table giving values of T at various times, t minutes, from the start of the experiment.

t (minutes)	0	10	20	30	40	50
T (°C)	96				30.4	

   (b) On graph paper draw the graph of T against t.
   (c) Taking readings from your graph, and showing clearly how your answers were obtained, find
      (i) how many minutes it took for the initial temperature reading to be halved,
      (ii) the average rate at which the temperature fell between $t = 15$ and $t = 45$, stating the units.
   (d) The equation of the graph is known to be $T = 96(0.75)^{t/k}$ where k is constant. What is the value of k?

CCEA 1998

5 (a) Factorise $x^2 - x - 12$.
(b) $f(x) = x^2 - x - 12$. Sketch the graph of $y = f(x)$, labelling the points at which the graph meets the axes.
(c) Sketch each of these graphs, labelling the points at which each graph meets the axes.
(i) $2f(x)$
(ii) $f(x + 2)$
(iii) $f(2x)$

6 The diagram shows a sketch of the function $y = f(x)$.

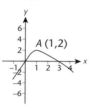

The curve cuts the x-axis at (0, 0) and (3, 0).
$A(1, 2)$ is a point on the curve.
The function is transformed.
On a copy of this grid, sketch the transformed function.
State the co-ordinates of A on each new curve.
(a) $y = f(x) - 2$
(b) $y = 2f(x)$
(c) $y = f(2x)$

NEAB 1998

7 (a) Draw the graph of $y = 9x - x^3$ for values of x between -3 and 3.
(b) Use the trapezium rule with six strips to estimate the area enclosed between the x-axis and the portion of the graph between 0 and 3.
(c) Use your answer to part (b) to estimate the total area enclosed between the x-axis and the graph.

8 A girl standing at the top of a tower throws a ball to her father on the ground below.
The height, h feet, of the ball above the ground after t seconds, is given by this equation:
$h = 20 + 10t - 4t^2$
(a) Draw the graph of h against t for values of t between 0 and 4.
(b) The father catches the ball 3 feet above the ground.
For how long was the ball in the air?
(c) By drawing a suitable tangent to the graph, find the vertical speed of the ball when the father catches it.

9 In the College Games, Michael Jackson won the 200 metres race in a time of 20.32 seconds.
(a) Calculate his average speed in metres per second.
Give your answer correct to 1 decimal place.
(b) Change your answer to part (a) to kilometres per hour. Give your answer correct to 1 decimal place.

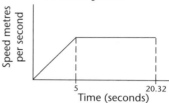

The diagram shows a sketch of the speed/time graph for Michael Jackson's race.
(c) Calculate his maximum speed in metres per second.
Give your answer correct to 1 decimal place.
(d) Calculate his acceleration over the first 5 seconds. State the units in your answer.
Give your answer correct to 2 significant figures.

Edexcel 1998

10 This graph shows the speed of the tip of a pendulum at different times.

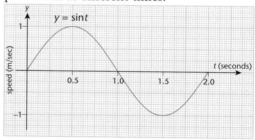

(a) How long does the pendulum take to travel between two consecutive points at which the speed is zero?
(b) Estimate how far the pendulum travels between these two points.
(c) Use the graph to estimate the maximum acceleration of the pendulum.

8: CIRCLES AND VECTORS

1 This diagram shows a circle with a chord AB and radius OP. The chord and the radius are perpendicular. X is the point where they intersect. Use congruent triangles to prove that X is the mid-point of AB.

2 BC is a diameter of a circle with centre O and A is a point on the circle. The tangent to the circle at C meets the line through AO at P. ∠BOA = 58°. Calculate the three angles of triangle APC.

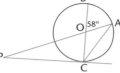

3 A, B, C and D are four points on a circle whose centre is O. PQ is a tangent to the circle, touching the circle at A. Calculate each of these angles.
(a) ∠AOC
(b) ∠ABC
(c) ∠DCA

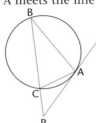

4 A, B and C are three points on a circle. The tangent to the circle at A meets the line through B and C at P. Prove that the triangles PAC and PBA are similar.

5 A, B, C and D are four points on a circle and chord BA is parallel to chord CD. Chords AC and BD intersect at X. ∠CAB = 50°.
(a) Prove that triangle AXB is isosceles.
(b) Find ∠CXB.
(c) Points B and C are fixed. Points A and D move round the major arc BC so that AB and CD remain parallel. Describe the locus of point X.

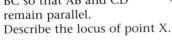

6 (a) Draw a kite ABCD with AB = AD = 6 cm, CB = CD = 10 cm and ∠ABC = ∠ADC = 110°.
(b) Draw and mark the locus of points which are equidistant from B and D.
(c) Draw a circle centre B through A and a circle centre D through A.
(d) A third circle is to be drawn. Its centre is to be on the locus drawn in part (b). Together with the other two circles, it must completely cover the kite. Its radius is to be as small as possible. Construct the position of the centre of this circle and then draw the circle.

7 A shape consists of an equilateral triangle joined to a semicircle, as shown.

The radius of the semicircle is 4 cm.
(a) Calculate the perimeter of the shape, correct to the nearest millimetre.
(b) Make an accurate drawing of the shape.
(c) Draw the locus of points outside this shape which are exactly 2 cm from the perimeter of the shape.
(d) Calculate the length of this locus.

8 ABCD is a trapezium in which AB and CD are parallel and DC is twice the length of AB. AB = **u** and BC = **v**. Express AC and BD in terms of **u** and **v**.

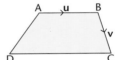

9 OABC is a quadrilateral. P, Q, X and Y are the midpoints of OA, BC, OB and AC respectively.

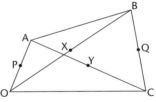

$\overrightarrow{OA}$ = **a**, $\overrightarrow{OB}$ = **b**, $\overrightarrow{OC}$ = **c**.
(a) Find and simplify expressions, in terms of **a**, **b** and **c**, for
(i) $\overrightarrow{PX}$, (ii) $\overrightarrow{OY}$, (iii) $\overrightarrow{OQ}$.
(b) Use your answers to parts (a)(ii) and (a)(iii) to find and simplify an expression for $\overrightarrow{YQ}$.
(c) What can you deduce about quadrilateral PXQY?
MEG 1998

10 (a) A circle has this equation.
$(x - 2)^2 + y^2 = 25$
What is the centre and the radius of this circle?
(b) Prove that the point (–1, 4) lies on this circle.
(c) Find the equation of the tangent to the circle through the point (–1, 4).

REVISION GUIDE

You will be given a lot of advice about how to revise for your GCSE examinations. Much of this advice is about how to find the key facts, and how to commit them to memory. Maths is a bit different from most other subjects. In Maths examinations, being able to solve problems is probably more important than remembering facts. Of course, there are also some things you have to remember. This REVISION GUIDE will help you with both.

Remembering facts and solving problems

In this REVISION GUIDE, your GCSE syllabus has been divided into small, easy-to-remember topics. You will find the facts you have to learn for each topic. You will also find worked examples for methods of solving problems.

Practising solving problems

For each topic, there is a set of problems for you to solve. Some of these are questions from past GCSE papers. The answers are on page 301 of this book.

"So where do I start?"

The syllabus has been divided into the four major areas:

Number	12 topics
Algebra	16 topics
Shape, space and measures	20 topics
Handling data	10 topics

A list of all the topics, in all four areas, is given on page 180. The topics are listed in the order they appear in the GCSE syllabus. They are *not* in order of difficulty.

The section for each area contains the topics and, then, a miscellaneous exercise. You could look through the list of topics on page 180,

and decide which topics you need to revise. Try some of the questions, and use the notes to help you.

Warning: You will want to do some of the questions on topics that you know you understand, to give yourself confidence. However, it also important that you try some of the questions you know you cannot do. It is also tempting to look at the worked examples and think "I can do that", *without actually doing the questions*.

> **Remember:**
> **Success in a Maths exam means solving problems – so successful Maths revision means solving problems.**

"How long do I spend on each topic?"

This will depend on how confident you are about the topic. If you are 'brushing up' on something you already know, it might only take you twenty minutes to reassure yourself that you have mastered the ideas. But, if the topic is one you never really understood, it will take you longer, and you may need to talk to your teacher about it.

"When do I start revising?"

Now! Even if you are reading this in the September of Y11, you may find it helpful to look at the list of topics on page 180, and to discuss with your teacher which topics you should already know. And, if you have forgotten some topics, then you can revise them now! Or, you might plan to revise one topic per week over the next two terms.

If it is now towards the end of Spring term (the time a lot of students start their revision), then there might not be enough time to spend a long while on each topic. You will need to plan what you are going to do. Read the previous two sections again, and decide what your priorities are.

"How do I keep track of my revision programme?"

Your teacher will probably give you a copy of the REVISION ORGANISER, which contains a list of all the revision topics. There are various ways in which you can use the spaces in the REVISION ORGANISER.

- Fill in the dates when you plan to revise each topic.
- Cross out or highlight the topics you have already revised and feel confident about.
- Highlight the topics you want to come back to.
- Make notes of key points you may forget.

Your teacher might also give you a copy of the revision notes in this text book. If so, you could carry this copy around with you all the time – so that you can revise wherever you are!

"What about my coursework exam?"

Some students do coursework for their GCSE; others do a 'coursework' examination. You will need to be clear about what you are doing. If you are doing the examination, you will be asked questions which test your ability to use and apply your knowledge of Mathematics.

You will need to:

- make decisions about how to tackle a problem
- write clearly about what you find out
- give reasons for your conclusions.

There is also a sheet giving criteria for assessing coursework or the coursework examination. Ask your teacher for Resource Sheet J. In many of the chapters in this book, and in *Book 1*, you will have noticed COURSEWORK OPPORTUNITIES. Tackling these will give you some idea about what to expect.

Also, you might have noticed flags like this next to some questions. This flag indicates that the question is a bit like the questions you might meet in the examination.

Making general statements

Most importantly, talk to your teacher about your coursework examination. You will want to see coursework examinations for the last year or two, set for the particular GCSE you are taking.

"Do I need to do any other revision?"

In this REVISION GUIDE, the questions have been organised into topics for you. This is the best way of starting your revision, because then you can concentrate on the topics you are least clear about.

But, in the examination, you will have to decide for yourself what topic the question is about. This is a skill you can practise by answering the questions in the six course revision exercises in this REVISION GUIDE.* But you also need to practise this skill, by doing past papers for the particular GCSE examination you are taking.

Talk to your teacher about getting hold of some past GCSE papers, and build these into the later stages of your revision programme.

*NOTE: It may be useful for you to know that there are six more course assessment tests in the *Teacher's Guide*. Also, half of the course revision exercises and tests are to be done without a calculator, just as some GCSE papers are to be done without a calculator.

EQUIVALENCE OF FRACTIONS, DECIMALS AND PERCENTAGES

EQUIVALENT FRACTIONS

These fractions are all equivalent.

$$\frac{1}{3}, \frac{2}{6}, \frac{3}{9}, \frac{4}{12}, \frac{30}{90}, \frac{250}{750}, \cdots$$

This means they all stand for the *same* number.
These fractions are all equivalent.

$$\frac{3}{4}, \frac{6}{8}, \frac{9}{12}, \frac{45}{60}, \frac{75}{100}, \cdots$$

Sometimes, you are asked to **simplify a fraction**.
This means writing an equivalent fraction with the *smallest* possible numbers.

Divide the top and bottom by the same number.

CHANGING PERCENTAGES TO FRACTIONS AND DECIMALS

$40\% = \frac{40}{100} = \frac{2}{5}$

Remember that % means 'divide by 100'.

or $40\% = 40 \div 100 = 0.4$

CHANGING FRACTIONS AND DECIMALS TO PERCENTAGES

$\frac{4}{5} = \frac{4}{5} \times 100\% = \frac{400}{5}\% = 80\%$

Multiply by 100%

$0.8 = 0.8 \times 100\% = 80\%$

EQUIVALENCE BETWEEN FRACTIONS AND DECIMALS

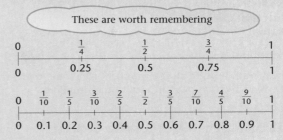

These are worth remembering

Remember that $\frac{a}{b}$ is the same as $a \div b$.

So $\frac{7}{8} = 7 \div 8 = 0.875$.

$\frac{40}{7} = 40 \div 7 = 5.71$ (correct to 3 significant figures)

This provides the easiest way of comparing the sizes of two fractions.

$\frac{5}{8} = 5 \div 8 = 0.625$

$\frac{2}{3} = 2 \div 3 = 0.667$ (correct to 3 decimal places)

So $\frac{2}{3}$ is bigger than $\frac{5}{8}$.

To convert a decimal to a fraction, use place value, and then simplify.

$0.6 = \frac{6}{10} = \frac{3}{5}$

$0.07 = \frac{7}{100}$

$0.375 = \frac{375}{1000} = \frac{3}{8}$

Do not use a calculator for this exercise.

1 Which fraction is the odd one out?
   Explain your answer.

   $\frac{5}{8}$ $\frac{40}{64}$ $\frac{25}{64}$ $\frac{15}{24}$ $\frac{25}{40}$

2 (a) Change each of these fractions to a decimal, correct to 2 decimal places.

   $\frac{3}{4}$ $\frac{4}{7}$ $\frac{7}{11}$ $\frac{7}{5}$

   $\frac{5}{3}$ $\frac{7}{10}$ $\frac{9}{13}$ $\frac{13}{9}$

   (b) List the fractions in part (a) in order of size.

3 Arrange these numbers in order of size, starting with the smallest.

   27% $\frac{2}{7}$ 2.7 $\frac{22}{7}$ 0.227

   22%   77% $\frac{7}{22}$ $\frac{7}{27}$ $2\frac{2}{7}$

4 Write each of these as a decimal, correct to 3 significant figures.

   $5\frac{1}{3}$ $8\frac{1}{6}$ $12\frac{5}{6}$ $7\frac{2}{3}$ $14\frac{1}{12}$ $1\frac{7}{12}$

N2 — RATIONAL AND IRRATIONAL NUMBERS

TYPES OF NUMBER

Natural numbers (counting numbers) 1, 2, 3, 4, ...

Integers .... –4, –3, –2, –1, 0, 1, 2, 3, 4, ...

Rational numbers are all the numbers that can be written as $\frac{\text{integer}}{\text{integer}}$. E.g. $\frac{2}{3}$, $-\frac{8}{5}$

> Rational numbers include the integers, e.g. $3 = \frac{6}{2}$.

Irrational numbers are numbers that *cannot* be written as $\frac{\text{integer}}{\text{integer}}$. E.g. π, $\sqrt{2}$, $2\sqrt{3} - 5$, $\sqrt[3]{7}$

Real numbers are all the numbers which are represented by points on the number line. They include rational and irrational numbers.

TERMINATING AND RECURRING DECIMALS

- All rational numbers can be expressed as terminating or recurring decimals.

- Fractions in which the denominator contains only powers of 2 and 5 produce decimals which terminate.

$$\frac{5}{8} = 0.625 \qquad \frac{37}{100} = 0.37 \qquad \frac{9}{25} = 0.36$$

- All other fractions produce recurring decimals.

$$\frac{2}{3} = 0.\dot{6} \qquad \frac{3}{7} = 0.\dot{4}2857\dot{1} \qquad \frac{7}{12} = 0.58\dot{3}$$

TURNING A RECURRING DECIMAL INTO A FRACTION

Example

What is $0.1\dot{2}$ as a fraction?

$$x = 0.121\,212\,12...$$
$$100x = 12.121\,212\,12$$

> Multiply by $10^2 = 100$, because the period is 2.

Subtract: $99x = 12$

$$x = \frac{12}{99} = \frac{4}{33}$$
$$0.1\dot{2} = \frac{4}{33}$$

To turn the recurring decimal $0.\dot{3}846\dot{1}5$ into a fraction, you multiply by 10^6.

To turn the recurring decimal $0.340\dot{5}$ into a fraction, you multiply by 10^3.

CALCULATING WITH SURDS

$$\sqrt{98} = \sqrt{49 \times 2} = 7\sqrt{2}$$
$$(\sqrt{2} + \sqrt{3})^2 = 2 + 2\sqrt{6} + 3 = 5 + 2\sqrt{6}$$

> An irrational number

$$(\sqrt{8} + \sqrt{18})^2 = 8 + 2\sqrt{144} + 18 = 26 + 24 = 50$$
or $(\sqrt{8} + \sqrt{18})^2 = (2\sqrt{2} + 3\sqrt{2})^2 = (5\sqrt{2})^2 = 50$

> Rational

Note $\sqrt{ab} = \sqrt{a} \times \sqrt{b}$

$$\sqrt{\frac{a}{b}} = \frac{\sqrt{a}}{\sqrt{b}}$$

But $\sqrt{a} + \sqrt{b} \ne \sqrt{a + b}$
and $\sqrt{a} - \sqrt{b} \ne \sqrt{a - b}$

Rationalising the denominator

$$\frac{3}{\sqrt{5}} = \frac{3 \times \sqrt{5}}{\sqrt{5} \times \sqrt{5}} = \frac{3\sqrt{5}}{5}$$

> Multiply top and bottom by $\sqrt{5}$.

$$\frac{2}{\sqrt{5} - 1} = \frac{2(\sqrt{5} + 1)}{(\sqrt{5} - 1)(\sqrt{5} + 1)} = \frac{2(\sqrt{5} + 1)}{4} = \frac{\sqrt{5} + 1}{2}$$

> Multiply top and bottom by $\sqrt{5} + 1$.

 Do not use a calculator for this exercise.

1 If $a = \sqrt{3}$, $b = \sqrt{6}$ and $c = \sqrt{12}$, evaluate each of these expressions.
Which are rational? Which are irrational?

(a) ab (b) $(ab)^2 - 1$ (c) $\frac{c}{a}$

(d) $(b - a)^2$ (e) $(a + c)^2$

2 Which of these numbers are irrational?
Which are rational?

(a) $\sqrt{6.25}$ (b) $\sqrt{6.4}$ (c) $\sqrt{3} \times \sqrt{12}$

(d) $\sqrt{3} \div \sqrt{12}$ (e) $\sqrt{5 + \sqrt{4}}$ (f) $\sqrt{5} + 4$

(g) $\sqrt{5 + 4}$ (h) $\sqrt{\frac{98}{242}}$

3 Replace the **?** between each of these pairs with one of the symbols <, =, or > to make a correct statement.
Justify your answers.

(a) $\sqrt{2} \times \sqrt{3}$ **?** $\sqrt{6}$ (b) $\sqrt{2} + \sqrt{3}$ **?** $\sqrt{5}$

(c) $\sqrt{3^2 + 2^2}$ **?** 3.6 (d) $\sqrt{\frac{169}{121}}$ **?** $1.\dot{1}\dot{8}$

(e) $(\sqrt{2} + \sqrt{3})^2$ **?** $5 + 2\sqrt{6}$ (f) $(\sqrt{5} - \sqrt{3})^2$ **?** 2

4 (a) Explain what a rational number is.

  (b) Using $(a + b)^2 = a^2 + 2ab + b^2$, or otherwise, show that
$$(\sqrt{2} + \sqrt{8})^2 = 18.$$

  (c) Tracey says

> $(\sqrt{2} + \sqrt{8})$ is an irrational number.
> $(\sqrt{2} + \sqrt{8})^2 = 18$
> I think that if you square an irrational number you always get a rational number!

Tracey is wrong.
Use an example to show that Tracey is wrong.

NEAB 1998

5 (a) Write down an irrational number between 5 and 6.

  (b) Write down a rational number between $\sqrt{5}$ and $\sqrt{6}$.

  (c) Write down a rational number which cannot be written as a terminating decimal.

  (d) Write down an irrational number whose square is rational.

  (e) Write down an irrational number whose square is irrational.

6 Write each of these fractions either as terminating or as recurring decimals.

  (a) $\frac{7}{8}$ (b) $\frac{6}{7}$

  (c) $\frac{5}{11}$ (d) $\frac{63}{125}$

7 (a) $x = 0.\dot{3}\dot{6}$. What is the value of $100x$?
       Use this answer to find the value of x as a fraction in its simplest form.

  (b) Write each of these recurring decimals as fractions in their simplest forms.

    (i) $0.19\dot{4}$

    (ii) $0.4\dot{5}\dot{9}$

    (iii) $0.0\dot{8}\dot{1}$

8 Which of these are possible for a right-angled triangle? Justify your answers.

  (a) All three sides are rational.

  (b) Two sides are rational and one is irrational.

  (c) One side is rational and two sides are irrational.

  (d) All three sides are irrational.

9 For each of these, give possible values for positive unequal numbers x and y.

  (a) x and y are both irrational and xy is rational.

  (b) x and y are both irrational and xy is irrational.

  (c) x and y are both irrational and $x + y$ is rational.

  (d) x and y are both irrational and $x - y$ is rational.

  (e) xy is irrational and x^2y is rational.

  (f) x, y and xy are irrational and $\frac{x}{y}$ is rational.

10 Solve these equations.

  (a) $\sqrt{18} = x\sqrt{2}$ (b) $\frac{1}{\sqrt{18}} = 3^{-1} \times 2^x$

  (c) $\sqrt{18} + \sqrt{50} = 2^x$ (d) $\frac{6}{\sqrt{3}} + \sqrt{147} = 3^x$

11 x is an irrational number. For each of these, say whether its value is definitely irrational, definitely rational, or you cannot tell which it is.
  Justify your answers.

  (a) $x + 2$ (b) x^2

  (c) $\frac{1 - x}{1 - x^2}$ (d) $x - (3 + x)$

12 Simplify each of these expressions.
  Which are rational? Which are irrational?

  (a) $\frac{12}{\sqrt{3}}$

  (b) $\frac{3}{\sqrt{2} - 1}$

  (c) $\frac{8}{\sqrt{5} - 1} - \frac{8}{\sqrt{5} + 1}$

MULTIPLES, FACTORS AND PRIMES

MULTIPLES

The first three multiples of 13 are 13, 26 and 39.
The smallest multiple of 7 bigger than 100 is 105.

FACTORS

The factors of 30 are 1, 2, 3, 5, 6, 10, 15 and 30.
The factors of 36 are 1, 2, 3, 4, 6, 9, 12, 18 and 36.
A *square* number has an *odd* number of factors.

Prime factors are factors which are prime numbers.

$30 = 2 \times 3 \times 5 \quad 36 = 6 \times 6 \qquad\qquad 525 = 25 \times 21$

Numbers
written as the
product of
prime factors

$= 2 \times 3 \times 2 \times 3 \qquad = 5 \times 5 \times 3 \times 7$

$= 2^2 \times 3^2 \qquad\qquad = 3 \times 5^2 \times 7$

The **lowest common multiple** and **highest common factor** of two numbers can be found using their prime factorisation.
The lowest common multiple of 30 and 525 is
$2 \times 3 \times 5^2 \times 7 = 1050$.
The highest common factor of 30 and 525 is
$3 \times 5 = 15$.

PRIME NUMBERS

A **prime number** does not have any factors, except 1 and the number itself.

These are the prime numbers less than 100:
2, 3, 5, 7, 11, 13, 17, 19, 23, 29, 31, 37, 41, 43, 47, 53, 59, 61, 67, 71, 73, 79, 83, 89, 97

- Apart from 2, no even number is prime (all even numbers have 2 as a factor).
- Apart from 5, no number ending in 0 or 5 is prime (it is divisible by 5).
- If the digits of a number add up to 3, that number is divisible by 3.
  So it is not prime, unless it is 3 itself.
- To test whether a number is prime, you only have to test whether another prime number is a factor. If 2, 3 and 5 are not factors, you need to test 7, 11 and 13. This is all you need to test for numbers up to 289 (which is 17×17).

Do not use a calculator for this exercise.

1 (a) What is the lowest number that is a multiple of 8 and 18?

   (b) What is the lowest number that is a multiple of 7, 11 and 13?

2 (a) Factorise 36, 56 and 54 into products of prime factors.

   (b) Find the highest common factor of 36 and 56.

   (c) Find the highest common factor of 36, 54 and 56.

3 (a) What is the highest common factor of the numbers 28 and 42?

   (b) What is the highest common factor of 280 and 420?

4 Write each of 224 and 280 as a product of prime factors.
   Hence, find the highest common factor and lowest common multiple of 224 and 280.

5 (a) Express 9800 as a product of prime factors.

   (b) Find the smallest square number which is a multiple of 9800.

   CCEA 1998

6 The highest common factor of X and 54 is 3.

   (a) What is the highest common factor of X and 108?

   (b) What is the lowest common multiple of 5X and 54?

7 (a) Write each of 220 and 284 as the product of prime factors.
      Hence, write down all the factors of 220 and all the factors of 284.

   (b) Check your answer by showing that 220 and 284 are amicable: in other words, the factors of 220 (apart from 220 itself) add to 284 and the factors of 284 (apart from 284 itself) add to 220.

N4 POWERS, ROOTS AND RECIPROCALS

POWERS, ROOTS AND INDICES

$5^3 = 125$ means the same as $\sqrt[3]{125} = 5$
$2^5 = 32$ means the same as $\sqrt[5]{32} = 2$

Rule	Example
$a^m \times a^n = a^{m+n}$	$3a^4 \times 4a^5 = 12a^9$
$a^m \div a^n = a^{m-n}$	$15b^7 \div 5b^2 = 3b^5$
$a^0 = 1$	$37^0 = 1$
$a^{-m} = \dfrac{1}{a^m}$	$(0.25)^{-1} = \dfrac{1}{0.25} = 4$
$(a^m)^n = a^{mn}$	$(3^5)^2 = 3^{10}$
$a^{\frac{1}{q}} = \sqrt[q]{a}$	$8^{\frac{1}{3}} = \sqrt[3]{8} = 2$ $49^{\frac{1}{2}} = \sqrt{49} = 7$
$a^{\frac{p}{q}} = (\sqrt[q]{a})^p$ $= \sqrt[q]{(a^p)}$	$27^{\frac{2}{3}} = \left(27^{\frac{1}{3}}\right)^2 = 3^2 = 9$ $16^{\frac{3}{4}} = \left(\sqrt[4]{16}\right)^3 = 2^3 = 8$ $27^{-\frac{4}{3}} = 1/\left(\sqrt[3]{27}\right)^4 = \dfrac{1}{3^4} = \dfrac{1}{81}$

Any number raised to the power of zero is equal to 1.

A negative power means a reciprocal

A fractional power means a root

RECIPROCALS

The **reciprocal** of n is $\dfrac{1}{n}$.

Number	Reciprocal
3	$\frac{1}{3}$
$\frac{1}{3}$	3
$\frac{2}{5}$	2.5
$\dfrac{a}{b}$	$\dfrac{b}{a}$

Do not use a calculator for this exercise.

1 Simplify these.
   (a) $(3a^4)^3$ (b) $\dfrac{a^5b^2}{ab^6}$ (c) $\sqrt{a^6b^4}$

2 Simplify these.
   (a) $x^3 \times x^{-2}$ (b) $\dfrac{x^{\frac{5}{2}}}{\sqrt{x}}$ (c) $\dfrac{\sqrt{x^3} \times \sqrt[3]{x}}{x \times \sqrt[6]{x}}$

3 Solve these equations.
   (a) $x^{-3} = 8$ (b) $2^x = \sqrt{8}$ (c) $8^x = x^6$

4 Evaluate these.
   (a) $16^{\frac{3}{4}}$ (b) $27^{\frac{4}{3}}$ (c) $\left(\frac{3}{4}\right)^{-2}$
   (d) $9^{-1.5}$

5 (a) If $a = 5^{-3}$ and $b = 5^3$, write $\dfrac{a^2}{\sqrt{b}}$ as a single power of 5.
   (b) If $x = \sqrt[3]{9}$ and $y = \sqrt{27}$, simplify $\dfrac{xy}{\sqrt[6]{3}}$

6 (a) Show that $\sqrt[3]{1500}$ lies between 11 and 12.
   (b) The solution of the equation $x^3 = 1\,225\,043$ is an integer. Find it.

7 A rectangle has sides of length $4y$ m and $4y\sqrt{2}$ m. The area of the rectangle is $1\,\text{m}^2$. Express the exact value of y as a power of 2.

8 The number a is greater than 1. List these numbers in order of size, starting with the smallest.

$$\sqrt{\dfrac{1}{a}} \qquad a^{-2} \qquad a^{\frac{1}{3}} \qquad \dfrac{1}{a^5} \qquad a^0$$

N5 STANDARD FORM

The number 1.083×10^5 is an example of a number in **standard form**.

$1.083 \times 10^5 = 1.083 \times 10 \times 10 \times 10 \times 10 \times 10 = 108\,300$

$2.2 \times 10^{-4} = 2.2 \div 10^4 = 2.2 \div 10\,000 = 0.000\,22$

$(1.3 \times 10^3) \times (5 \times 10^{-5}) = 1.3 \times 5 \times 10^3 \times 10^{-5} = 6.5 \times 10^{-2}$

$(1.8 \times 10^{-6}) \div (3 \times 10^4) = (1.8 \div 3) \times (10^{-6} \div 10^4) = 0.6 \times 10^{-10} = 6 \times 10^{-11}$

$\sqrt{4 \times 10^{-6}} = 2 \times 10^{-3}$

$(6 \times 10^3) + (7 \times 10^{-2}) = 6000 + 0.07 = 6000.07 = 6.000\,07 \times 10^3$

$(4 \times 10^{-3}) - (8 \times 10^{-4}) = 0.004 - 0.0008 = 0.0032 = 3.2 \times 10^{-3}$

> All these can be worked out, and the answers given in standard form, *without* using a calculator.

> You will also need to know how to *use a calculator* to do calculations in standard form, such as these.

$(4.65 \times 10^7) + (6.38 \times 10^9) = 6.43 \times 10^9$ (to 2 d.p.)

$(3.68 \times 10^3) \div (4.93 \times 10^5) = 7.46 \times 10^{-3}$ (to 2 d.p.)

Do not use a calculator for Questions 1 to 4.

1 Write these numbers in standard form.
 (a) 57 300
 (b) 0.009 056
 (c) Twenty five million
 (d) Double 7.5×10^4
 (e) 643.577
 (f) Seventy-three millionths

2 Calculate these.
 Give your answer in standard form.
 (a) $3 \times (2.3 \times 10^5)$
 (b) $(3 \times 10^2) \times (2 \times 10^3)$
 (c) $(5 \times 10^5) \times (7 \times 10^6)$
 (d) $(3 \times 10^2) \times (5 \times 10^3) \times (2 \times 10^4)$
 (e) $(4 \times 10^7)^2$
 (f) $(6.4 \times 10^8) \div 4$
 (g) $(3.6 \times 10^5) \div (1.2 \times 10^2)$
 (h) $(2.7 \times 10^6) \div (5.4 \times 10^2)$

3   Calculate these.
    Give your answers in standard form.
    (a) $(2.5 \times 10^3) \times (6 \times 10^5)$
    (b) $(3.6 \times 10^2) \times (2 \times 10^{-3})$
    (c) $(2.8 \times 10^7) \div (4 \times 10^5)$
    (d) $(4.8 \times 10^{-4}) \div (8 \times 10^{-7})$
    (e) $(6 \times 10^5) + (9 \times 10^3)$
    (f) $(3 \times 10^4) - (2 \times 10^2)$
    (g) $4.7 \times 10^{11} + 5.3 \times 10^{10}$
    (h) $1.44 \times 10^{-18} - 5.6 \times 10^{-20}$

4   There are approximately 5.7×10^7 people living
    in Great Britain. On average, each person uses
    20 litres of water per day.
    (a) How many litres of water are used
         throughout Great Britain each day?
    (b) How many litres of water are used in Great
         Britain each year?

5   Evaluate these, giving your answer in standard
    form.
    (a) $(3.47 \times 10^7) \times (7.68 \times 10^9)$
    (b) $(4.53 \times 10^{12})^3$
    (c) $(6.43 \times 10^{-5}) \times (7.38 \times 10^{-4})$
    (d) $\dfrac{4.72 \times 10^5}{9.37 \times 10^{-4}}$
    (e) $\sqrt{6.457 \times 10^{15}}$
    (f) $((9.31 \times 10^{-9}) \div (1.77 \times 10^8))^{-\frac{3}{4}}$

6   A rectangular picture measures 1.2×10^2 cm by
    4.3×10^3 cm.
    (a) What is the perimeter of the picture?
         Give your answer in standard form.
         Remember to state the units in your
         answer.
    (b) What is the area of the picture?
         Give your answer in standard form.
         Remember to state the units in your
         answer.
                                        NEAB 1999

7   The mass of an electron is 9.109×10^{-28} g and
    the mass of a proton is 1.6726×10^{-24} g.
    How many times bigger is the mass of a proton
    than the mass of an electron?
    Give your answer to the nearest whole number.

8   The star Sirius is 81 900 000 000 000 km from
    the Earth.
    (a) Write 81 900 000 000 000 in standard form.

    Light travels 3×10^5 km in 1 second.
    (b) Calculate the number of seconds that light
         takes to travel from Sirius to the Earth.
         Give your answer in standard form correct
         to 2 significant figures.
    (c) Convert your answer to part (b) to days.
         Give your answer as an ordinary number.
                                        Edexcel 1998

9   The area of the Earth covered by sea is
    362 000 000 km².
    (a) Write 362 000 000 in standard form.

    The surface area, A km², of the Earth may be
    found using the formula
    $A = 4\pi r^2$
    where r km is the radius of the Earth.
    $r = 6.38 \times 10^3$.
    (b) Calculate the surface area of the Earth.
         Give your answer in standard form,
         correct to 3 significant figures.
    (c) Calculate the percentage of the Earth's
         surface which is covered by sea.
         Give your answer correct to 2 significant
         figures.
                                        Edexcel 1997

10 When a female baby is born, its length is
    typically 20 inches.
    By the age of 16, a female is typically
    5ft 6 inches.
    Find the average rate of growth between birth
    and the age of 16 for such a female.
    Give your answer in miles per hour.

STRATEGIES FOR MENTAL ARITHMETIC

$246 + 399 = 246 + 400 - 1 = 645$
$24 \times 32 = 24 \times 30 + 48 = 720 + 48 = 768$
$56 \times 49 = 56 \times 50 - 56 = 2800 - 56 = 2744$

$14 \times 16 = 7 \times 2 \times 8 \times 2 = 56 \times 2 \times 2 = 224$
$64 \times 9 = 8 \times 2 \times 2 \times 2 \times 9 = 72 \times 2 \times 2 \times 2 = 576$

Rounding and then adjusting is often helpful.

Doubling is useful with multiplying.

23×57

	50	7
20	1000	140
3	150	21

When multiplying two 2-digit numbers, this might be a useful model.

$42 \times 38 = (40 + 2)(40 - 2) = 1600 - 4 = 1596$
$29^2 = 29^2 - 1 + 1 = (29 - 1)(29 + 1) + 1 = 28 \times 30 + 1 = 841$

The difference of two squares can sometimes help.

$23 \times 57 = 1000 + 140 + 150 + 21 = 1311$

$8 \times 19 = 8 \times 20 - 8 = 152$
and now we know, for example, that

- $8 \times 1.9 = 15.2$
- $1520 \div 19 = 80$
- $0.08 \times 0.019 = 0.00152$

An important thing to know is how to use place value.

 Do not use a calculator for this exercise.

1 (a) How many months are there in a millennium?

    (b) How many seconds are there in November?

    (c) How many hours are there in a year that is not a leap year?

2 A 100-litre container of wine is used to fill bottles with a capacity of 70 cl.
How many bottles can be filled from the container?

3 A ball of string contains 5.5 m of string.

    (a) How many pieces of string, each 35 cm long, can be cut from this ball of string?

    (b) What is the length of the piece of string that is left over?

4 Coaches can seat 49 passengers.
How many coaches are needed for 356 people?

5 Calculate these.

    (a) 7×28 (b) 70×180

    (c) 0.8×1.6 (d) 320×0.09

6 Calculate these.

    (a) $560 \div 4$ (b) $490 \div 0.7$

    (c) $2000 \div 25$ (d) $300 \div 0.75$

7 Calculate these.

    (a) 12×13 (b) 41×42

    (c) 49×51 (d) 97×103

    (e) 91^2 (f) 55^2

8 (a) Calculate 34×47.

    (b) Use your answer to part (a) to deduce the value of these.

        (i) 0.34×4700 (ii) $15.98 \div 340$

        (iii) $1598 \div 0.47$ (iv) $159.8 \div 68$

9 Calculate these, giving each answer as a decimal.

    (a) $\dfrac{0.02 \times 0.03}{12}$ (b) $\dfrac{1}{0.64}$

    (c) $\dfrac{(0.36)^2}{0.16}$ (d) $\sqrt{0.25}$

    (e) $\sqrt{1.44}$ (f) $\sqrt{1.6} \div \sqrt{1000}$

Nelson GCSE Maths   REVISION GUIDE: NUMBER (HIGHER)

THE FOUR RULES OF DECIMALS

Quite often, you can add, subtract, multiply or divide decimals *mentally*. Sometimes, you will need to use a *written* method. You will want to use the one you are already familiar with.

> It is sensible to estimate the answer as a check on your working.

MULTIPLYING DECIMALS

Here are two methods you *could* use to multiply decimals.

Method 1
Example 1: 4.6 × 8.3

Estimate: 5 × 8 = 40

4	× 8.3	=	33.2
0.1 × 8.3		=	0.83
0.5 × 8.3		=	4.15
4.6 × 8.3		=	38.18

Example 2: 0.38 × 6.5

Estimate: 0.4 × 6 = 2.4

0.1 × 6.5	=	0.65
0.3 × 6.5	=	1.95
0.01 × 6.5	=	0.065
0.08 × 6.5	=	0.52
0.38 × 6.5	=	2.47

Method 2
Example 1: 4.6 × 8.3
46 × 83 = 3818

4.6 × 8.3 = 38.18

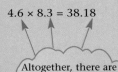

Altogether, there are two digits after the decimal point; so the same must be true in the answer.

Example 2: 0.38 × 6.5
38 × 65 = 2470
There are three digits after the decimal point.
0.38 × 6.5 = 2.470 = 2.47

Be careful not to lose the final zero until after you have counted the digits.

DIVIDING DECIMALS

Here are two methods you *could* use to divide decimals.

Method 1
Example 1: 4.2 ÷ 0.03

			4.2
100 × 0.03	=	−3	
			1.2
10 × 0.03	=	−0.3	
			0.9
30 × 0.03	=	−0.9	
			0

So 4.2 ÷ 0.03 = 140

Example 2: 46.54 ÷ 0.13

			46.54
300 × 0.13	=	−39	
			7.54
50 × 0.13	=	−6.5	
			1.04
4 × 0.13	=	−0.52	
			0.52
4 × 0.13	=	−0.52	
			0

So 46.54 ÷ 0.13 = 358

Method 2
Example 1: 4.2 ÷ 0.03
4.2 ÷ 0.03 = 42 ÷ 0.3 = 420 ÷ 3
420 ÷ 3 = 140
So, 4.2 ÷ 0.03 = 140

Keep multiplying both numbers by 10, until the second number is a whole number, and then do the division.

Example 2: 46.54 ÷ 0.13
46.54 ÷ 0.13 = 465.4 ÷ 1.3 = 4654 ÷ 13
4654 ÷ 13 = 358
So, 46.54 ÷ 0.13 = 358

Do not use a calculator for this exercise.

1 The mean of five numbers is exactly 7.83. Four of the numbers are 6.38, 4.49, 7.21 and 8.11.

   (a) Calculate the fifth number.

   (b) What is the range of the numbers?

   (c) What is the median of the four biggest numbers?

2 Calculate these.

   (a) 0.023 × 45   (b) 1.3 × 25.4

   (c) 4.22 × 5.7   (d) 3.8^2

3 Calculate these, correct to 2 significant figures.

   (a) 25.8 ÷ 4.2   (b) 4.7 ÷ 6.3

   (c) 13 ÷ 0.81   (d) 0.2 ÷ 0.77

N8 — THE FOUR RULES OF FRACTIONS

ADDING AND SUBTRACTING FRACTIONS

$\frac{1}{4} + \frac{3}{8} = \frac{2}{8} + \frac{3}{8} = \frac{5}{8}$

The numbers at the bottom of each fraction must all be the same, before you can add the fractions.

You make them the same by multiplying top and bottom of each fraction by a suitable number.

Multiply top and bottom by 3.

Multiply top and bottom by 8.

The same is true when you are subtracting fractions.

$\frac{5}{8} + \frac{1}{3} = \frac{15}{24} + \frac{8}{24} = \frac{23}{24}$

$\frac{3}{4} - \frac{5}{16} = \frac{12}{16} - \frac{5}{16} = \frac{7}{16}$

Example
Work out $2\frac{3}{4} + 1\frac{5}{8}$.

Either
$2\frac{3}{4} + 1\frac{5}{8}$
$= 3 + \frac{3}{4} + \frac{5}{8}$
$= 3 + \frac{6}{8} + \frac{5}{8}$
$= 3 + \frac{11}{8}$
$= 4\frac{3}{8}$

Or
$2\frac{3}{4} + 1\frac{5}{8}$
$= \frac{11}{4} + \frac{13}{8}$
$= \frac{22}{8} + \frac{13}{8}$
$= \frac{35}{8}$
$= 4\frac{3}{8}$

Example
Work out $5\frac{2}{5} - 3\frac{1}{2}$

Either
$5\frac{2}{5} - 3\frac{1}{2}$
$= 2 + \frac{2}{5} - \frac{1}{2}$
$= 2 + \frac{4}{10} - \frac{5}{10}$
$= 2 - \frac{1}{10}$
$= 1\frac{9}{10}$

Or
$5\frac{2}{5} - 3\frac{1}{2}$
$= \frac{27}{5} - \frac{7}{2}$
$= \frac{54}{10} - \frac{35}{10}$
$= \frac{19}{10}$
$= 1\frac{9}{10}$

MULTIPLYING AND DIVIDING FRACTIONS

$\frac{1}{6} \times \frac{3}{4} = \frac{1 \times 3}{6 \times 4} = \frac{3}{24} = \frac{1}{8}$

$\frac{2}{3} \times \frac{3}{10} = \frac{2 \times 3}{3 \times 10} = \frac{6}{30} = \frac{1}{5}$

When multiplying or dividing fractions, always change mixed numbers into top-heavy fractions

$2\frac{2}{3} \times 4\frac{1}{2} = \frac{8}{3} \times \frac{9}{2} = \frac{8 \times 9}{3 \times 2} = 12$

$1\frac{3}{4} \div 2\frac{1}{3} = \frac{7}{4} \div \frac{7}{3} = \frac{7}{4} \times \frac{3}{7} = \frac{3}{4}$

You multiply the top numbers together and the bottom numbers.

Multiply by the reciprocal.

Do not use a calculator for this exercise.

1   When doing some cooking, John used $\frac{1}{4}$ of the flour.
    Anne used $\frac{2}{3}$ of the flour remaining.
    What fraction of the original amount of flour is left?

2   Calculate these.

   (a) $\frac{3}{5}$ of $22\frac{1}{2}$ (b) $\frac{5}{8}$ of $10\frac{2}{5}$

   (c) $\frac{2}{3}$ of $5\frac{1}{4}$ (d) $\frac{3}{4}$ of $2\frac{6}{7}$

3   Calculate these.

   (a) $2\frac{3}{4} + 1\frac{1}{3}$ (b) $3\frac{2}{5} + 4\frac{1}{10}$

   (c) $5 - 2\frac{3}{8}$ (d) $5\frac{1}{3} - 3\frac{3}{4}$

4   Calculate these.

   (a) $3\frac{1}{2} \times 2\frac{2}{7}$ (b) $4\frac{1}{3} \times 5$

   (c) $2\frac{2}{3} \div \frac{8}{9}$ (d) $2\frac{3}{8} \div 1\frac{1}{4}$

5   In a village, $\frac{1}{2}$ of the males are married to $\frac{3}{5}$ of the females.
    What fraction of the population of the village is married?

N9   PERCENTAGES

WHAT DOES PERCENTAGE MEAN?

37% is the same as $\frac{37}{100}$ or 0.37

RECOGNISING SIMPLE PERCENTAGES

$1\% = \frac{1}{100}$ $10\% = \frac{1}{10}$ $20\% = \frac{1}{5}$

$25\% = \frac{1}{4}$ $33\frac{1}{3}\% = \frac{1}{3}$ $50\% = \frac{1}{2}$

$75\% = \frac{3}{4}$ $100\% = 1$

> You should know these simple percentages.

FINDING PERCENTAGES

If you can, work it out in your head!

Examples

10% of £2 = 20p   30% of £40 = £12
15% of £240 = £36   2% of £36 = 72p

Here are some tips.

- 1% means 1p in the £. So, 1% of £28 is 28p, and then you can work out 2%, 3%, etc.
- You can find 10% by dividing by 10.
- If you want 5%, halve 10%.
- If you want 15%, work out 10% and 5%, and add.
- If you want 17.5%, use 10% + 5% + 2.5%.

Examples

15% of £36 = £3.60 + £1.80 = £5.40
17.5% of £44 = £4.40 + £2.20 + £1.10 = £7.70

When you cannot work it out in your head, here is a method.

Example
37% of 16 = 37 ÷ 100 × 16 = 5.92

FINDING ONE NUMBER AS A PERCENTAGE OF ANOTHER

Example
The sale price of a coat is £70. The original price was £120. What is the percentage saving?
You save £50 out of £120. Percentage saving is
£50 ÷ £120 × 100% = 42% (to the nearest 1%)

Example
What percentage is 48 minutes of 4 hours?

> Two quantities in different units need to be put into the same unit first.

4 hours = 240 minutes

Percentage is 48 minutes ÷ 240 minutes × 100% = 20%.

COMPARING AMOUNTS

Example: A student scores 17 out of 25 on a Science test, and 15 out of 20 on a Maths test. At which subject did she do best?
    Change both scores to a percentage:
    Science: 17 ÷ 25 × 100 = 68%
    Maths: 15 ÷ 20 × 100 = 75%
    The student did better at Maths.

INCREASING BY A PERCENTAGE

Example: Increase £68 by 14%.
Either
    First find 14 ÷ 100 × 68 = £9.52 and then add this to £68, giving
    £68 + £9.52 = £77.52
Or
    14% = 0.14
    So, multiply by 1 + 0.14, i.e. 1.14.
    £68 × 1.14 = £77.52

DECREASING BY A PERCENTAGE

Example: Decrease £68 by 14%.
Either
    First find 14% of £68 (14 ÷ 100 × £68 =) £9.52 and then subtract this from £68, giving
    £68 − £9.52 = £58.48
Or
    Multiply by 1 − 0.14, i.e. 0.86.
    £68 × 0.86 = £58.48

REPEATED PERCENTAGE INCREASE

Keep multiplying by the same amount as many times as you need.
Example: If you put £800 into a bank for four years at 7.5% **compound interest** per annum, you will end up with a total of £800 × 1.075 × 1.075 × 1.075 × 1.075, i.e. £1068.38.

REVERSE PERCENTAGES

Example: When a number is increased by 20%, it becomes 48. What is the number?
Either
    The original number must be 100%.
    120% = 48
    10% = 4 (Divide both sides by 12)
    100% = 40
Or
    To increase by 20%, multiply by 1.20.
    So, divide by 1.20 to reverse the process.
    48 ÷ 1.20 = 40

1 A woman's wages increase from £234 a week to £245.70 a week.
What percentage increase is this?

2 Anne usually buys petrol at the garage at the end of the road. It costs 68.9 pence per litre.
A bit further away is a garage which sells the same grade of petrol at 61.9p per litre.
What percentage saving could she make if she bought petrol from the further garage?

3 £1200 is invested for three years at 7% compound interest.
Find, correct to the nearest penny, the total amount in the account after three years.

4 £1500 is invested in an account which pays 6% compound interest.
After how many years will the amount invested have doubled?

5 In a sale, a suit is reduced in price first by 20% and later by a further 25%.
What is the total percentage reduction?

6 If inflation increases by 2.5% per year for three years, what will be the total percentage increase over the three years, correct to the nearest 0.1%?

7 (a) The cost of a chair is £356 + VAT at $17\frac{1}{2}$%.
What is the total cost of the chair?

(b) The cost of a table is £499 including VAT at $17\frac{1}{2}$%.
What is the cost of the table before VAT is added?

8 Between 1998 and 1999, the number of students in a school increased by exactly 28%.
The number of students in 1999 was 1984.
What was the number in 1998?

9 A man bought a car which depreciated in value by 64%.
He sold it for £4500.
How much did he pay for it?

10 (a) In Britain there are 5.80×10^7 people.
The number of retired people is 1.04×10^7.
What percentage of people in Britain are retired?
Give your answer to an appropriate degree of accuracy.

(b) 13.8% of the world's population live in Europe.
The population of the world is 5.72×10^9.
Calculate the population of Europe.

SEG 1998

11

| 1 pint = 568 ml |
| 8 pints = 1 gallon |

Sally uses the approximate rule

| 1 gallon = 4.5 litres |

Show that this rule is correct to within 1%.

NEAB 1997

12 Ten per cent is cut from the length *and* the width of a rectangle.
What is the percentage decrease in area?

N10 RATIO AND PROPORTIONAL DIVISION

RATIO

Ratios are used to compare different amounts.

12:30 = 2:5

700 g:2 kg
= 700:2000
= 7:20

Ratios are used for map scales.
If 5 cm on a map represents 1 km, the scale on the map is 5:100 000 = 1:20 000

PROPORTIONAL DIVISION

Example
Share £45 in the ratio 2:3:4.
You need to divide the money into (2 + 3 + 4) shares, i.e. 9 shares.
£45 ÷ 9 = £5
Each share is worth £5.
The three amounts of money are
  2 × £5 = £10
  3 × £5 = £15
  4 × £5 = £20
You can check your answer.
£10 + £15 + £20 = £45 ✔

Example
Divide a line 12 cm long in the ratio 7:3.
12 cm ÷ (7 + 3) = 1.2 cm
So, the parts are 8.4 cm and 3.6 cm.

---

1 The perimeter of a triangle is 24 cm.
   The sides are in the ratio 5:4:3.
   What is the length of each side of the triangle?

2 35% of the members of a sports club are females.
   Express the ratio of females to males in its simplest form.

3 Two daughters are left £80 000 in their mother's will. The mother's will specifies that the money is divided in the ratio of their ages at their mother's death. The older daughter is 45 and the difference between their ages is 10 years. How much does each daughter receive?

4 The plan of a house has been drawn using a scale of 1:20.
   (a) On the plan the kitchen is 21 cm long and 16 cm wide.
       What is the area of the kitchen in square metres?
   (b) The actual bathroom measures 3.5 m by 2.8 m.
       What are the dimensions of the bathroom on the plan?

5 When a metal rod is heated, its length increases in the ratio 5:4.
   (a) If the rod measured 30 cm when cold, how long will it be when heated?
   (b) Another rod increases its length in the ratio 8:5 when heated.
       This rod measured 40 cm when hot.
       What was its length before it was heated?

6 The line AB is 15 cm long.
   The points X and Y divide AB internally and externally in the ratio 1:2.
   In other words, the lengths AX:XB and AY:YB are both in the ratio 1:2; X is between A and B and Y is not.
   Find the distance between X and Y.

```
Y                           A    X              B
●───────────────────────────●────●──────────────●
```

N11 ORDER OF OPERATIONS AND EFFICIENT USE OF A CALCULATOR, INCLUDING ESTIMATION

This is the order for doing operations.

B brackets   ( )
I indices x^2, x^3, etc.
D division
M multiplication
A addition   } working from
S subtraction } left to right

Check that you understand why these answers are correct.

$4 \times 8 - 3 \times 6 = 14$

$5 \times 7 - (3 + 6) = 26$

$7 + 3 \times 5^2 = 82$

$\dfrac{13 - 12 \div 4}{4 + 3 \times 2} = 1$

Making an estimate of the answer to a calculation is a way of checking that your answer is correct.

Calculation	Roughly	Using a calculator
4.15×9.89	$4 \times 10 = 40$	41.0 to 3 s.f.
$\dfrac{2914 - 363}{47}$	$\dfrac{3000 - 350}{50} = 53$	54.3 to 3 s.f.
$63 \times 28 - 33 \times 48$	$60 \times 30 - 30 \times 50 = 300$	180
$47 \times 52 - (3284 - 2669)$	$50 \times 50 - (3300 - 2700) = 1900$	1829
$\dfrac{136 - 4326 \div 345}{427 + 326 \times 219}$	$\dfrac{140 - 4000 \div 400}{400 + 300 \times 200} = \dfrac{130}{60400} = \dfrac{1}{500} = 0.002$	0.0017 to 2 s.f.
$\dfrac{4.96^2 + 3.11^2}{16.89}$	$\dfrac{25 + 9}{17} = 2$	2.03 to 3 s.f.

 Do not use a calculator for Question 2(a) or Question 4.

1 Use a calculator to work out the following. In each case write down the full calculator display.

(a) $8.6 - (3.05 - 1.7)$ (b) $\dfrac{6.4 - 2.7}{6.4 + 2.7}$

(c) $\dfrac{1}{4 - \sqrt{3}}$

NEAB 1997

2 (a) Show clearly how you would obtain an ESTIMATE for the following calculation.

$$\dfrac{610 \times 4.98}{0.213}$$

(b) **Use your calculator** to find, correct to 3 significant figures, the value of

$\sqrt{54.6^2 - 9.37^3}$.   *WJEC 1998*

3 Use a calculator to work out each of these, giving each answer correct to 3 significant figures.

(a) $5.43 - (6.57 - 2.85)$ (b) $\dfrac{4.79 - 3.68}{4.79 + 3.68}$

(c) $\dfrac{5 + 2.9\sqrt{3}}{5 - 2.9\sqrt{3}}$ (d) $\dfrac{34.9 \times 42.5}{14.7 - 2.63}$

4 Show how to estimate the answer to each of these calculations, without using a calculator.

(a) $882 \div 28$ (b) 3.84×0.517

(c) $0.787 \div 0.195$ (d) $\sqrt{3.15^2 + 4.23^2}$

(e) $\dfrac{5.7}{12.2} + \dfrac{28.2}{57.6}$ (f) $\dfrac{(0.31)^2 \times 411.34}{58.9 \times 0.0113}$

5 The value x is given by this formula.

$$x = \dfrac{2p - 3q}{p - q^2}$$

It is required to evaluate x when $p = 20.9$ and $q = 4.04$.

(a) Estimate the value of x. Show your working.

(b) Use a calculator to find the value of x, correct to 3 significant figures.

DIRECT AND INVERSE PROPORTION

DIRECT PROPORTION

- A is directly proportional to B
- $A \propto B$
- $A \div B$ is constant
- $A = kB$ (k is called the constant of proportionality)
- B halved $\Rightarrow$ A halved

These all mean the same.

Sometimes one variable is directly proportional to a power of another.

Examples

$N \propto M^2$ means the same as $N = kM^2$.
If M increased by 10% ($\times 1.1$) then N increased by 21% ($\times 1.1^2$).

$T \propto \sqrt{Q}$ means the same as $T = k\sqrt{Q}$.

Direct proportion can be represented by a **straight-line graph**.

Example
If $A \propto B$ plotting A against B will give a straight line.

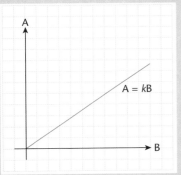

If $N \propto M^2$ plotting N against M^2 will give a straight line. The gradient of the line is the constant of proportionality.

INVERSE PROPORTION

- C is inversely proportional to D
- $C \propto \frac{1}{D}$
- $C \times D$ is constant
- $C = \frac{k}{D}$ (k is called the constant of proportionality)
- D doubled $\Rightarrow$ C halved

These mean the same.

Sometimes one variable is inversely proportional to a power of another.

Example

$H \propto \frac{1}{R^2}$ means the same as $HR^2 = k$.
If R is decreased by 10% ($\times 0.9$) then H is increased by 23.5% ($\div 0.9^2$).

Inverse proportion can be represented by a **hyperbola graph**.

Example
If $C \propto \frac{1}{D}$ plotting C against D will give a curve (hyperbola).

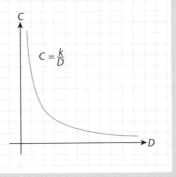

However, plotting C against $\frac{1}{D}$ will give a straight line.

1 It is given that p is inversely proportional to q, and that $p = 4$ when $q = 5$.

   (a) Find an expression for p in terms of q.

   (b) Find p when $q = 2$.

   (c) Find q when $p = 20$.

2 When a heavy object falls, the distance, d feet, it has travelled is directly proportional to the square of the time, t seconds.
After 1.25 seconds, the distance is 25 feet.

   (a) Find a formula for d in terms of t.

   (b) How far has the object fallen after 0.8 seconds?

   (c) How long does it take the object to fall 200 feet?

3 Given that y is inversely proportional to x^3,
   copy and complete this table.

x	15		30	1.5
y	40	1080		

4 The wavelength, w metres, of radio waves is
   inversely proportional to the frequency, f kHz,
   of the waves.

   (a) A radio wavelength of 1000 metres has a
       frequency of 300 kHz.
       The frequency is doubled to 600 kHz.
       What is the new wavelength?

   (b) Calculate the frequency when the
       wavelength is 842 metres.

   (c) Radio NEAB has a frequency in kHz which
       is numerically equal to its wavelength
       in metres.
       Calculate the wavelength of Radio NEAB.

                                        NEAB 1998

5 If Y is proportional to X^2, what happens

   (a) to Y, when X is doubled?

   (b) to X, when Y is divided by 25?

   (c) to Y, when X is increased by 10%?

   (d) to X, when Y is decreased by 36%?

6 If Y is inversely proportional to X,
   what happens

   (a) to Y, when X is doubled?

   (b) to X, when Y is multiplied by $\frac{6}{7}$?

   (c) to Y, when X is increased by 60%?

7 Decide which graph matches each relationship.
   Graphs

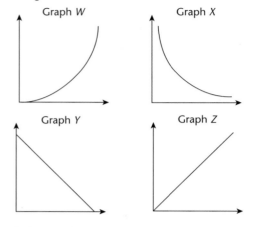

   Relationships
   A: The area of a circle plotted against its radius.
   B: The circumference of a circle plotted against
      its radius.
   C: The length of a rectangle of area 24 cm²
      plotted against its width.

                                        SEG 1996

8 An experiment involves measurements x and y.
   It is believed that y varies inversely as x or
   inversely as the square of x.

   (a) Given that $y = 0.8$ when $x = 0.2$, find the
       two possible equations giving y in terms of x.

   (b) For the value $x = 0.4$, y was measured as
       being 0.5 approximately.
       Which of the two equations seems more
       likely to be correct?
       Explain your answer.

                                        CCEA 1995

Do not use a calculator for Question 5 onwards.

1 Light travels at 186 284 miles per second.
The planet Jupiter is 483.6 million miles from the Sun.

(a) Calculate how long light takes to travel from the Sun to Jupiter.
Give your answer to the nearest minute.

(b) Use approximation to check that your answer is of the right order of magnitude.
You **must** show all your working.

SEG 1998

2 When a tractor travels the length of a ten-acre field, the number of turns, n, made by a wheel of the tractor, is inversely proportional to d, the diameter of the wheel in metres.

(a) When $d = 0.9$, $n = 56$.
Find an equation connecting n and d.

(b) Calculate d when $n = 31.5$.

(c) A tractor has front and rear wheels whose diameters are in the ratio 3 : 7.
When this tractor is being driven at constant speed, find the value of the ratio

$$\frac{\text{turns per minute}}{\text{of front wheel}} : \frac{\text{turns per minute}}{\text{of rear wheel}}.$$

CCEA 1996

3

Four Star Leaded Petrol	Unleaded Petrol
62p per litre	54p per litre

Susan calls at a petrol station and puts £23.87 worth of four-star leaded petrol into her car.

Susan is thinking of converting her car to be able to use unleaded petrol. What would be the percentage drop in the cost of her petrol bills, if prices remained as they are now?

WJEC 2000 specimen

4 (a) Video tapes are sold at £9.99 each and the shop makes a profit of 35% of their cost price.
What did the shop pay for the video tapes?

(b) After the videos have been in the shop for six months, their selling price is reduced by 15%.
What is the percentage profit made by the shop on the videos sold at the reduced price?

5 John made the statement
"If you are given a number written correct to 2 decimal places it is more accurate than when written correct to 2 significant figures."

John chose 6.60 and 6.6 as examples.

(a) Explain clearly how John could use these numbers to justify his statement.

(b) Is John's statement always true?
Justify your answer.

Edexcel 1996

6 The intensity of illumination varies inversely with the square of the distance from the light.
How does the intensity of illumination, at a point 2 m from the light, compare with that at a point 6 m from the light?

7 Estimate the value of these calculations.

(a) $\dfrac{(0.38)^2 \times 518.36}{49.7 \times 0.0387}$

(b) $\dfrac{1}{7.83} + \dfrac{1}{3.76}$

8 (a) Find an approximate value of the expression

19.7 × 41.2 ÷ 0.0483.

(b) All six faces of this cuboid are to be painted. There is enough paint to cover 5 m².

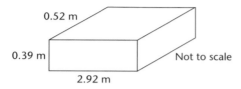

0.52 m

0.39 m

2.92 m

Not to scale

Use approximations to estimate whether there is enough paint to paint the cuboid.
You must show all your working.

SEG 2000 specimen

9 (a) Find the value of $\frac{a}{b} - \frac{b}{a}$ when $a = \frac{2}{5}$ and $b = -6$.

(b) Find the value of $\frac{p^2}{q}$ when $p = 0.6$ and $q = 0.003$.

10 Simplify each of the following, indicating in each case whether your answer is rational or irrational.

(a) $\frac{6}{\sqrt{3}} + \sqrt{48}$

(b) $(3 - \sqrt{2})^2$

(c) $25^{\frac{1}{2}} \times 3^{-2}$

WJEC 2000 specimen

11 Find the value of

(a) $32^{\frac{1}{5}}$

(b) $(3\frac{3}{8})^{\frac{2}{3}}$

(c) $2^{-3} \times 64^{\frac{1}{2}}$

(d) $(16^{\frac{1}{4}} - 3^{\frac{1}{2}})(16^{\frac{1}{4}} + 3^{\frac{1}{2}})$

12 (a) A Mathematics student attempted to define an 'irrational number' as follows:

'An irrational number is a number which, in its decimal form, goes on and on.'

Give an example to show that there are numbers satisfying this definition which are not irrational numbers.

(b) Which of the following numbers are rational and which irrational?

$\sqrt{4\frac{1}{4}}$, $\sqrt{6\frac{1}{4}}$, $(\sqrt{2} + \sqrt{3})^2$, $(\frac{1}{3}\sqrt{3})^2$

Express each of the rational numbers in the form $\frac{p}{q}$ where p and q are integers.

OCR 2000 specimen

13 Convert these decimals into fractions, expressed in their simplest form.

(a) 0.375

(b) $0.7\dot{2}$

(c) $0.14\dot{8}$

14 (a) 9 has exactly three factors: 1, 3 and 9. Find two more numbers which have exactly three factors.
What can you say about numbers which have exactly three factors?

(b) Express these as a product of prime factors.
(i) 168　　　　**(ii)** 630

(c) Find the smallest number of which 168 and 630 are factors.

(d) Find the largest number which is a factor of both 168 and 630.

15 (a) (i) Calculate the value of $3 \times 10^{-4} \times 7 \times 10^6$. Give your answer in standard form.

(ii) Give your answer to part (i) as a product of prime numbers.

(b) Write down the smallest value of n so that $(7 \times 10^6)^n$ is divisible by 5^{12}.

SEG 1996

LINEAR, QUADRATIC AND OTHER SEQUENCES

This is how to find the nth term of the sequence 5, 7, 9, 11, 13, ...

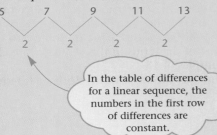

In the table of differences for a linear sequence, the numbers in the first row of differences are constant.

The formula for this sequence begins $2n$ because the first row of differences is always 2.

The full formula is $2n + 3$ because $5 - 2 = 3$.

It is always worth checking that your formula is correct.
For example, when $n = 4$, $2n + 3 = 11$.
This agrees with the fourth term of the sequence.

This is how to find the nth term of the sequence 5, 7, 11, 17, 25, ...

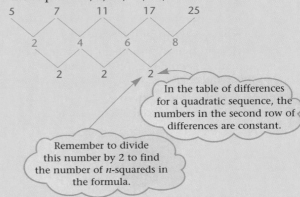

In the table of differences for a quadratic sequence, the numbers in the second row of differences are constant.

Remember to divide this number by 2 to find the number of n-squareds in the formula.

The formula will begin with $1n^2$ (although you write just n^2). Now take the n^2 sequence away from the original sequence to work out the formula for the sequence left over.

So the rest of the formula is $-n + 5$.
The full formula is $n^2 - n + 5$.

It is always worth checking that your formula is correct.
For example, when $n = 5$, $n^2 - n + 5 = 25$.
This agrees with the fifth term of the sequence.

1 Find an expression for the nth term of each of these linear sequences.

(a) 3, 8, 13, 18, ...

(b) −4, 3, 10, 17, ...

(c) 50, 39, 28, 17, ...

(d) $a - b, a, a + b, a + 2b, ...$

2 Find a formula for the nth term of each of these quadratic sequences.

(a) 1, 4, 9, 16, 25, ...

(b) 0, 3, 8, 15, 24, ...

(c) 3, 12, 27, 48, 75, ...

3 Find an expression for the nth term of each of these quadratic sequences.

(a) 2, 6, 12, 20, ...

(b) 3, 7, 15, 27, ...

(c) 4, 7, 13, 22, ...

(d) 30, 29, 27, 24, ...

4 Here are the first three patterns in a sequence.

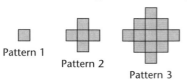

Pattern 1

Pattern 2

Pattern 3

(a) Find the number of squares in each of the first four patterns of the sequence.

(b) Assuming that the number of squares form a quadratic sequence, find a formula for this sequence.

(c) Here is the third pattern of the sequence with squares coloured alternately red and blue.

If the fourth term of the sequence is coloured in this way, how many red and how many blue squares are there?

(d) What kind of numbers are the numbers of red and blue squares in each term of the sequence?

(e) Use your answer to part (d) to prove the formula you obtained in part (b) is in fact the formula for the number of squares in the sequence.

5 Here are the first three patterns in a sequence.

Pattern 1

Pattern 2

Pattern 3

(a) Write down the number of red squares and the number of blue squares in the first five patterns.

(b) Write down the number of red squares and the number of blue squares in the nth pattern.

(c) Use your answer to part (b) to verify that the number of red squares in Pattern k is equal to the total number of squares in Pattern $k - 2$.

6 (a) The nth term of a sequence is $n^2 + 5n + 6$. Factorise this expression for the nth term. Hence, or otherwise, explain why every term in the sequence is an even number.

(b) The nth term of another sequence is $n^3 + 3n^2 + 2n$. Factorise this expression for the nth term. Hence, or otherwise, explain why every term in this sequence is a multiple of 6. Some of the terms in this sequence are also multiples of 18. Work out the value of the 10th such term.

GRAPHS OF REAL-LIFE SITUATIONS

Sometimes graphs are drawn to help solve practical problems.

Here is a graph showing a girl's journey.

> She rested between 10.00 a.m. and 11.30 a.m., and between 12.30 p.m. and 2.00 p.m., before starting her return journey.

> She walked ten miles there altogether and ten miles home.

> After her rest, her speed was 4 miles in 1 hour, i.e. 4 m.p.h.

> Before her rest, her speed was 6 miles in 2 hours, i.e. 3 m.p.h.

> She started at 8.00 a.m.

> On her return journey, she walked 10 miles in 4 hours, i.e. at a speed of 2.5 m.p.h.

On a **distance–time graph**:
- speed is represented by the gradient (see A3)
- the steeper the graph, the faster the speed
- a flat bit of graph is where someone or something has stopped
- a graph sloping down represents a return journey.

This container is filled with water at a steady rate.

The graph shows the depth of water plotted against time.

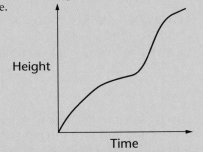

1 A woman went on a 12 mile walk, leaving home at 12 noon. She called on a friend on the way. Her daughter travelled the same route by bicycle.

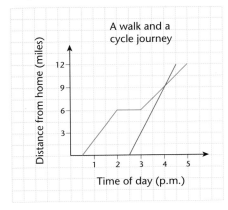

(a) Which line represents the woman's journey, the red line or the blue line?

(b) At what speed did the woman walk before she called on her friend?

(c) How long did she spend at her friend's house?

(d) How far is it between her house and her friend's house?

(e) At what speed did she walk *after* she left her friend's house?

(f) At what time did she finish her walk?

(g) How long did it take her daughter to cycle 12 miles?

(h) At what speed did her daughter cycle?

(i) At what time did her daughter overtake her?

(j) How long did her daughter have to wait for her mother at the end of the journey?

2 A ferry left harbour at 1000 hours and sailed, at constant speed, to an island 8 km away. The journey took 45 minutes. The ferry remained at the island for 25 minutes before setting out on the return journey. Travelling at constant speed, it arrived back at harbour at 1150 hours.

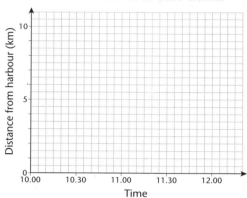

(a) On graph paper like this, draw a travel graph to represent the ferry's complete journey.

(b) Calculate the speed, in km/h, of the return journey.

CCEA 1998

3 Steve travelled from home to school by walking to a bus stop and then catching a school bus. Steve left home at 0800. He walked at 6 km/h for 10 minutes. He then waited for 5 minutes before catching the bus. The bus took him a further 8 km to school at a steady speed of 32 km/h.

(a) Use this information to construct a travel graph showing Steve's journey.
Use axes like these.

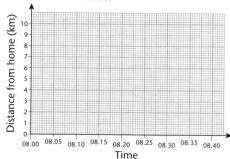

(b) How long would it take Steve to cycle from home to school at an average speed of 15 km/h?
Give your answer in minutes.

MEG 1998

4 This diagram shows three water storage tanks.

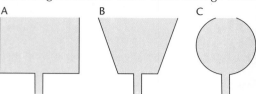

The tanks are full when the tap at the base is opened. Water then flows out of each tank at a constant rate.
For each tank, sketch a graph showing how the height of water varies over time.

5 **Every hour**, on the hour, a train leaves Toronto for Montreal.
At the same times, trains leave Montreal for Toronto.
All the trains travel at a speed of 75 mph.
The distance between Toronto and Montreal is 300 miles.

(a) On a copy of this grid, draw the distance-time graphs of the trains.
(One of the distance-time graphs has been drawn for you.)

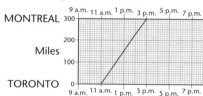

(b) Use your graphs to find

(i) When the 2 p.m. train from Toronto passes the 1 p.m. train from Montreal,

(ii) how many trains will be passed by the train leaving Toronto at 12 noon on its run to Montreal.

NEAB 1997

LINEAR AND NON-LINEAR GRAPHS

GRADIENTS

Gradient = $\dfrac{\text{distance up}}{\text{distance across}}$

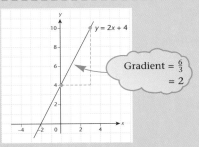

Gradient = $\dfrac{6}{3}$
= 2

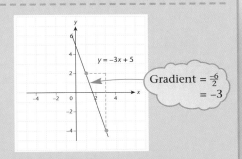

Gradient = $\dfrac{-6}{2}$
= −3

EQUATIONS OF GRAPHS OF STRAIGHT LINES $y = mx + c$

The value of m is the **gradient** of the graph. The value of c tells you the point where the graph crosses the y-axis, sometimes called the y-**intercept**.

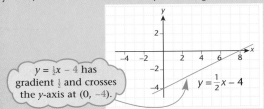

$y = \frac{1}{2}x − 4$ has gradient $\frac{1}{2}$ and crosses the y-axis at (0, −4).

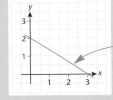

This graph of $2x + 3y = 6$ can be plotted by finding some points on it. The points (3, 0), (0, 2) and (1.5, 1) all lie on the graph.

GRAPHS INVOLVING x^2

All **quadratic graphs** have the shape of a **parabola**. They all have *one* line of symmetry.

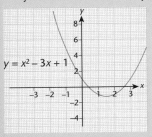

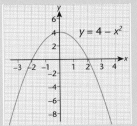

GRAPHS INVOLVING x^3

Cubic graphs are always shaped like one of these.

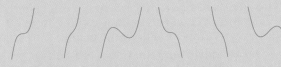

Here are two examples of cubic graphs.

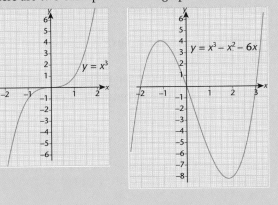

RECIPROCAL GRAPHS

These have equations like $y = \dfrac{6}{x}$ and $y = \dfrac{12}{x}$.
This is the graph of $y = \dfrac{1}{x}$.

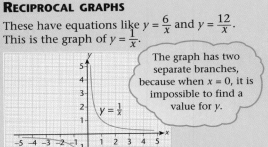

The graph has two separate branches, because when $x = 0$, it is impossible to find a value for y.

![X] **Do not use a calculator for this exercise.**

1 The equation of almost any straight line can be written in the form $y = mx + c$.

  (a) The equations of three of these four straight lines can be written as $y = mx + c$. Which one cannot? What is its equation?

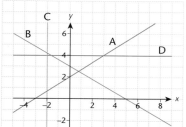

  (b) Find the value of m and c for each of the other three lines.

2 Tracey's monthly pay, £P, is made up of a fixed basic wage plus commission. The commission is a percentage of the amount of her sales, £S. This table shows some amounts of sales and the corresponding monthly pay.

Sales £S	1000	1500	2500	3500
Pay £P	970	1030	1150	1270

  (a) **(i)** Use a horizontal axis for S from £0 to £5000, and a vertical axis for P from £0 to £1300 and draw the graph.

    (ii) Explain why the values of S and P satisfy a law of the form $P = aS + b$.

  (b) **(i)** Use the graph to calculate the values of a and b.

    (ii) Write down the law connecting S and P.

  (c) Hence find

    (i) Tracey's fixed basic wage,

    (ii) the percentage commission on her sales.

CCEA 1998

3 OAEC is a kite. The sides of the kite are the two coordinate axes and two lines. The equation of one of these lines is $2x + 3y = 60$.

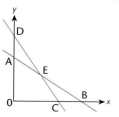

(a) Write down the equation of the other line which is a side of the kite.

(b) Work out the coordinates of the points A, B, C and D, and finally E.

(c) Calculate the area of the kite.

4 **(a)** Below are three graphs. Match each graph with one of the following equations.

    A: $y = 3x - p$ B: $y = x^2 + p$
    C: $3x + 4y = p$ D: $y = px^3$

    In each case p is a positive number

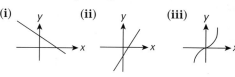

  (b) Sketch a graph of the equation you have not yet chosen.

NEAB 1998

5 Here are four equations.

$$y = x^2 - 3 \qquad y = x^3 - 3x \qquad y = -\frac{3}{x} \qquad y = \frac{3}{x^2}$$

Here are the graphs of three of the equations.

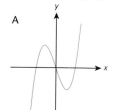
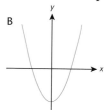

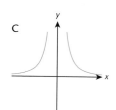

There is more practice in drawing and sketching graphs in A4 and A15.

(a) Match each graph with one of the equations.

(b) One of the equations does not have a graph. Sketch this graph.

TRANSFORMATIONS OF GRAPHS

These pictures show how graphs of functions are transformed when the functions are changed.

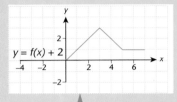

$y = f(x) + 2$

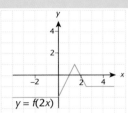

$y = f(2x)$

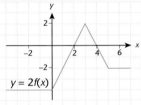

$y = 2f(x)$

A translation $\begin{pmatrix} 0 \\ 2 \end{pmatrix}$

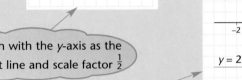

A stretch with the y-axis as the invariant line and scale factor $\frac{1}{2}$

A stretch with the x-axis as the invariant line and scale factor 2

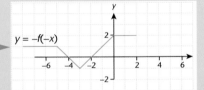

$y = -f(-x)$

A half turn about the origin

A reflection in the y-axis

$y = f(x)$

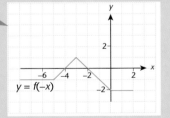

$y = f(-x)$

A translation $\begin{pmatrix} -3 \\ 0 \end{pmatrix}$

A reflection in the x-axis

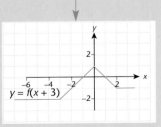

$y = f(x + 3)$

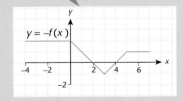

$y = -f(x)$

Do not use a calculator for this exercise.

1 Each of these graphs is a translation of the graph of $y = x^2$.

A

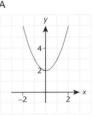

B

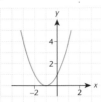

C

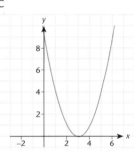

D   E

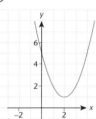

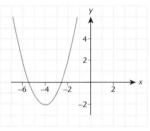

Write down the equation of each graph.

2 Draw *sketches* of each of these, marking the points where the graph meets each of the axes.

(a) $y = x^2$ (b) $y = x^2 - 4$

(c) $y = (x - 2)^2$ (d) $y = 3x^2$

(e) $y = 2(x + 3)^2$ (f) $y = (x + 3)^2 + 4$

3 This is a sketch of the graph $y = x^3$.

Draw a sketch of each of these, marking any points where the graph crosses the axes.

(a) $y = x^3 + 1$ (b) $y = (x + 1)^3$

(c) $y = -x^3$

4 (a) Sketch the graph of $y = \cos x$ for values of x between $0°$ and $360°$.

(b) On the same axes, sketch the graph of $y = \cos x - 1$.

5 (a) Sketch the graph of $y = \sin x$ for values of x between $0°$ and $360°$.

(b) On the same axes, sketch the graph of $y = \sin 2x$.

6 This picture shows four quadratic graphs. One is the graph of $y = x^2$. The other three are either translations or reflections of $y = x^2$. Each graph meets at least one other graph at its minimum or maximum point. Find the equations of the other three graphs.

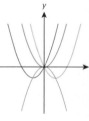

7 This diagram shows the graph of $y = f(x)$.

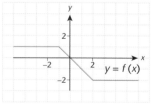

Sketch the graph of

(a) $y = f(x) - 2$ (b) $y = f(x + 2)$

(c) $y = 2f(x)$ (d) $y = f(2x)$

(e) $y = -f(x)$ (f) $y = -f(-x)$

AREA UNDER A GRAPH AND TANGENTS TO CURVES

AREA UNDER A CURVE

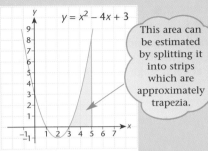

This area can be estimated by splitting it into strips which are approximately trapezia.

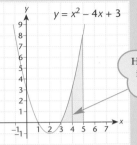

Here the area is split into two strips.

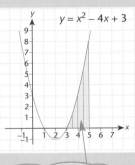

Here the area is split into four strips.

The more strips used, the more accurate is the estimate.

Applications
- Finding area of cross-sections
- Finding the distance travelled from a speed–time graph
- Finding volumes

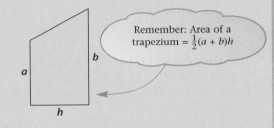

Remember: Area of a trapezium = $\frac{1}{2}(a + b)h$

TANGENTS TO GRAPHS

The gradient of a graph at a point is the gradient of its tangent at that point.
This diagram shows $y = x^2$ and two of its tangents.
The gradient of the tangent to $y = x^2$ at (2, 4) is 4, and the gradient of the tangent to $y = x^2$ at (–1, 1) is –2.
The gradient of the tangent at the origin is zero.

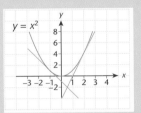

Applications
- Finding speed from a distance–time graph
- Finding acceleration from a speed–time graph

1 (a) Draw the graph of $y = x^3 - 5x + 4$ for values of x between –3 and 3.

(b) Estimate the gradient of the graph when $x = 2$ and when $x = -1$.

2 The diagram shows the speed/time graph of a bus as it travels between two bus stops.

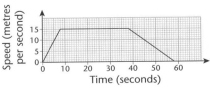

Calculate the time it takes to travel **half** the distance between the bus stops.

SEG 1998

Nelson GCSE Maths REVISION GUIDE: ALGEBRA (HIGHER)

3 A stone is thrown from the top of a cliff.
The height, h metres, of the stone above the sea
after t seconds is given by the equation
$h = 20 + 15t - 5t^2$.

(a) Copy and complete this table.

Time in seconds, t	0	1	1.5	2	3	4
Height in metres, h	20					

(b) On axes like these, plot a graph of
$h = 20 + 15t - 5t^2$

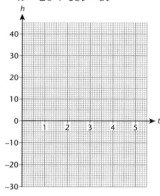

(c) Use your graph to find a solution of the
equation $20 + 15t - 5t^2 = 10$.

(d) Explain what happens to the stone after 4
seconds.

(e) By drawing a tangent find the gradient of
the curve at the point where $t = 3$. State
the units of the gradient.

MEG 1998

4 Here is the velocity time graph for an
oscillating particle.

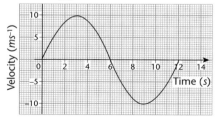

**In part (a) you must write down the units
with your answer.**

(a) Calculate an estimate for the acceleration
of the particle at 10 seconds.

(b) Calculate an estimate for the distance
travelled by the particle in the first
6 seconds.

Edexcel 1997

5 A ball is rolled down a slide and along a table.
The table has a smooth surface and a
rough surface.

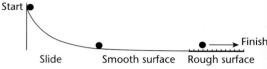

The ball takes 8 seconds from start to finish.
The velocity v metres per second at time
t seconds at each stage is shown on this graph.

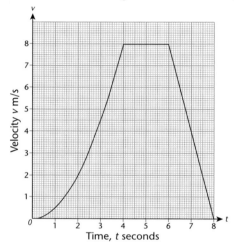

(a) Estimate the acceleration of the ball when
$t = 1.5$.
State the units of acceleration.

(b) Estimate the total distance travelled by
the ball.

NEAB 1998

6 This table shows the cross-sectional areas for a
tree trunk 10 m high.

Height above ground (m)	0	2	4	6	8	10
Cross-sectional area (cm²)	360	290	230	180	130	90

(a) Plot a graph of cross-sectional area against
height above ground.

(b) Use the trapezium rule to estimate the
volume of the tree trunk.
Specify the units.

(c) Does your answer give an overestimate or
an underestimate?

A6 MANIPULATING ALGEBRAIC EXPRESSIONS

For most of the work on this card, you will need to be able to work with brackets (card A7) and to factorise (card A8).

SIMPLIFYING EXPRESSIONS

You need to be able to simplify expressions such as these.

$$a^2 + 2ab + 3a^2 - 4ab - 5b = 4a^2 - 2ab - 5b$$
$$4a^2b \times 6ab^3 = 24a^3b^4$$
$$\frac{6x^2y}{25z^2w} \div \frac{4xyw}{5z} = \frac{6x^2y}{25z^2w} \times \frac{5z}{4xyw} = \frac{3x}{10zw^2}$$

ALGEBRAIC FRACTIONS

These can often be simplified by factorising. Cancel the $(x + 1)$.

$$\frac{x^2 - 1}{x + 1} = \frac{(x - 1)(x + 1)}{x + 1} = x - 1$$

$$\frac{2}{y - 1} - \frac{2}{y + 1} = \frac{2(y + 1)}{(y - 1)(y + 1)} - \frac{2(y - 1)}{(y - 1)(y + 1)}$$

Cancel the 2 and $(x + 1)$.

$$\frac{2x + 4}{x^2 - 1} \times \frac{x^2 + 2x + 1}{6} = \frac{2(x + 2)}{(x - 1)(x + 1)} \times \frac{(x + 1)(x + 1)}{6}$$

$$= \frac{(x + 2)(x + 1)}{3(x - 1)}$$

$$= \frac{2(y + 1) - 2(y - 1)}{(y + 1)(y - 1)}$$

$$= \frac{2y + 2 - 2y + 2}{(y - 1)(y + 1)}$$

$$= \frac{4}{(y - 1)(y + 1)}$$

Use the same rules for combining algebraic fractions as you use for numerical fractions.

---

1 Simplify these expressions.
(a) $x^2 + 2xy - 3x^2 + 7xy$
(b) $p^3 - q^3 + 3pq^2 - 6q^3 - 4p^3$
(c) $3x^2 \times 4x^3$
(d) $5x^2y \times 7xy^3$
(e) $(3a^2)^3$
(f) $4a^2bc^3 \div 12a^2b^2c$
(g) $\frac{(6a^2b)^2}{(2ab)^3}$
(h) $\sqrt{4p^2q \times 9p^2q^3}$

2 Find the perimeters and areas of these shapes, giving your answers in their simplest form.

  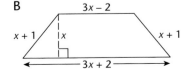

3 Write each of these as a single fraction in its simplest form.
(a) $\frac{3}{x - 2} - \frac{2}{x + 7}$ (b) $\frac{4}{a - 1} - \frac{4}{a + 1}$
(c) $\frac{a}{2a + 4b} - \frac{b}{4a + 2b}$ (d) $\frac{1}{p} + \frac{1}{q} - \frac{2}{p + q}$

4 Simplify these expressions.
(a) $\frac{x^2 - 2x - xy + 2y}{x^2 - 4}$ (b) $\frac{2x^2 - 7x + 3}{x^2 - 9}$
(c) $\frac{a^2 + a - 6}{a^2 + 5a + 6}$ (d) $\frac{2a^2 - 5a + 2}{4a^2 - 4a + 3}$

5 Write each of these as a single fraction in its simplest form.
(a) $\frac{n^2 - 4n + 3}{n^2 - 4} \times \frac{n + 2}{n - 3}$
(b) $\frac{n^2 + 5n + 4}{n^2 - 2n - 3} \div \frac{n^2 + 2n - 8}{n^2 - 5n + 6}$
(c) $\frac{3}{n^2 - 5n} - \frac{3}{n^2 - 4n - 5}$
(d) $\frac{n + 3}{n^2 - 4n + 3} + \frac{n - 3}{n^2 + 2n - 3}$

ALGEBRAIC EXPRESSIONS USING BRACKETS

ONE BRACKET

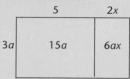

$3a(5 + 2x) = 15a + 6ax$

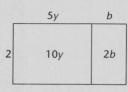

$2(5y + b) = 10y + 2b$

Here are some more examples.

$2(3a + 4b - 2c) = 6a + 8b - 4c$
$-6(2x - 5) = -12x + 30$
$3(6d + 1) - 2(7d + 4) = 18d + 3 - 14d - 8$
$\qquad\qquad\qquad\qquad = 4d - 5$
$2x(x - 3y) = 2x^2 - 6xy$
$pq(p^2 + q^2) = p^3q + pq^3$

TWO BRACKETS

This is how two brackets are multiplied out.

$(x + 2)(x + 3) = x^2 + 2x + 3x + 6$
$\qquad\qquad\quad = x^2 + 5x + 6$

$(x - 5)^2 = (x - 5)(x - 5)$
$\qquad\quad = x^2 - 5x - 5x + 25$
$\qquad\quad = x^2 - 10x + 25$

$(a + b)(a - b) = a^2 + ab - ab - b^2$
$\qquad\qquad\quad = a^2 - b^2$

	x	2
x	x^2	$2x$
3	$3x$	6

	x	-5
x	x^2	$-5x$
-5	$-5x$	25

	a	b
a	a^2	ab
$-b$	$-ab$	$-b^2$

$(a + b + c)^2 = (a + b + c)(a + b + c)$
$\qquad\qquad\quad = a^2 + b^2 + c^2 + 2ab + 2bc + 2ac$

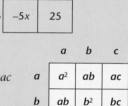

This method can be extended to more complicated examples

1 Expand and simplify where possible.
  (a) $a(3a^2 - 7)$ (b) $5(2x + 3) - 4(x - 5)$
  (c) $3(a + 2) + 5(2a - 1)$
  (d) $x(x^2 + xy - y^2) - y(x^2 - xy + y^2)$

2 Write each of these expressions without brackets.
  (a) $(2x - 5)(x - 3)$ (b) $(x - 4)(2x + 3)$
  (c) $(3x - 1)(2x - 3)$ (d) $(3x - 2)(2x + 1)$

3 Expand and simplify these expressions.
  (a) $(x - 2y)^2$ (b) $(a^2 + b^2)^2$
  (c) $(a + b)^2 - (a - b)^2$ (d) $(p + 2q)^2 + (2p + q)^2$

4 Expand and simplify these expressions.
  (a) $(a + b + 1)^2$ (b) $(x + y + 2)(x - y + 1)$
  (c) $(x + 2y - 3z)^2$
  (d) $(a + b - c)^2 + (b + c - a)^2 + (c + a - b)^2$

5

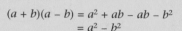

Diagram NOT accurately drawn

In the diagram each side of the square $ABCD$ is $(3 + x)$ cm.

(a) Write down an expression in terms of x for the area, in cm^2, of the square $ABCD$.

The actual area of the square $ABCD$ is 10 cm^2.

(b) Show that $x^2 + 6x = 1$.

Edexcel 1997

A8 FACTORISING, INCLUDING COMPLETING THE SQUARE

COMMON FACTORS

$$4a^2 + 12a = 4a(a + 3)$$

$$10ab - 6b^2 = 2b(5a - 3b)$$

DIFFERENCE OF TWO SQUARES

$$a^2 - b^2 = (a + b)(a - b)$$

$$25y^2 - 9z^2 = (5y + 3z)(5y - 3z)$$

QUADRATIC FACTORS

$$a^2 + 4a + 3 = (a + 3)(a + 1)$$

$$x^2 - x - 6 = (x - 3)(x + 2)$$

$$n^2 - 5n + 6 = (n - 2)(n - 3)$$

$$2x^2 + 5x + 2 = (2x + 1)(x + 2)$$

COMPLETING THE SQUARE

Halve the coefficient of x and square it.

$$\begin{aligned} x^2 + 6x + 3 &= x^2 + 6x + 9 - 9 + 3 \\ &= (x + 3)^2 - 6 \end{aligned}$$

$$\begin{aligned} 2x^2 - 10x - 5 &= 2(x^2 - 5x) - 5 \\ &= 2(x^2 - 5x + 6.25) - 12.5 - 5 \\ &= 2(x - 2.5)^2 - 17.5 \end{aligned}$$

1   Factorise each of these expressions.
   (a) $4x - 16x^2$
   (b) $4a^2 + 6ab$
   (c) $4ab^2 - 8a^2b$
   (d) $20x^2y^2z - 36xy^2z^2 + 24x^2yz^2$

2   Factorise each of these expressions.
   (a) $a^2 - 4a - 12$ (b) $a^2 + 3ab - 18b^2$
   (c) $a^2 - 25b^2$ (d) $a^2 + 4ab + 4b^2$

3   Factorise each of these expressions.
   (a) $ab - cd - bc + ad$
   (b) $6x^2 - 4x - 3xy + 2y$
   (c) $a^2 + ab + ac - ad - bd - cd$
   (d) $6ab + 8ad - 9bc - 12cd$

4   Factorise each of these expressions.
   (a) $3x^2 - 19x + 20$ (b) $4x^2 - 12x + 9$
   (c) $6a^2 - 13ab + 6b^2$ (d) $24x^2 - 2xy - 15y^2$

5   Factorise these completely.
   (a) $2x^2 - 8y^2$ (b) $12n^2 - 3$
   (c) $63x^2 - 28y^2$ (d) $3a^3 - 75ab^2$

6   The expression $x^2 + 6x + 19$ can be written in the form $(x + a)^2 + b$, for appropriate numerical values of a and b.
   Find the values of a and b.

7   Complete the square for each of these expressions.
   (a) $x^2 - 8x + 18$ (b) $x^2 + 4x - 5$
   (c) $2x^2 + 4x + 1$ (d) $x^2 - 7x + 7$

Nelson GCSE Maths   REVISION GUIDE: ALGEBRA (HIGHER)

A9   CHANGING THE SUBJECT OF A FORMULA

Make T the subject of this equation: $A = P + \dfrac{PRT}{100}$

Multiply by 100	$100A = 100P + PRT$
Rearrange terms	$PRT = 100A - 100P$
Divide by PR	$T = \dfrac{100A - 100P}{PR}$

Make I the subject of this equation: $L = W - I^2R$

Rearrange terms	$I^2R = W - L$
Divide by R	$I^2 = \dfrac{W - L}{R}$
Take the square root	$I = \sqrt{\dfrac{W - L}{R}}$

Make l the subject of this equation: $T = 2\pi\sqrt{\dfrac{l}{g}}$

Rearrange terms	$\dfrac{T}{2\pi} = \sqrt{\dfrac{l}{g}}$
Square both sides	$\dfrac{T^2}{4\pi^2} = \dfrac{l}{g}$
Multiply by $4\pi^2 g$	$T^2 g = 4\pi^2 l$
Divide by $4\pi^2$	$l = \dfrac{T^2 g}{4\pi^2}$

Make n the subject of this equation: $S = 180 - \dfrac{360}{n}$

Multiply by n	$Sn = 180n - 360$
Rearrange terms	$180n - Sn = 360$
Factorise	$n(180 - S) = 360$
Divide by bracket	$n = \dfrac{360}{180 - S}$

Make R the subject of this equation: $V = \dfrac{12R}{r + R}$

Multiply by $(r + R)$	$V(r + R) = 12R$
Multiply out bracket	$Vr + VR = 12R$
Rearrange terms	$12R - VR = Vr$
Factorise	$R(12 - V) = Vr$
Divide by bracket	$R = \dfrac{Vr}{12 - V}$

Make v the subject of this equation: $\dfrac{1}{f} = \dfrac{1}{u} + \dfrac{1}{v}$

Rearrange terms	$\dfrac{1}{v} = \dfrac{1}{f} - \dfrac{1}{u}$
Write as one fraction	$\dfrac{1}{v} = \dfrac{u - f}{uf}$
Invert both sides	$v = \dfrac{uf}{u - f}$

1   Make p the subject of this formula.
$y = 5p - 49$

2   (a)   Make v the subject of this formula.
$s = \frac{1}{2}(u + v)t$
  (b)   Make u the subject of this formula.
$v^2 = u^2 + 2as$

3   The total energy (kinetic plus potential) is given by this formula.
$E = \frac{1}{2}mv^2 + mgh$
  (a)   Make h the subject of the formula.
  (b)   Make v the subject of the formula.

4   Make a the subject of this formula.
$2(a - 5) = b(7 - 3a)$

5   R, S and T are connected by the formula

$$\frac{1}{R} = \frac{1}{S} + \frac{1}{T}$$

  (a)   Rewrite the formula in the form $R = \cdots$
  (b)   Rewrite the formula in the form $T = \cdots$

6   The number of coins, N, with diameter d cm and with a fixed thickness that can be made from a given volume of metal can be found by using the formula
$$N = \frac{k}{d^2}$$
where k is a constant.
    (a) Given that 8000 coins of diameter 2 cm can be made from the given volume of metal, calculate how many coins of diameter 1 cm can be made from an equal volume of metal.
    (b) Rearrange the formula $N = \frac{k}{d^2}$ to make d the subject.
    (c) 2000 coins are to be made using an equal volume of metal.
        Estimate the diameter of these coins.
                                    OCR 2000 specimen

7   (a) (i) The focal length (f) of a lens is connected to the distance (u) of an object from the lens and distance (v) of its image by this formula.
$$f = \frac{uv}{u + v}$$
Rearrange this equation to express v in terms of u and f.
        (ii) An object is 40 cm from a lens of focal length 30 cm.
        Find the distance of the image from the lens.
    (b) (i) The combined resistance R of two resistances, R_1 and R_2, in parallel is given by this formula.
$$R = \frac{R_1 R_2}{R_1 + R_2}$$
Rearrange the equation to express R_2 in terms of R and R_1.
        (ii) What resistance should be used in parallel with a resistance of 40 ohms to produce a combined resistance of 30 ohms?

8   x and y are connected by this formula.
$$\frac{4}{x} - \frac{7}{y} = \frac{1}{x}$$
Make x the subject of the formula.

9   a, b and c are connected by this formula.
$$a + b\sqrt{c} = b - 2a\sqrt{c}$$
    (a) Make b the subject of the formula.
    (b) Make c the subject of the formula.

10 When a wire of length l cm is supported between two points a distance d cm apart, the sag, s cm, at its centre is given by this formula.
$$s = \sqrt{\tfrac{3}{8}d(l - d)}$$
    (a) Make l the subject of this formula.
    (b) Find, correct to the nearest centimetre, the length of wire that produces a sag of 67.5 cm when supported by two points which are 1.45 m apart.

11 The period of oscillation for a system consisting of two masses, M and m, which uses strings of length L is given by this formula.
$$T = 4\pi \sqrt{\frac{ML + 3mL}{3Mg + 2mg}}$$
Make m the subject of this formula.

12 The surface area of a closed cylinder of radius r and height h has its minimum value A for a given volume V, when $h = 2r$.
    (a) Show that, for the minimum value of A,
$$r = \sqrt[3]{\frac{V}{2\pi}}.$$
    (b) Show that $A = 6\pi\left(\frac{V}{2\pi}\right)^{\frac{2}{3}}$.
    (c) A can of tomatoes needs to have a volume of 495 cm³.
        What is the minimum surface area possible for this can?

LINEAR EQUATIONS

FORMING AND SOLVING LINEAR EQUATIONS

A girl is y years old.
Her father is 3 times as old as she is.
Her mother is 2 years younger than her father.
The total of their ages is 103.
How old are they?

Father's age is $3y$. So, mother's age is $3y - 2$.
$$y + 3y + 3y - 2 = 103$$
$$7y - 2 = 103$$
$$7y = 105$$
$$y = 15$$

The girl is 15, the father is 45, and the mother is 43.

EQUATIONS WITH FRACTIONS

There are several ways of tackling equations with fractions. Sometimes, it is simplest to work with the fractions. At other times, it is easier to multiply through by a suitable number to clear the fractions.

$$5x + 2 = \tfrac{3}{2}x + 16$$
$$\Rightarrow \quad 5x - \tfrac{3}{2}x = 16 - 2$$
$$\Rightarrow \quad \tfrac{7}{2}x = 14$$
$$\Rightarrow \quad 7x = 28$$
$$\Rightarrow \quad x = 4$$

$$3x - \tfrac{1}{2}(x - 2) = 6$$
$$\Rightarrow \quad 3x - \tfrac{1}{2}x + 1 = 6$$
$$\Rightarrow \quad \tfrac{5}{2}x + 1 = 6$$
$$\Rightarrow \quad \tfrac{5}{2}x = 5$$
$$\Rightarrow \quad \tfrac{1}{2}x = 1$$
$$\Rightarrow \quad x = 2$$

$$\frac{x + 3}{5} - 1 = \frac{x - 4}{3}$$ ← Multiply each term by 15.
$$\Rightarrow \quad 3(x + 3) - 15 = 5(x - 4)$$
$$\Rightarrow \quad 3x + 9 - 15 = 5x - 20$$
$$\Rightarrow \quad 14 = 2x$$
$$\Rightarrow \quad x = 7$$

$$\frac{1}{x + 2} = \frac{6}{x}$$ ← Multiply each term by $x(x + 2)$.
$$\Rightarrow \quad x = 6(x + 2)$$
$$\Rightarrow \quad x = 6x + 12$$
$$\Rightarrow \quad -5x = 12$$
$$\Rightarrow \quad x = -2.4$$

Do not use a calculator for this exercise.

1 Solve this equation.
$$7x - 4(x - 3) = 48 - 2(x + 3)$$

2 Solve these equations.
   (a) $6(x + 2) + 3(3x - 1) = 21$
   (b) $2(2x + 3) - 3(x - 2) = 3 - 5x$

3 Solve these equations.
   (a) $\frac{2}{3}x = 12$ (b) $\frac{3}{2x} = 10$

4 Solve these equations.
   (a) $9 - \frac{5x}{2} = 11$ (b) $\frac{4}{x} + 9 = 2$

5 Solve this equation.
$$\frac{2x + 3}{6} - \frac{x - 1}{8} = 10$$

6 Solve these equations.
   (a) $\frac{1}{x - 3} = \frac{11}{x}$ (b) $\frac{x - 1}{5 - 3x} = 3$
   (c) $\frac{4}{x + 2} = \frac{7}{x - 2}$

INEQUALITIES AND LOCATING REGIONS BY LINES

Inequalities use the symbols $<$, $\leq$, $>$, and $\geq$. They show the range of values for which a statement is true.

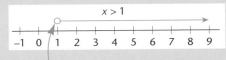

$$2x - 5 \leq 7$$
$$\Rightarrow \quad 2x \leq 12$$
$$\Rightarrow \quad x \leq 6$$

$$6 - x < 5$$
$$\Rightarrow \quad 6 < 5 + x$$
$$\Rightarrow \quad 1 < x$$
$$\Rightarrow \quad x > 1$$

Inequalities can be shown on a number line.

$x \leq 6$

$x > 1$

The filled circle means the end point is included in the range. The empty circle means it is *not*.

Inequalities are used to describe **regions** on a graph.

The dotted line means that the points on the boundary line are *not* included in the region. The solid line means that they are.

In this shaded region, $x \geq 0$, $y > 1$ and $x + y \leq 4$

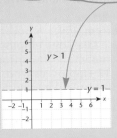

$y > 1$
$y = 1$

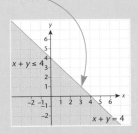

$x + y \leq 4$
$x + y = 4$

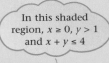
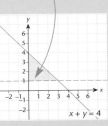

$x + y = 4$

Do not use a calculator for this exercise.

1 Solve these inequalities.

(a) $9x > 7x - 3$ (b) $8 - 3y > 2(y + 14)$

(c) $9x + 5 > 19 + 7x$ (d) $4 < 2x + 3 < 8$

(e) $x - 1 \leq 4x + 5 \leq x + 17$

2 (a) Find the greatest integer y for which $3y < 22$.

(b) Find the least integer x for which $x^2 < 22$.

(c) Find the least integer n for which $5n - 9 > 28 + 2n$.

3 Solve these inequalities.

(a) $(x + 2)^2 > 49$ (b) $(x + 2)^2 < x^2 + 6x + 5$

(c) $(x + 2)^2 < 4$ (d) $(x + 2)^2 > (x - 5)^2$

4 (a) Show on a graph the region satisfying all these inequalities.

$x + y < 6 \quad y > 2x - 2 \quad y > 0 \quad x > 0$

(b) Write down the coordinates of all the points with integer coordinates which lie within this region.

5 (a) On graph paper, draw the region which satisfies all of the following inequalities.

$y > 3 \quad y \geq 2x - 2 \quad y \leq 7 - x \quad x \geq 0$

Make sure that you indicate clearly the region that is your answer.

(b) Write down the coordinates of all the points whose coordinates are integers and lie in the region which satisfies all the inequalities given in (a).

WJEC 1998

Nelson GCSE Maths   REVISION GUIDE: ALGEBRA (HIGHER)

6 This is the graph of $y = x^3 - 9x$.

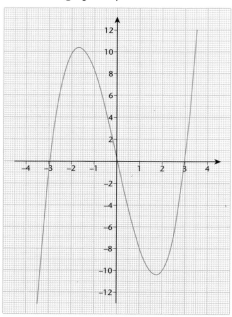

Use the graph to solve these inequalities.

(a) $x^3 - 9x > 11$

(b) $x^3 - 9x < -6$

(c) $x^3 < 9x + 8$

7 To help meet the cost of producing the annual school magazine, the editor invites local businesses to pay for either a full-page advertisement or a half-page advertisement in the magazine. The magazine will have x **full-page** advertisements and y **half-page** advertisements.

(a) There are certain restrictions on the numbers of each type of advertisement.

    I   The total number of pages **filled** by advertisements has to be in the range 15 to 24, inclusive.

    (i) Write down two inequalities in x and y which express this restriction.

    II   The number of full-page advertisements must not exceed the number of half-page advertisements.

    (ii) Write down an inequality in x and y which expresses this restriction.

    III There cannot be more than 20 half-page advertisements.
       That is, $y \leq 20$.

(b) Illustrate the above four inequalities by a suitable diagram on graph paper. Identify the region containing the set of points which satisfy all four inequalities.

(c) The cost of a full-page advertisement is £90 and the cost of a half-page advertisement is £60. Find the maximum total income that the editor can expect to receive from businesses which advertise in the magazine.

CCEA 1996

8 A lead crystal manufacturer has decided to introduce a new range of vases – the Beechill model and the Clady model.
Let x be the number of Beechill vases produced per week and y be the number of Clady vases produced per week.
Total manufacturing costs are £50 for each vase and the manufacturer's total weekly outlay must not exceed £4000.

(a) Write down an inequality in x and y which expresses this condition.

The Beechill vase takes one employee 6 hours to make and the Clady vase takes one employee 10 hours to make. The manufacturer can afford to employ not more than 12 employees who work 9 hours a day (Monday to Friday) and 5 hours on Saturday making these vases.

(b) Show that this condition can be expressed in the form

$$3x + 5y \leq 300$$

The manufacturer needs to produce at least 30 Beechill vases and at least 20 Clady vases per week.

(c) **(i)** Write down an inequality in x.

    (ii) Write down an inequality in y.
    Using a scale of 1 cm = 5 units on both x and y axes, draw a graph to illustrate the four inequalities. Identify the region containing the set of points satisfying all four inequalities.

The manufacturer sells all the Beechill vases for £60 each and all the Clady vases for £80 each.

(d) Write down an expression for the weekly profit £P.

(e) How many of each type of vase should be made in order to produce maximum profit?

CCEA 1996

TRIAL AND IMPROVEMENT INCLUDING SOLVING EQUATIONS

Example: Solve $x^3 - 5x + 3 = 0$, correct to 2 decimal places.
First, a table of values can be used to locate the approximate solutions.

x	-4	-3	-2	-1	0	1	2	3
$x^3 - 5x + 3$	-41	-9	5	7	3	-1	1	15

> The value of $x^3 - 5x + 3$ changes sign for x between -3 and -2, between 0 and 1 and between 1 and 2, and so there are solutions to the equation in these intervals.

Alternatively, a graph can be used to locate the solutions.
To find the smallest solution, trial and improvement can be used.

Trials	Calculation	Sign
Try $x = -2.5$	$-2.5^3 - 5 \times (-2.5) + 3 = -0.125$	Negative
Try $x = -2.3$	$-2.3^3 - 5 \times (-2.3) + 3 = 2.333$	Positive
Try $x = -2.4$	$-2.4^3 - 5 \times (-2.4) + 3 = 1.176$	Positive
Try $x = -2.45$	$-2.45^3 - 5 \times (-2.45) + 3 = 0.544$	Positive
Try $x = -2.48$	$-2.48^3 - 5 \times (-2.48) + 3 = 0.147$	Positive
Try $x = -2.49$	$-2.49^3 - 5 \times (-2.49) + 3 = 0.0118$	Positive
Try $x = -2.495$	$-2.495^3 - 5 \times (-2.495) + 3 = -0.056$	Negative

> The solution is between -2.49 and -2.495 and is thus -2.49, correct to 2 decimal places.

Trial and improvement can also be used to find the other solutions to the equation. Approximate solutions can often be obtained from a graph and a more accurate solution found using trial and improvement.

1 (a) Use either a graph or a table to locate the solution of $x^3 - 6x = 50$.

  (b) Find this solution correct to 1 decimal place.

2 A cuboid has three sides of length x cm, $(x - 4)$ cm and $(x + 4)$ cm. Its volume is 300 cm^3.

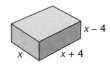

  (a) Find and simplify an equation satisfied by x.

  (b) Use trial and improvement to solve this equation, correct to 2 decimal places.

3 Find *all* the solutions of each of these equations, correct to 1 decimal place.

  (a) $x^4 + 3x = 80$

  (b) $x^3 - 6x^2 + 4 = 0$

4 (a) Sketch the graph of $y = x^3$.

  (b) The graph is transformed by a translation with vector $\binom{2}{3}$.
  Find, by trial and improvement where necessary, the coordinates of the points where this new graph cuts the axes, correct to 2 decimal places.

5 (a) Draw a sketch of the graph of $y = x(x - 1)(x - 2)$.

  (b) There are two points on the graph where the tangent is parallel to the x-axis.
  Find the coordinates of each of these points, correct to 1 decimal place.

$\overbrace{\text{A13}}$ QUADRATIC EQUATIONS

SOLVING EQUATIONS BY FACTORISING

$$2x^2 + 9x - 5 = 0$$
$$\Rightarrow (2x - 1)(x + 5) = 0$$

Either $2x - 1 = 0$ or $x + 5 = 0$.

So $\qquad x = \frac{1}{2}$ or $\qquad x = -5$.

$$x(x - 5) = 36$$
$$\Rightarrow x^2 - 5x - 36 = 0$$
$$\Rightarrow (x - 9)(x + 4) = 0$$

So, $x = 9$ or $x = -4$.

> Equations may need to be rearranged before they can be factorised.

SOLVING QUADRATIC EQUATIONS BY COMPLETING THE SQUARE

$$x^2 + 6x + 7 = 0$$
$$x^2 + 6x + 9 - 2 = 0$$
$$(x + 3)^2 = 2$$
$$x + 3 = \pm\sqrt{2}$$

> This equation does not factorise, so we complete the square.

> Now take the square root of both sides.

So, the two solutions are $x = -3 + \sqrt{2}$ and $x = -3 - \sqrt{2}$.
These are the *exact* solutions.
Decimal approximations can be found using a calculator to evaluate $\sqrt{2}$.

SOLVING QUADRATIC EQUATIONS BY USING THE FORMULA

If $ax^2 + bx + c = 0$ then $x = \dfrac{-b \pm \sqrt{b^2 - 4ac}}{2a}$.

$$3x^2 + 11x - 5 = 0$$

Here, $a = 3$, $b = 11$ and $c = -5$.

So, $x = \dfrac{-11 \pm \sqrt{11^2 - (-60)}}{6}$

$$\Rightarrow x = \dfrac{-11 \pm \sqrt{181}}{6}$$

So, $x = -4.08$ or $x = 0.41$ (to 2 decimal places).

SOLVING QUADRATIC EQUATIONS USING AN ITERATIVE FORMULA

This is illustrated by Questions 11 and 12 on page 219.

ROOTS OF QUADRATIC EQUATIONS

Consider the equation $ax^2 + bx + c = 0$.

- If $b^2 - 4ac > 0$, this equation has two real roots and the graph of $y = ax^2 + bx + c$ crosses the x-axis twice.

- If $b^2 - 4ac$ is a perfect square, the roots are rational. Otherwise, they are irrational.

- If $b^2 - 4ac = 0$, the equation has one real root (sometimes called a repeated root because, when the quadratic is factorised, it has a repeated factor). The graph of $y = ax^2 + bx + c = 0$ touches the x-axis.

- If $b^2 - 4ac < 0$, the equation does not have real roots (it does have two complex number roots). The graph of $y = ax^2 + bx + c$ does not meet the x-axis.

QUADRATIC EQUATIONS INVOLVING ALGEBRAIC FRACTIONS

$$x + \frac{25}{x} = 10$$
$$\Rightarrow x^2 + 25 = 10x$$
$$\Rightarrow x^2 - 10x + 25 = 0$$
$$\Rightarrow (x - 5)^2 = 0$$
$$\Rightarrow x = 5$$

> Multiply through by x.

$$\frac{9}{(x - 4)} - \frac{15}{(2x + 1)} = 2$$
$$\Rightarrow 9(2x + 1) - 15(x - 4) = 2(x - 4)(2x + 1)$$
$$\Rightarrow 4x^2 - 17x - 77 = 0$$
$$\Rightarrow (x - 7)(4x + 11) = 0$$
$$\Rightarrow x = 7 \text{ or } x = -2\frac{3}{4}$$

> Multiply through by $(x - 4)(2x + 1)$.

  Do not use a calculator for Questions 1, 2, 3 and 5.

1 (a) Factorise this expression.
$$3x^2 - 2x - 16$$

   (b) Hence, solve this equation.
$$3x^2 - 2x - 16 = 0$$

2 (a) Factorise $x^2 + 7x - 18$.

   (b) Hence, or otherwise, solve $x^2 + 7x = 18$.

3 Solve these equations by factorising.

   (a) $x^2 + 12x + 35 = 0$ (b) $2x^2 - 7x - 15 = 0$
   (c) $4x^2 + 28x + 49 = 0$ (d) $12x^2 - 44x + 35 = 0$

4 Solve these equations, giving your answer to 2 decimal places.

   (a) $x^2 - 4x - 16 = 0$ (b) $2x^2 - 5x - 11 = 0$
   (c) $x^2 = x + 1$ (d) $7x^2 + 13x + 4 = 0$

5 The lengths of the sides of this triangle are $(x - 9)$cm, $3x$cm and $(3x + 1)$ cm.

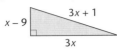

(a) Use Pythagoras' theorem to obtain a quadratic equation for x. Simplify the equation.

(b) Solve the equation and, hence, find the sides of the triangle.

(c) What right-angled triangle does the other solution to the equation suggest?

6 Solve this equation.

$$\frac{2}{y + 6} + \frac{3}{2y + 7} = 1$$

7 Solve this equation, giving your answers correct to 2 decimal places.

$$\frac{3}{x - 1} + \frac{2}{x - 2} = 5$$

8 The surface area of a cuboid is $1000 \, \text{cm}^2$. The lengths of its edges are $(x + 4)$ cm, $(2x + 2)$ cm and $(3x - 3)$ cm.

(a) Find and simplify a quadratic equation satisfied by x.

(b) Solve the equation and, hence, find the volume of the cuboid.

9 The sum of a set of x numbers is 272. When the number 34 is added to the set the mean increases by 1. Write down and solve an equation for x. Hence, find the possible values for the mean after the number 34 is added.

10 The volume of a cuboid is $210 \, \text{cm}^3$. The base and top of the cuboid are rectangles with dimensions $(x + 2)$ cm and $(2x - 1)$ cm. The other four faces of the cuboid have a total surface area of $130 \, \text{cm}^2$.

(a) Show that the x satisfies this equation.

$$\frac{420}{x + 2} + \frac{420}{2x - 1} = 130$$

(b) Solve this equation and, hence, find the area of the base of the cuboid.

11 A rectangular lawn has width x metres and length $2x$ metres. The length is increased by 3 metres and the width by 1 metre.

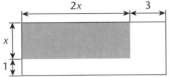

Not to scale

(a) Multiply out the expression $(2x + 3)(x + 1)$ to give the area of the new larger lawn.

(b) The new lawn has an area of $66 \, \text{m}^2$. Form an equation and solve it to find the area of the original lawn.

(c) Another lawn is 3 metres longer than it is wide. Its area is $92 \, \text{m}^2$.

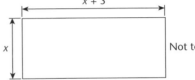

Not to scale

To find the width, x, this iteration is used

$$x_{n + 1} = \frac{92}{x_n + 3}.$$

Starting with $x_1 = 8$, find the width, x, correct to **one** decimal place.

SEG 1996

12 The equation $x^2 - x - 7 = 0$ can be rearranged to give $x = \sqrt{x + 7}$. This information can be used to obtain the iterative formula

$$x_{n + 1} = \sqrt{x_n + 7}.$$

(a) Starting with $x_1 = 4$ calculate the values of x_2, x_3 and x_4, giving all the figures on your calculator display.

(b) Find one solution of $x^2 - x - 7 = 0$ correct to 3 decimal places.

SEG 1995

LINEAR SIMULTANEOUS EQUATIONS

SOLUTION BY ELIMINATION

$$3x + 2y = 8 \qquad ①$$
$$5x + 3y = 13 \qquad ②$$
$$①×3 \quad 9x + 6y = 24 \qquad ③$$
$$②×2 \quad 10x + 6y = 26 \qquad ④$$
$$④-③ \qquad x = 2$$
$$\text{In} ① \qquad 6 + 2y = 8$$
$$2y = 2$$
$$y = 1$$
$$\text{Check in} ② \quad 5x + 3y = 10 + 3 = 13 ✔$$

SOLUTION BY SUBSTITUTION

$$y = x + 8 \qquad ①$$
$$x + y = 14 \qquad ②$$
$$\text{Substitute} ① \text{in} ② \quad x + x + 8 = 14$$
$$2x = 6$$
$$x = 3$$
$$\text{In} ① \qquad y = 3 + 8 = 11$$
$$\text{Check in} ② \qquad x + y = 3 + 11 = 14 ✔$$

SOLVING SIMULTANEOUS EQUATIONS BY DRAWING GRAPHS

Find where the graphs of these equations intersect.
$$x + y = 5$$
$$y = 2x + 1$$

The lines appear to cross at $(1\frac{1}{3}, 3\frac{2}{3})$ so the solution is $x = 1\frac{1}{3}$, $y = 3\frac{2}{3}$. This is the exact solution, which can be checked by substitution.

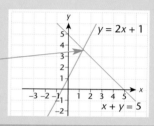

Do not use a calculator for this exercise.

1 Solve these pairs of simultaneous equations.
   (a) $2x + y = 3$
        $x + 3y = -1$
   (b) $x - y = 1$
        $3x + 5y = 15$

2 Solve these pairs of simultaneous equations
   (a) $4x - 3y = 31$
        $3x - 4y = 25$
   (b) $2x + 5y = 1$
        $5x - 3y = 49$
   (c) $5x = 7y + 3$
        $4x + 2y = 29$
   (d) $3x - 4y = 39$
        $x = 2y + 16$

3 Solve these pairs of simultaneous equations by drawing graphs.
   (a) $y = \frac{1}{2}x + 4$
        $y = 3x - 1$
   (b) $3x + 2y = 6$
        $2y - x = 2$

4 Tickets for a concert are sold at two prices.
   One party buys 7 of the dearer tickets and 5 of the cheaper. They pay £138.25.
   Another party buys 5 of the dearer tickets and 3 of the cheaper. They pay £93.75.
   Find the cost of the dearer and the cheaper tickets.

5 Members of a youth club can either pay a nightly fee or buy a season ticket.
   When 8 members paid nightly fees and 3 members bought season tickets, the treasurer collected £50.50.
   When 5 members paid nightly fees and 2 members bought season tickets, the treasurer collected £33.
   Use simultaneous equations, solving them algebraically, to calculate the nightly fee and the cost of a season ticket.
   Show your working.

   CCEA 1998

6 Cans of beans are packed into packets or cartons. 5 cans of beans can fit in a packet and 14 cans of beans can fit in a carton.
   A packet costs £4 and a carton costs £6.
   I spent £32 buying 53 cans of beans.
   How many packets and how many cartons did I buy?

A15   SOLVING EQUATIONS USING GRAPHS

- -

QUADRATIC EQUATIONS

To solve $x^2 - 3x - 1 = 0$, draw the graph of $y = x^2 - 3x - 1$ and see where it crosses the x-axis.

Another way of solving $x^2 - 3x - 1 = 0$ is to draw the graphs of $y = 3x + 1$ and $y = x^2$, and to see where they intersect.

There are many other pairs of graphs whose intersection solves this quadratic, for example $y = x^2 - 4x$ and $y = 1 - x$.

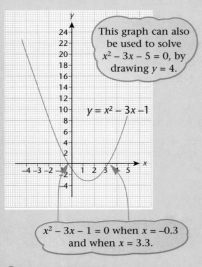

This graph can also be used to solve $x^2 - 3x - 5 = 0$, by drawing $y = 4$.

$y = x^2 - 3x - 1$

$x^2 - 3x - 1 = 0$ when $x = -0.3$ and when $x = 3.3$.

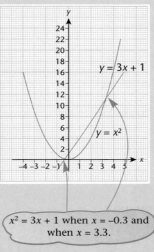

$y = 3x + 1$

$y = x^2$

$x^2 = 3x + 1$ when $x = -0.3$ and when $x = 3.3$.

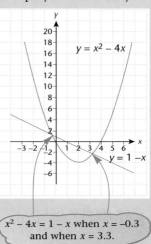

$y = x^2 - 4x$

$y = 1 - x$

$x^2 - 4x = 1 - x$ when $x = -0.3$ and when $x = 3.3$.

CUBIC EQUATIONS

Cubic equations can be solved in the same way.

Example

Solve $x^3 - 3x^2 + 1 = 0$

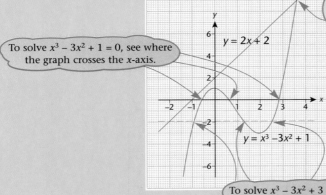

To solve $x^3 - 3x^2 + 1 = 0$, see where the graph crosses the x-axis.

$y = 2x + 2$

$x^3 - 3x^2 - 2x - 1 = 0$ is equivalent to $x^3 - 3x^2 + 1 = 2x + 2$. To solve $x^3 - 3x^2 - 2x - 1 = 0$, see where the graph crosses $y = 2x + 2$.

$y = x^3 - 3x^2 + 1$

To solve $x^3 - 3x^2 + 3 = 0$, see where the graph crosses $y = -2$.

1 (a) Solve the equation $x^2 + 2x - 2 = 0$ by drawing a graph of $y = x^2 + 2x - 2$ for values of x between -5 and 3.

   (b) Use your graph to solve the equation $x^2 + 2x - 2 = 5$.

   (c) Use your graph to solve the equation $x^2 + 2x - 2 = -3$.

2 (a) Draw the graph of $y = x^2 + x - 4$ for values of x between -3 and 4.

   (b) Use your graph to solve these equations.
      (i) $x^2 + x - 4 = 0$
      (ii) $x^2 + x - 4 = -2$
      (iii) $x^2 - x - 7 = 0$

3 (a) Draw the graph of $y = x^2 + 2x - 4$ for values of x between -6 and 3.

   (b) On the same axes, draw the graph of $y = 1 - 2x$.

   (c) Use your graphs to solve the equation $x^2 + 4x - 5 = 0$.

   (d) Draw another line on your graph to solve the equation $x^2 + x - 8 = 0$.

4 (a) Draw the graph of $y = x^3 - 6x + 3$ for values of x between -3 and 3.

   (b) By drawing appropriate lines on your graph, estimate solutions to each of these equations.
      (i) $x^3 - 6x - 8 = 0$
      (ii) $x^3 - 7x + 1 = 0$

5 (a) Draw the graph of $y = 2^x$ for values of x between -3 and 3.

   (b) Draw an appropriate line on your graph to solve $2^x - x = 3$.

   (c) Draw an appropriate curve on your graph to solve $2^x = \frac{1}{2}x^2$.

6 (a) Draw the graph of $y = x^3 - 2x^2 - 3x + 4$ for values of x between -2 and 3.

   (b) Use your graph to solve $x^3 - 2x^2 - 3x + 2 = 0$.

   (c) The equation $x^3 - 2x^2 - x - 1 = 0$ can be solved by superimposing the graph of $y = px + q$. State the values of p and q.

   (d) Draw the graph of $y = px + q$ and, hence, solve this equation.
      $x^3 - 2x^2 - x - 1 = 0$

7 (a) Draw the graph of $y = 3 - \frac{1}{x^2}$ for values of x between -2 and 3.

   (b) Explain why superimposing the graph of $y = x$ helps to solve the equation $x^3 - 3x^2 + 1 = 0$.
      Solve this equation.

   (c) By superimposing another graph, solve the equation $x^4 - 3x^2 + 1 = 0$.

SELECTING FUNCTIONS TO FIT SETS OF DATA

Example
Fit a function to this data.

X	1	2	3	4	5
Y	4	13	28	49	76

> The technique described on card A1 is useful here.

This is the difference pattern for Y.

> This indicates a quadratic function starting $3X^2$.

The function is $Y = 3X^2 + 1$.

Example
Fit a function to this data.

X	2	4	6	12
Y	36	9	4	1

> Here the ideas on card N12 about proportion are helpful.

Since Y increases when X decreases, try inverse proportion. Evaluate XY, X^2Y, XY^2, etc.
You will discover that $YX^2 = 144$. Hence, the function is $Y = \dfrac{144}{X^2}$.

Example
This table gives times (t seconds) taken for a ball to roll different distances (d cm) down a slope.
Fit a function to this data.

t	1.18	1.47	1.87	2.29	2.52	2.72	2.94	3.19	3.31	3.52
d	10	20	30	40	50	60	70	80	90	100

Plotting d against t produces a curve.
Plotting d against t^2 produces a straight line more or less.

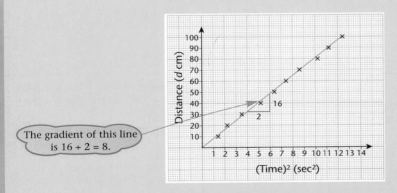

> The gradient of this line is $16 \div 2 = 8$.

The line of best fit provides a function which approximates the data.
So the function is $d = 8t^2$.

1 This table lists the diameter (d mm) and mass (m g) of ball bearings of different sizes.

d	1	2	3	4	5
m	4	7	12	19	28

Find a relationship connecting m and d.

2 This was displayed on a crane on a building site.

Load in tonnes(L)	2	1.5	1	0.75
Radius in metres(R)	7.5	10	15	20

Find a relationship between the load, L, and the radius, R.

3 Timothy knows that there is a relation of the form $s = kt^n$ between the distance s metres fallen from rest by a small body and the time t seconds for which that body has been falling. He experiments and obtains the following results.

Time (t seconds)	0.2	0.4	0.6	0.8	1.0
Distance (s metres)	0.2	0.8	1.8	3.4	5.0

(a) By considering his last pair of values, find k.

(b) By considering his first pair of values, find n.

(c) Show that one of his other pairs of values is inaccurate.

MEG 1996

4 The manager of a production company records the production costs in £(P) and the number (N) of items produced as in this table.

N	100	500	1000	2000	3000	4000
P	7500	13 500	21 000	36 000	51 000	66 000

Plot these values on graph paper.

(a) After completing the graph, explain why the values of P and N are connected by a relationship of the form

$P = aN + b$ where a and b are constants.

(b) From the graph, determine appropriate values for a and b.

(c) What are the production costs for 3500 items?

(d) How many items can be produced for £45 000?

(e) The company sells the items for £25 each. How many must be produced before it breaks even?

CCEA 1996

5 The temperature, T°C of the tea in a vacuum flask h hours after it is filled is believed to be given by the formula

$T = a \times (0.5)^h + b$.

(a) If the formula is correct, what sort of graph will be obtained if T is plotted against $(0.5)^h$?

The table shows a series of measurements of the temperature of the tea in a vacuum flask.

h (hours)	0.333	0.750	1.083	1.500	2.167
T (°C)	78	65	54	46	40

(b) Copy and complete this table and plot a graph of T against $(0.5)^h$.

h (hours)	0.333	0.750	1.083	1.500	2.167
$(0.5)^h$	0.794				
T (°C)	78	65	54	46	40

(c) Use your graph to estimate the values of a and b.

(d) (i) State the value of $(0.5)^0$.

(ii) Estimate the temperature of the tea when the flask was filled.

MEG 1998

6 A child throws a stone out to sea from the top of a high cliff. The height of the stone above the sea at different times is given in this table.

Time (t secs)	0	1	1.5	2	2.5
Height (h metres)	40	35	29	20	9

The relationship between h and t is known to be of the form $h = a + bt^2$, where a and b are constants.

Draw a suitable graph and estimate the values of a and b.

Do not use a calculator for Questions 1 to 9.

1 (a) The first two terms of a linear sequence are 4 and 7.
Find a formula for the nth term of the sequence.

(b) The first three terms of a quadratic sequence are 4, 7 and 12.
Find a formula for the nth term of the sequence.

(c) The nth term of another sequence is $2n^2 - 3n + 5$.

  (i) Write down the first three terms.

  (ii) Which is the first term of the sequence which exceeds 500?

2 Solve these equations.

(a) $x^2 = 9x$

(b) $x^2 = 9x + 10$

(c) $x^2 = 9x - 20$

(d) $2x^2 = 9x + 5$

(e) $5x^2 = 9x + 2$

3 Solve these simultaneous equations.

(a) $3x + 2y = 5$ **(b)** $7x - 5y = 32$
    $2x - 3y = 12$ $5x - 3y = 22$

4 (a) Factorise these expressions.

  (i) $7p^2 - 63$

  (ii) $2n^2 - n - 6$

(b) Simplify these expressions.

  (i) $\dfrac{x^2 - 2x + xy - 2y}{x^2 - y^2}$

  (ii) $\dfrac{a}{a + b} + \dfrac{b}{a - b}$

  (iii) $\dfrac{y + 3}{y(y + 2)} - \dfrac{1}{y + 2}$

5 (a) (i) Express $x^2 - 6x + 10$ in the form $(x + p)^2 + q$, where p and q are whole numbers.

  (ii) Sketch the graph of $y = x^2 - 6x + 10$.

  (iii) How many solutions does the equation $x^2 - 6x - 8 = 0$ have?

(b) Show that $\frac{1}{2}(3 + \sqrt{7})$ and $\frac{1}{2}(3 - \sqrt{7})$ are the solutions of the equation $2x^2 - 6x + 1 = 0$.

6 (a) Given that
$x^2 + 4x + 8 = (x + p)^2 + q$
find the value of p and show that $q = 4$.

(b) The graph below shows a sketch of the curve with equation
$$y = \frac{40}{x^2 + 4}.$$

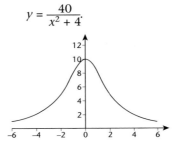

Use your result from part (a) to sketch the curve with equation
$$y = \frac{40}{x^2 + 4x + 8}.$$

MEG 1995

7 For a particular resort a tour operator offers package holidays of two types, Self-catering and Partial board.
Let x be the number of Self-catering and y the number of Partial board holidays booked.
The total number of holidays cannot exceed 80.

(a) Write down an inequality in x and y which expresses this condition.

To keep his hotel contract he must ensure that there are at least 20 Self-catering holidays and at least 15 Partial board holidays booked.

(b) Write down two inequalities to express these conditions.

He pays a handling fee of £5 per Self-catering holiday and £8 per Partial board holiday.
He must ensure that the total of the handling fees is at least £240.

(c) Write down an inequality which expresses this condition.

(d) Illustrate the four inequalities by a suitable diagram.

Identify the region containing the set of points satisfying all four inequalities.

(e) His profit for a Self-catering holiday is 20% greater than that for a Partial board holiday. What values of x and y would give

  (i) maximum profit,

  (ii) minimum profit?

CCEA 1995

Nelson GCSE Maths   REVISION GUIDE: ALGEBRA (HIGHER)

8 The diagram shows the graph of $y = x^2 + \frac{20}{x} - 10$ in the range $1 \le x \le 4$.

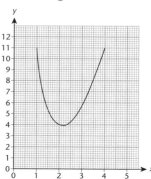

(a) Use the graph to estimate the solutions of $x^2 + \frac{20}{x} - 10 = 9$ in the range $1 \le x \le 4$.

(b) Use the graph to estimate one of the solutions of
$$x^2 + \frac{20}{x} - 15 = 0$$
in the range $1 \le x \le 4$.

(c) The graph $y = x^2 + \frac{20}{x} - 10$ and a graph of the form $y = px + q$ can be used to estimate solutions of the equation
$$x^3 - 2x^2 - 11x + 20 = 0.$$
Find the values of p and q.

SEG 2000 specimen

9 This table shows values of $y = x^3 - 7x^2 + 7x + 15$ for values of x between -1 and 6.

x	−1	0	1	2	3	4	5	6
y	0	15	16	9	0	−5	0	21

(a) Using the points in the table, draw the graph of $y = x^3 - 7x^2 + 7x + 15$ for values of x between $x = -1$ and 6 on graph paper. Your scale on the y-axis should at least allow for values of y between -10 and 25.

(b) Estimate the gradient of the curve $y = x^3 - 7x^2 + 7x + 15$ when $x = 1.5$.

(c) Using your graph, write down the maximum value of y for values of x between 0 and 5 together with the value of x for which it occurs.

(d) By drawing an appropriate line on the graph, solve the equation
$$x^3 - 7x^2 + 9x + 10 = 0$$

WJEC 2000 specimen

10 This is the graph of a function $y = f(x)$.

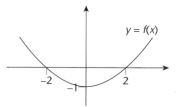

Sketch these graphs.

(a) $y = f(x) + 1$ (b) $y = -f(x)$

(c) $y = 3f(x)$ (d) $y = f(\frac{1}{2}x)$

(e) $y = f(x + 2)$

11 The normal rate of flow of water in a stream under a particular bridge is $50\,m^3$ per minute. One afternoon, there was a thunderstorm which changed the rate of flow, as shown in this table.

Time (mins)	0	30	60	90	120	150	180	210	240	270	300
Rate of flow (m^3/min)	50	50	80	130	200	230	190	130	50	50	50

(a) Draw a graph of rate of flow against time.

(b) What volume of water flowed under the bridge during the 5-hour period?

12

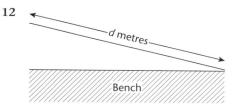

Julie carried out an experiment which involved rolling a ball down an inclined plane. She measured the time, t seconds, taken by the ball to roll a distance d metres down the plane. She obtained these results.

d	0.50	0.75	1.00	1.25	1.50
t	1.32	1.60	1.83	2.05	2.25
t^2					

She was told that $d = kt^2$, where k is a constant.

(a) (i) Copy and complete the table.

    (ii) Plot these values of d against t^2.

(b) Explain why these points suggest that $d = kt^2$.

(c) Hence find the value of k.

NEAB 1995

13 (a) Water flows into a cylinder at a constant rate.

Sketch the graph of the depth of water against time on axes like these.

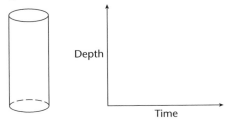

(b) Water flows into another container at a constant rate.

Sketch the cross-section of the container that generated this graph.

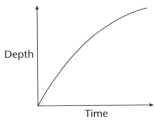

(c) The values of depth, d, against time, t, for a different container are shown in the table.

Time t (secs)	1	2	3	4	5	6	7	8	9	10
Depth d (cm)	0.1	0.4	0.9	1.6	2.5	3.6	4.9	6.4	8.1	10

(i) Find the equation connecting t and d.

The graph of depth against time is shown.

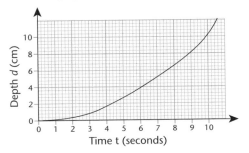

(ii) Find the rate of increase of depth after six seconds.

SEG 1995

14 (a) If a sum of money is invested for T years at $R\%$ per annum *simple* interest, then the amount £A accumulated is

$$A = P + \frac{PTR}{100}.$$

(i) Rewrite this formula in the form $P = \cdots$

(ii) Some money was invested and earned 4.5% *simple* interest per annum. The amount of money after 6 years was £2540. How much money was invested?

(b) Usually compound interest is paid when money is invested. If £2000 is invested at a rate of $r\%$ per annum, the amount of money £A accumulated after n years is

$$A = 2000\left(1 + \frac{r}{100}\right)^{n}.$$

After 6 years, the £2000 invested has grown to £2577.72. Use trial and improvement to find the value of r, correct to 2 decimal places.

15 Fred cycled from home to his friend's house and back again.
The distance from Fred's home to his friend's house is 20 km.
On his way from home to his friend's house, Fred cycled at x km per hour.
On the way back, Fred's speed had decreased by 2 km per hour.
It took Fred 4 hours altogether to cycle to his friend's house and back.

(a) Write down an equation for x.

(b) Show that the equation can be written as $x^2 - 12x + 10 = 0$.

(c) Solve the equation in part **(b)**. Give your answers correct to 1 decimal place.

Only one of the answers in part **(c)** can be Fred's speed.

(d) Explain why.

Edexcel 1995

S1 3D OBJECTS AND THEIR 2D REPRESENTATION

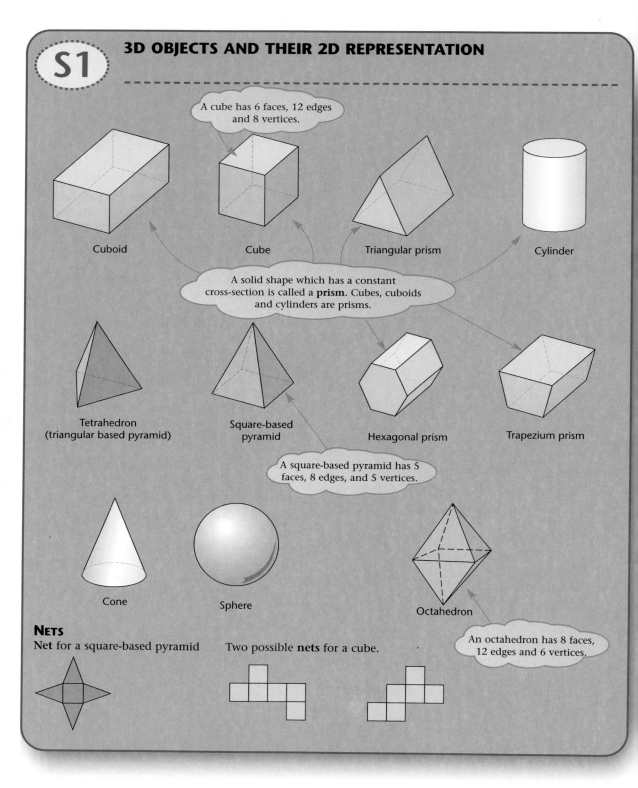

A cube has 6 faces, 12 edges and 8 vertices.

Cuboid

Cube

Triangular prism

Cylinder

A solid shape which has a constant cross-section is called a **prism**. Cubes, cuboids and cylinders are prisms.

Tetrahedron (triangular based pyramid)

Square-based pyramid

Hexagonal prism

Trapezium prism

A square-based pyramid has 5 faces, 8 edges, and 5 vertices.

Cone

Sphere

Octahedron

An octahedron has 8 faces, 12 edges and 6 vertices.

NETS
Net for a square-based pyramid

Two possible **nets** for a cube.

1 Which of these nets will fold to make a pyramid?

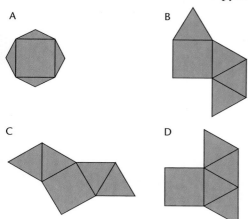

A

B

C

D

2 This pyramid has all its faces right-angled triangles.

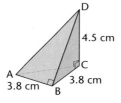

DC = 4.5 cm, BC = 3.8 cm and AB = 3.8 cm.
Draw an accurate net for this pyramid.

3 (a) How many faces, edges and vertices does a tetrahedron have?

(b) Each of three vertices of the tetrahedron is sliced off by a plane close to the vertex.

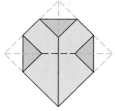

How many faces, edges and vertices does the shape remaining have?

4 This cuboid has a path drawn on it, which joins opposite vertices of the cuboid.

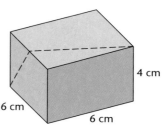

6 cm

4 cm

6 cm

Find the length of the shortest path on the surface of the cuboid which joins opposite vertices.

5 One way of cutting a tetrahedron in half is to draw a plane through the mid-points of four of the edges.

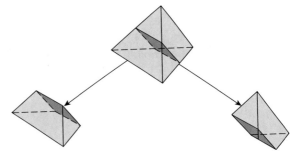

Draw a net for one of the halves.

Nelson GCSE Maths REVISION GUIDE: SHAPE, SPACE AND MEASURES (HIGHER)

CONGRUENT TRIANGLES

S2

Two triangles are congruent if one fits exactly on the other (after turning over if necessary).

> Triangles are congruent if three pairs of sides are equal.

> Triangles are congruent if both triangles have a right angle and the hypotenuses and another pair of sides are equal

> Triangles are congruent if two pairs of sides and the included angle are equal.

> Triangles are congruent if one pair of sides and two pairs of angles (in corresponding positions) are equal.

1 (a) Draw a square. Draw lines on it to cut it into four congruent triangles.

   (b) Draw another square. Find a different way of cutting it into four congruent triangles.

2 These triangles are congruent.
    Find y.

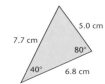

3 Explain why these triangles cannot be congruent.

4 AB is a diameter of a circle with centre O and OC is a radius perpendicular to AB. E is a point on OC.

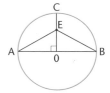

Prove that triangles AEO and OEB are congruent. Deduce that triangle AEB is isosceles.

5 ABCDEF is a regular hexagon inscribed in a circle with centre O. The circle with centre F through A and E meets diagonal FB at Y. The radius OX is perpendicular to side CD.

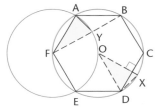

Prove that triangle AFY is congruent to triangle XOD.

6 ABC is a triangle. Equilateral triangles ABD and ACE are drawn on sides AB and AC. Lines DC and BE meet at X.

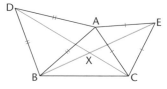

   (a) Prove that triangles ADC and ABE are congruent.

   (b) Hence, prove that ∠ADX = ∠ABX.

   (c) Deduce that ∠BXC is 120°.

Nelson GCSE Maths REVISION GUIDE: SHAPE, SPACE AND MEASURES (HIGHER)

ANGLE AND SYMMETRY PROPERTIES OF TRIANGLES AND QUADRILATERALS

PARALLEL LINES
All the red angles are equal. All the white angles are equal.

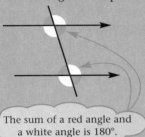

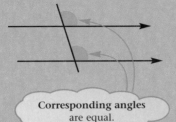

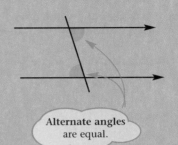

The sum of a red angle and a white angle is 180°.

Corresponding angles are equal.

Alternate angles are equal.

TRIANGLES

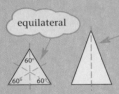

equilateral

isosceles

right-angled

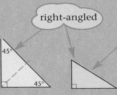

scalene

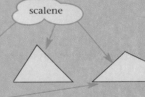

obtuse-angled

Exterior angle theorem
This angle is equal to $x + y$

The sum of the interior angles of a triangle is 180°.
$x + y + z = 180°$

QUADRILATERALS

A quadrilateral has four sides. Here are some special quadrilaterals.

Shape	Lines of symmetry	Order of rotational symmetry	Diagonals			
			same length	cross at right angles	always cross at mid-points	bisect angles of quad
Square Regular quadrilateral		4	YES	YES	YES	YES
Rectangle All angles right angles		2	YES	NO	YES	NO
Rhombus All sides equal		2	NO	YES	YES	YES
Parallelogram Opposite sides parallel		2	NO	NO	YES	NO
Kite Two pairs of adjacent sides equal		none (or 1)	NO	YES	NO	NO
Trapezium One pair of opposite sides parallel		none (or 1)	NO	NO	NO	NO
Isosceles trapezium Trapezium with non-parallel sides equal		none (or 1)	YES	NO	NO	NO

The sum of the interior angles of a quadrilateral is 360°.
$p + q + r + s = 360°$

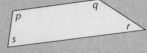

Nelson GCSE Maths   REVISION GUIDE: SHAPE, SPACE AND MEASURES (HIGHER)

1 Look at this diagram.

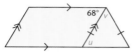

  (a) Calculate the value of *u*.
     Give reasons for your answer.
  (b) Calculate the value of *v*.
     Give reasons for your answer.

2 This diagram shows a kite.

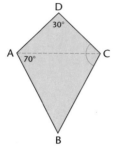

Calculate these angles, giving reasons for your answers.

  (a) ∠ABC

  (b) ∠BCD

3 (a) Use angle properties to find as many angles as you can in this rectangle.

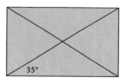

  (b) Use angle properties to find as many angles as you can in this parallelogram.

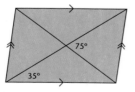

4 (a) Draw a quadrilateral which has rotational symmetry of order 2 but no lines of symmetry.

  (b) Draw a quadrilateral which has exactly two lines of symmetry.

5 A quadrilateral has one line of symmetry. Its diagonals are the same length. Which of these statements *must* be true.

A: Two of its sides are parallel.

B: Two of its internal angles are equal.

C: At least one pair of its sides are equal in length.

D: One of the diagonals meets the other diagonal at its mid-point.

S4 ANGLE AND SYMMETRY PROPERTIES OF POLYGONS

Polygon	Number of sides
Triangle	3
Quadrilateral	4
Pentagon	5
Hexagon	6
Heptagon	7
Octagon	8
Nonagon	9
Decagon	10
Dodecagon	12

A **regular polygon** has all its sides equal *and* all its angles equal.

SUM OF THE ANGLES OF A POLYGON

Divide the polygon into triangles.

A hexagon can be divided into four triangles. The sum of the angles of a hexagon is 4 × 180°, i.e. 720°.

SYMMETRY

Regular pentagon
Five lines of symmetry
Rotational symmetry of order 5

Hexagon
Three lines of symmetry
Rotational symmetry of order 3

Pentagon
One line of symmetry

Octagon
Rotational symmetry of order 4

INTERIOR AND EXTERIOR ANGLES

exterior angle
interior angle

At a vertex:
interior angle + exterior angle = 180°.

360° ÷ 5 = 72° So, the exterior angle is 72°.

180° − 72° = 108°
So, each interior angle of a regular pentagon is 108°.

The exterior angles of a polygon add up to 360°. In a **regular polygon** with *n* sides all the **exterior angles** are equal, and are found by dividing 360 by *n*.

1 Look at this diagram.
   Work out the size of angle *j*.

   85° 136° 100°

2 (a) The angle sum of a polygon is 900°.
        How many sides does it have?

   (b) A nonagon has 9 sides.
        What is the size of each interior angle of a regular nonagon?

3 A regular decagon, an equilateral triangle and a square are fitted together as shown.
   Work out the size of angle *p*.

   Decagon

4 (a) Each exterior angle of a regular polygon is equal to 20°.
        How many sides does the polygon have?

   (b) Half of the exterior angles of a polygon are equal to 16° and half of them are equal to 20°.
        How many sides does the polygon have?

5 (a) Draw a sketch showing a regular pentagon and all its lines of symmetry.

   (b) A pentagon is irregular.
        How many lines of symmetry could it have? Draw sketches to illustrate your answer.

6 Draw a regular pentagon and the two diagonals from one of its vertices.
   What size are the angles in each of the triangles into which the pentagon is divided?

Nelson GCSE Maths   REVISION GUIDE: SHAPE, SPACE AND MEASURES (HIGHER)

CIRCLE THEOREMS

CHORDS AND TANGENTS TO CIRCLES

AB is a chord. Centre O lies on the perpendicular bisector of AB.

A tangent to a circle is perpendicular to the diameter.

The two tangents from a point to a circle are equal in length.

ANGLE PROPERTIES OF CIRCLES

The angle in a semicircle is a right angle.

The angle at the centre of a circle is twice the angle at the circumference.

$\angle AOB = 2\angle APB$ Reflex $\angle AOB = 2\angle APB$

Angles in the same segment are equal.

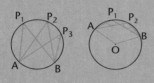

The exterior angle of a cyclic quadrilateral is equal to the interior opposite angle.

The opposite angles of a cyclic quadrilateral add to 180°.

The angle between a chord and a tangent is equal to the angle in the alternate segment.

1 In this diagram find angles *e*, *f* and *g*.

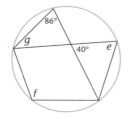

2 In this diagram, find angle *h*.

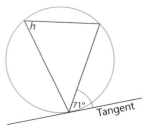

3 In this diagram, find angle *i*.

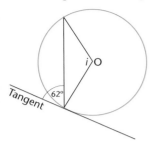

Tangent 62°

4 In this diagram, find angles *j* and *k*.

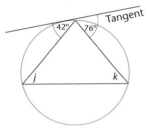

Tangent 42° 76°

j   *k*

5 In this diagram, two of the lines are tangents.

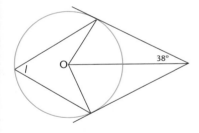

l   38°

Find angle *l*.

6 (a) The opposite angles of a quadrilateral add up to 180°.
Is the quadrilateral cyclic?

(b) Use your answer to part **(a)** to say whether each of these types of quadrilateral is *always* cyclic, *sometimes* cyclic or *never* cyclic.

A: Rectangle

B: Parallelogram

C: Rhombus

D: Square

E: Trapezium

F: Kite

7

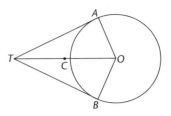

TA and *TB* are tangents to a circle centre *O*.
The mid-point of *TO* is *C*.

(a) Give geometrical reasons why

    (i) angle *TAO* = 90°,

    (ii) angle *ATO* = angle *BTO*,

    (iii) *CA* = *CT*.

(b) Angle *ACO* = 40°.
Calculate the size of angle *ATO*.

NEAB 1996

8

Not drawn to scale

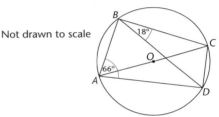

18° 66°

ABCD is a cyclic quadrilateral.
AC is a diameter of the circle, centre *O*,
which passes through *A*, *B*, *C* and *D*.
Angle *BAD* = 66°, angle *DBC* = 18°.
Calculate the size of

(a) angle *BDA*,   **(b)** angle *AOD*.

NEAB 1996

9 This circle has radius 5 cm. P is 13 cm from the centre of the circle and PA and PB are tangents meeting the circle at A and B.

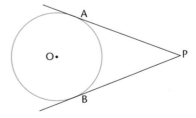

Find the lengths of PA and PB.

10 Two parallel chords are drawn in a circle with radius 25 cm. One of the chords is 14 cm long and the other is 30 cm long.
How far apart are these chords?

Nelson GCSE Maths   REVISION GUIDE: SHAPE, SPACE AND MEASURES (HIGHER)

Area of square A + Area of square B = Area of square C
or $a^2 + b^2 = c^2$

Example
$6^2 + b^2 = 17^2$
$36 + b^2 = 289$
$b^2 = 289 - 36$
$= 253$
$b = \sqrt{253}$
$= 15.9$ (to 3 s.f.)

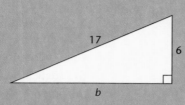

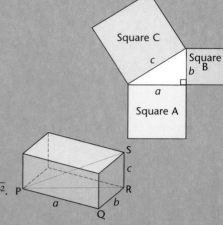

USING PYTHAGORAS' THEOREM IN THREE DIMENSIONS

Applying Pythagoras' theorem to triangle PQR gives PR $= \sqrt{a^2 + b^2}$.

Applying Pythagoras' theorem to triangle PSR gives PS $= \sqrt{a^2 + b^2 + c^2}$.

  Do not use a calculator for Questions 1 and 6.

1 Calculate the length of the sides marked a and b.

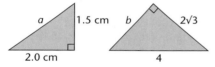

2 Find the distance between the points $(-3, -4)$ and $(2, 8)$.

3 In this cuboid, AB is 2.2 m, AE is 3.4 m and BC is 4.3 m.

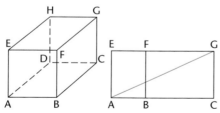

(a) A mathematical ant crawls from A to G on the surface of this cuboid, taking the shortest route.
Calculate the distance of its journey correct to 2 significant figures.

(b) A mathematical fly flies in a straight line inside the cuboid from A to G.
By how much is the fly's journey shorter than the ant's?

4 The vertex of this square-based pyramid is directly above the centre of the base.

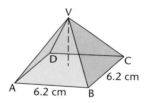

AB is 6.2 cm and the height of the pyramid is 3.7 cm. Calculate the length of VC.

5 The vertices of a triangle are at $(-3, 2)$, $(1, -5)$ and $(2, 3)$.
Prove that the triangle is isosceles.

6 The two shorter sides of a right-angled triangle are $(2 + \sqrt{3})$ cm and $(2 - \sqrt{3})$ cm. The two shorter sides of another right-angled triangle are $(3 + \sqrt{5})$ cm and $(3 - \sqrt{5})$ cm.

Prove that the lengths of the hypotenuses of these triangles are in the ratio $1:\sqrt{2}$.

TRIGONOMETRY

BEARINGS

A bearing is an angle measured clockwise from North. A bearing can be any angle between 0° and 360°.

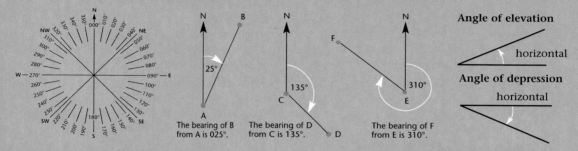

The bearing of B from A is 025°.

The bearing of D from C is 135°.

The bearing of F from E is 310°.

Angle of elevation

horizontal

Angle of depression

horizontal

THE TRIGONOMETRIC FORMULAE

$$\sin x = \frac{\text{opp}}{\text{hyp}}$$

$$\cos x = \frac{\text{adj}}{\text{hyp}}$$

$$\tan x = \frac{\text{opp}}{\text{adj}}$$

Examples

Find the side labelled *a*.

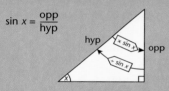

$a = 6.3 \text{ cm} \times \cos 40°$
$= 4.8 \text{ cm}$

Find the side labelled *b*.

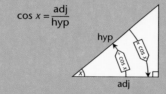

$b = 5.8 \text{ cm} \div \sin 55°$
$= 7.1 \text{ cm}$

Find the angle marked *x*.

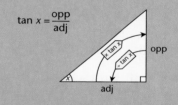

$\tan x = \dfrac{4.7}{3.8}$
$= 1.237$
$x = 51°$

TRIGONOMETRY IN THREE DIMENSIONS

The angle between an edge and a face
The angle between the edge CP and the base PQRS is ∠CPN. If lengths are known this angle can be calculated using trigonometry in triangle CPN.

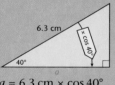

The angle between two faces
The angle between the face PQC and the base PQRS is ∠CMN. Note that both CM and NM are at right angles to the edge PQ where the faces meet. The angle can be calculated using trigonometry in triangle CMN.

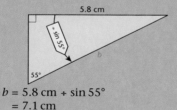

TRIGONOMETRY WITHOUT A CALCULATOR

If you know, for example, that $\cos y = \frac{15}{17}$, then you can calculate $\sin y$ and $\tan y$ by using Pythagoras' theorem to find the third side of the appropriate right-angled triangle.

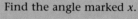

$\sin y = \frac{8}{17}$, $\tan y = \frac{8}{15}$

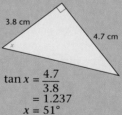

Nelson GCSE Maths   REVISION GUIDE: SHAPE, SPACE AND MEASURES (HIGHER)

237

1 Find a, b, p and q correct to 2 significant figures, and x and y correct to the nearest degree.

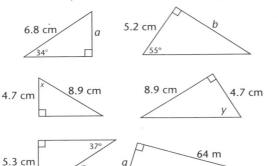

2 (a) Find the hypotenuse of this triangle.

(b) Find the exact values of
   (i) $\tan x$
   (ii) $\sin x$
   (iii) $\cos x \div \tan x$

3 These diagrams show an equilateral triangle and a right-angled isosceles triangle.

With the help of these diagrams, find exact values for

(a) $\cos 60°$ **(b)** $\tan 60°$ **(c)** $\cos 30°$
(d) $\tan 30°$ **(e)** $\sin 45°$ **(f)** $\tan 45°$

4 A ship sails 16 km from U to V on a bearing of 058°, and then 23 km from V to W on a bearing of 141°. Draw a sketch to show this. How far East of U is W? Give your answer to 2 significant figures.

5 For safety, the angle between Jake's ladder and the ground should be between 70° and 80°.
  (a) Jake leans a ladder 4.5 m long against a wall, so that it reaches 4.1 m up the wall. Is the ladder safely placed?
  (b) If the ladder is placed so that it is safe, what are the distances its foot can be from the bottom of the wall?

6 A, B and C are three communications satellites orbiting the Earth on a circular path. They are equal distances from each other.
The radius of the Earth is approximately 6400 km.
Calculate the radius of the orbit.

7 This diagram shows a cuboid. ABCD is the base of the cuboid.

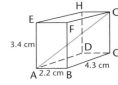

  (a) Calculate the angle between AG and the base of the cuboid, giving your answer correct to the nearest degree.
  (b) Calculate the angle between AG and AB, correct to the nearest degree.

8 The vertex of this square-based pyramid is above the centre of the base.

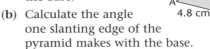

  (a) Calculate the angle one of the triangular faces of the pyramid makes with the base.
  (b) Calculate the angle one slanting edge of the pyramid makes with the base.

9 Two ships leave the same harbour. Ship A travels 23.8 nautical miles on a bearing of 241°. Ship B travels 16.3 nautical miles on a bearing of 317°.
  (a) How far North of ship A is ship B?
  (b) How far East of ship A is ship B?
  (c) What is the bearing of ship B from ship A?

10 The faces of a regular octahedron are all equilateral triangles with sides of length 4 cm.

  (a) Find the distance between opposite vertices of the regular octagon.
  (b) Find the angle between two adjacent faces of the regular octagon.
  (c) Find the angle between two edges of the regular octagon which meet but which do not lie in the same face.

SINE, COSINE AND TANGENT OF ANGLES OF ANY SIZE, INCLUDING TRIGONOMETRIC EQUATIONS

SINE, COSINE AND TANGENT OF ANGLES OF ANY SIZE

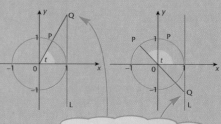

The coordinates of any point P on the circle of radius 1 are $(\cos t, \sin t)$.

The y-coordinate of Q is $\tan t$.

GRAPHS OF TRIGONOMETRIC FUNCTIONS

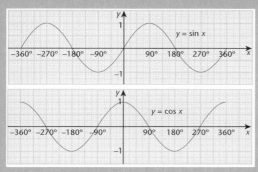

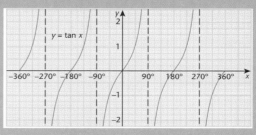

TRIGONOMETRIC EQUATIONS

Example 1: Find the values of x between 0° and 360° for which $\sin x = 0.4$.
Obtain approximate solutions from the graph.
Use a calculator to obtain more accuracy.
One solution is 23.6°.
So, the other solution is $180° - 23.6° = 156.4°$.

Example 2: When $h = 5$, find the first four positive solutions for t to the equation $h = 4 + 3\sin(10t°)$.
$5 = 4 + 3\sin(10t°) \Rightarrow 3\sin(10t°) = 1$
$\Rightarrow \sin(10t°) = \frac{1}{3}$
So $10t = 19.47, 160.53, 360 + 19.47, 360 + 160.53$,
..., and the first four positive solutions are $t = 1.95$, $t = 16.1$, $t = 37.9$ and $t = 52.1$.

1 (a) Find two values of θ between 0° and 360° for which
　　(i) $\cos \theta = 0.5$　　(ii) $\tan \theta = 1.5$
　　(iii) $\sin \theta = -0.63$

　(b) State two values of x, other than 360°, for which $\sin x = \sin 36°$.

2 Suggest an equation for this graph.

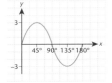

3 Sketch the graph of $y = 3\cos x + 2$ for $0° \le x \le 360°$.

4 Find the *exact* values of x between 0° and 360° which are solutions of these equations.

　(a) $\sin x = \frac{\sqrt{3}}{2}$　(b) $\cos x = \frac{-1}{\sqrt{2}}$　(c) $\tan x = \frac{1}{\sqrt{3}}$

5 The formula $h = 8 + 5\sin(30t)°$ gives the height of the tide in metres, t hours after midnight.
　(a) Calculate the height of the tide at
　　(i) 3 a.m.　(ii) 1.30 a.m.　(iii) 7.15 a.m.
　(b) Sketch the graph of $h = 8 + 5\sin(30t)°$ for values of t between 0 and 12.
　(c) Between what times is the depth of water greater than 10.5 m?

Nelson GCSE Maths　REVISION GUIDE: SHAPE, SPACE AND MEASURES (HIGHER)

S9   SINE AND COSINE RULES AND $\frac{1}{2}ab$SIN C

THE SINE RULE

$$\frac{a}{\sin A} = \frac{b}{\sin B} = \frac{c}{\sin C}$$

You can use the sine rule

- *either* if you know two sides
  of a triangle and the angle opposite one of them
  and want to find the other angles of the triangle

- *or* if you know all three angles and one of the
  sides, and want to find one or both of the other
  sides.

AREA OF A TRIANGLE

The area of triangle ABC is $\frac{1}{2}ab$ sin C.

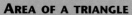

THE COSINE RULE

$$c^2 = a^2 + b^2 - 2ab\cos C$$

You can use the cosine rule

- *either* if you know two sides of a triangle and the
  angle between them and
  want to find the third side

- *or* if you know all three sides, and want to find
  one or more of the angles.

Using the cosine rule to find an angle
To find angle D

$$8^2 = 7^2 + 5^2 - 2 \times 7 \times 5 \times \cos D$$
$$\Rightarrow 64 = 74 - 70\cos D$$
$$\Rightarrow 70\cos D = 10$$
$$\Rightarrow \cos D = \tfrac{1}{7}$$
$$\Rightarrow D = 81.8° \text{ approximately.}$$

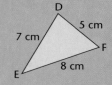

---

1   Calculate angle LMN in this triangle.

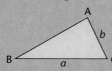

2   Look at triangle PQR.
   (a) Calculate the area of
       triangle PQR.
   (b) Calculate the length
       of PR.
   (c) Find ∠QPR.

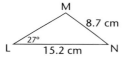

3   In triangle ABC, AB = 4.6 cm, BC = 7.5 cm
    and AC = 8.1 cm. Calculate angle ACB.

4   In this diagram, triangle ABC is isosceles.

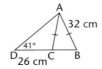

   (a) Calculate ∠DAC.
   (b) Calculate the length of CB.

5   From A, the angle of elevation of the top a
    building is 16°.

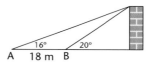

    From B, 18 m nearer the building, it is 20°.
    How tall is the building?

6   A square-based pyramid has a base with edges
    of length 10 cm, two slant edges of length 12 cm
    and two slant edges of length 14 cm.
    Two of the faces of the pyramid are isosceles
    triangles.

   (a) Calculate the surface area of the pyramid.
   (b) Calculate the angle between the smallest
       triangular face and the base of the
       pyramid.

TRANSFORMATIONS

Transforming shapes means changing them in some way. The shape you start with is called the **object**; the result of changing the shape is called the image.

Reflections need a mirror line. Every point on the object is the same distance from the mirror as the corresponding point on the image.

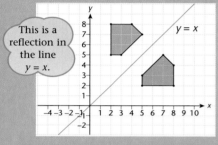

This is a reflection in the line $y = x$.

Rotations need a centre, an angle of rotation and a direction of rotation.

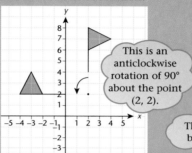

This is an anticlockwise rotation of 90° about the point (2, 2).

Translation is a sliding movement. **Vectors** are used to describe translations.

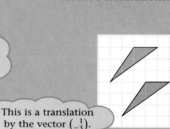

This is a translation by the vector $\binom{1}{-3}$.

Enlargements need a scale factor and a centre of the enlargement. Even if the object becomes smaller, it is still called an enlargement.

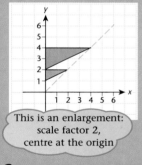

This is an enlargement: scale factor 2, centre at the origin

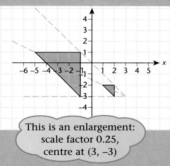

This is an enlargement: scale factor 0.25, centre at (3, −3)

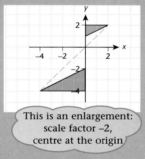

This is an enlargement: scale factor −2, centre at the origin

COMBINING TRANSFORMATIONS

Two reflections in intersecting lines, AB and AC, meeting at angle θ, are equivalent to a rotation of 2θ about A.

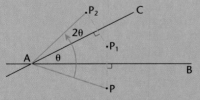

Two reflections in parallel lines produce a translation which is twice the distance between the lines and perpendicular to them.

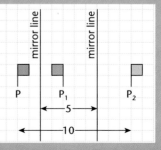

Two enlargements with the same centre and with scale factors h and k, are equivalent to an enlargement with the same centre and with scale factor hk. This works for both positive and negative scale factors.

Nelson GCSE Maths   REVISION GUIDE: SHAPE, SPACE AND MEASURES (HIGHER)

1 (a) In a translation, the point (1, 7) maps to the point (–3, 4).
What is the vector for this translation?

(b) In a translation, the point (2, 1) maps to the point (7, 3).
To what point does (–2, 7) map in this translation?

2 (a) Draw this shape and its reflection in the line y = x. Call the image P.

(b) Reflect P in the line y = 1.
Call this image Q.

(c) What transformation maps the original shape on to Q?

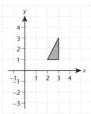

3 (a) Draw this shape and rotate it 90° clockwise about the point (1, 0).
Call the image U.

(b) Reflect U in the line x = 1.
Call this image V.

(c) What transformation maps the original shape on to V?

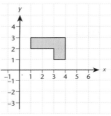

4 (a) An enlargement has centre (2, 0) and the point P is at (8, 2).
If the image of P is (14, 4), what is the scale factor of the enlargement?

(b) If a different enlargement has the same centre and its scale factor is $\frac{1}{2}$, what are the coordinates of the image of P?

5 (a) Draw axes with x between 0 and 9 and y between –5 and 9.
Draw the triangle PQR where P is at (2, 1), Q is at (4, 1) and R is at (4, 4).

(b) Enlarge triangle PQR by scale factor 2, using (0, 0) as the centre of enlargement.
Label the image P'Q'R'.

(c) Enlarge P'Q'R' by scale factor $-\frac{1}{2}$, using (6, 0) as the centre of enlargement.
Label the image P''Q''R''.

(d) What transformation maps PQR to P''Q''R''?

(e) If a scale factor of $\frac{1}{2}$ is used in part (c) instead of a scale factor of $-\frac{1}{2}$, what transformation maps PQR to P''Q''R'' in this case?

6 Give an example for each of these to show that the statement is false.
A: Two reflections always combine to give a rotation.

B: Two enlargements always combine to give an enlargement.

C: Two rotations always combine to give a rotation.

7 (a) Study these shapes.
Describe fully the single transformation which will map
(i) A onto C,
(ii) B onto C.

(b) Copy the diagram, and on it, draw the image of B

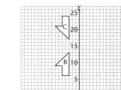
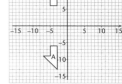

(i) under a reflection in the y-axis, labelling this image D,

(ii) under a rotation of 180° about 0, labelling this image E,

(iii) under a rotation of 90° anticlockwise about 0, labelling this image F.

(c) Describe fully, **two** successive transformations which are together equivalent to a reflection in the x-axis.
CCEA 1998

8 Copy this diagram which shows three triangles A, B and C.

(a) Describe fully the single transformation which maps triangle A onto triangle B.

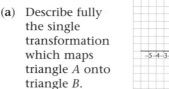
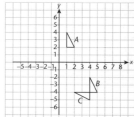

(b) Describe fully the single transformation which maps triangle B onto triangle C.

(c) P is a clockwise rotation of 90° with centre (3, –2).
Q is a reflection in the line y = x – 1.

Triangle B maps onto triangle D by P followed by Q.
Draw triangle D on your diagram.
SEG 2000 specimen

MATRICES (CCEA ONLY)

Reflection in the x-axis transforms the point (x, y) to the point $(x, -y)$, and can be expressed like this:

$$\begin{pmatrix} x_1 \\ y_1 \end{pmatrix} = \begin{pmatrix} 1 & 0 \\ 0 & -1 \end{pmatrix}\begin{pmatrix} x \\ y \end{pmatrix} = \begin{pmatrix} x \\ -y \end{pmatrix}$$

Here are some more matrices for transformations.

> Given a matrix, you can investigate what transformation it represents by applying it to particular points written as column vectors.

$$\begin{pmatrix} 0 & -1 \\ -1 & 0 \end{pmatrix} \qquad \begin{pmatrix} 0 & -1 \\ 1 & 0 \end{pmatrix} \qquad \begin{pmatrix} 2 & 0 \\ 0 & 2 \end{pmatrix}$$

Reflection in $y = -x$ Rotation anticlockwise through 90°   Enlargement, centre the origin, scale factor 2

This is the rule for matrix multiplication:

$$\begin{pmatrix} x_1 \\ y_1 \end{pmatrix} = \begin{pmatrix} a & b \\ c & d \end{pmatrix}\begin{pmatrix} x \\ y \end{pmatrix} = \begin{pmatrix} ax + by \\ cx + dy \end{pmatrix}$$

1 (a) Write down a matrix which represents each of these transformations.

    (i) Reflection in the line $y = x$

    (ii) Enlargement with centre the origin and scale factor 3.

(b) Hence, or otherwise, find a matrix which represents reflection in $y = x$ followed by enlargement with centre the origin and scale factor 3.

2 Triangle T has vertices at $(2, 4)$, $(3, 1)$ and $(0, 0)$.

(a) Draw triangle T on a coordinate grid and transform it using this matrix.

$$\begin{pmatrix} 0.8 & 0.6 \\ 0.6 & -0.8 \end{pmatrix}$$

Label the image T′.

(b) Describe the transformation represented by this matrix as clearly as possible.

3 On graph paper, draw the triangle ABC with vertices A $(-2, 2)$, B $(-4, 6)$ and C $(-6, 4)$.

(a) Draw the image of the triangle ABC under the transformation defined by the matrix

$$\begin{pmatrix} 1 & 0 \\ 0 & -1 \end{pmatrix}$$

Label this image $A_1B_1C_1$.

(b) Draw the image of the triangle $A_1B_1C_1$ under the transformation defined by the matrix

$$\begin{pmatrix} -1 & 0 \\ 0 & -1 \end{pmatrix}$$

Label this image $A_2B_2C_2$.

(c) Describe in geometrical terms the transformation of

    (i) triangle ABC onto triangle $A_2B_2C_2$,

    (ii) triangle $A_1B_1C_1$ onto triangle $A_2B_2C_2$.

CCEA 1996

4

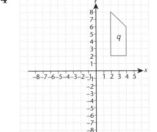

(a) (i) Draw the image of q under a reflection in the x-axis followed by a reflection in the line $y = x$. Label this image q'.

    (ii) Describe fully the single transformation which maps q to q'.

(b) (i) Draw the image of q under a rotation of 180° about the origin followed by an enlargement, scale factor $-\frac{1}{2}$, centre the origin. Label this image q''.

    (ii) Describe fully the single transformation which is the inverse of the combination of transformations in **(b) (i)**.

    (iii) Find the 2×2 matrix associated with the transformation which maps q'' to q.

CCEA 1995

5 (a) Copy this diagram on to squared paper.

(b) Transform the triangle Q using this matrix.

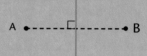

$$\begin{pmatrix} 1 & 1 \\ -1 & 1 \end{pmatrix}$$

Label the image R.

(c) The transformation defined by this matrix is a rotation followed by an enlargement. Find the centre and angle of the rotation and the centre and scale factor of the enlargement.

S12 LOCUS

The **locus** of a point that is always a constant distance away from a fixed point is a **circle**.

The locus of a point which is equidistant from two fixed points A and B is the **perpendicular bisector** of the line joining A and B.

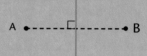

This is the locus of a point that is always a constant distance from a line of fixed length.

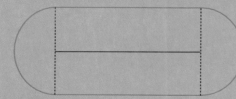

The locus of a point which is equidistant from two fixed lines is made up of both **angle bisectors** of the two lines.

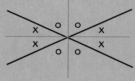

S13 explains how to construct perpendicular bisectors and angle bisectors, using a compass.

If A and B are fixed points, the locus of a point X, such that ∠AXB is fixed, consists of the arcs of two circles.

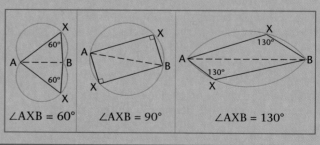

$\angle AXB = 60°$ $\angle AXB = 90°$ $\angle AXB = 130°$

1 (a) Mark two points, X and Y, 8 cm apart.

(b) Draw the locus of points that are 6 cm from Y.

(c) Draw the locus of points that are equidistant from X and Y.

(d) Shade the region where the points are less than 6 cm from Y and are nearer to X than to Y.

2 (a) Draw a rectangle with sides of length 5 cm and 3 cm.

(b) Draw the locus of points that are *inside* the rectangle and 1 cm from its perimeter.

(c) Draw the locus of points that are *outside* the rectangle and 1 cm away from its perimeter.

3 A new tree is being put into this garden.

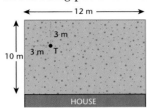

It must follow these three rules.

A: It must be at least 4 m from the house.

B: It must be at least 2 m from the other three edges of the garden.

C: It must be more than 4 m from an existing tree (T).

Draw the garden to a scale of 2 cm to 1 m.
Shade the region where the tree may be put.

4 The letter L is made from two perpendicular rods *AB* and *BC*.

AB = 3 cm, *BC* = 2 cm.

The letter L is rotated through 90° clockwise about the point *C*.

Draw accurately the locus of the point *A*.

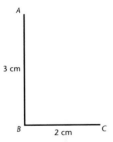

SEG 1996

5 The shape of a flower bed is an equilateral triangle joined to a semicircle.

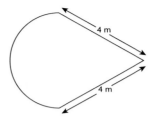

(a) Draw an accurate plan of the flower bed using a scale of 1 cm to represent 1 metre.

(b) A path is made around the flower bed. The outer edge of the path is 2 metres from the flower bed all the way round. Draw accurately the outer edge of the path on your plan.

6 The diagram shows a rectangle *ABCD* standing on a horizontal table. *AB* = 5 cm, *BC* = 3 cm. The rectangle is rotated clockwise in its own plane about *C* until *BC* is horizontal. It is then rotated clockwise about *B* until *AB* is horizontal.

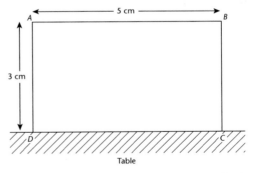

(a) Copy the diagram and construct the locus of the point *A*.

(b) Calculate the length of the path of *A*.

NEAB 1996

S13 RULER AND COMPASS CONSTRUCTIONS

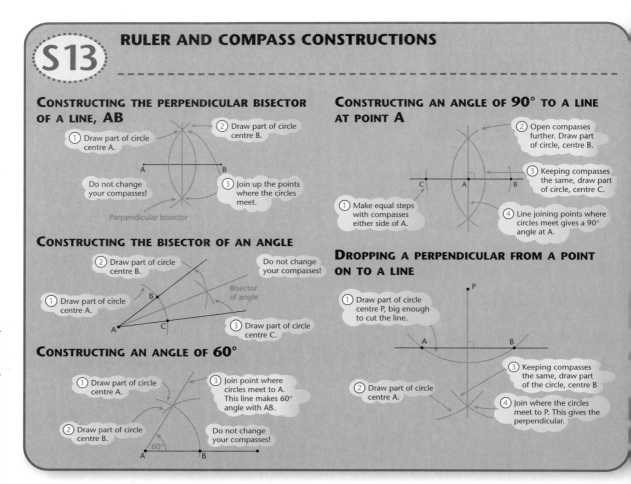

CONSTRUCTING THE PERPENDICULAR BISECTOR OF A LINE, AB

① Draw part of circle centre A.

② Draw part of circle centre B.

Do not change your compasses!

③ Join up the points where the circles meet.

Perpendicular bisector

CONSTRUCTING THE BISECTOR OF AN ANGLE

② Draw part of circle centre B.

Do not change your compasses!

Bisector of angle

① Draw part of circle centre A.

③ Draw part of circle centre C.

CONSTRUCTING AN ANGLE OF 60°

① Draw part of circle centre A.

③ Join point where circles meet to A. This line makes 60° angle with AB.

② Draw part of circle centre B.

Do not change your compasses!

60°

CONSTRUCTING AN ANGLE OF 90° TO A LINE AT POINT A

② Open compasses further. Draw part of circle, centre B.

③ Keeping compasses the same, draw part of circle, centre C.

① Make equal steps with compasses either side of A.

④ Line joining points where circles meet gives a 90° angle at A.

DROPPING A PERPENDICULAR FROM A POINT ON TO A LINE

① Draw part of circle centre P, big enough to cut the line.

③ Keeping compasses the same, draw part of the circle, centre B

② Draw part of circle centre A.

④ Join where the circles meet to P. This gives the perpendicular.

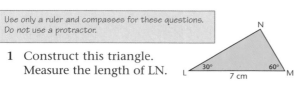

Use only a ruler and compasses for these questions. Do not use a protractor.

1 Construct this triangle. Measure the length of LN.

2 (a) Construct this triangle accurately.

(b) Construct a perpendicular from B on to AC. Measure the length of this perpendicular.

3 Draw a circle with radius 4 cm. Construct a square which has its vertices on the circle. Measure the side of the square.

4 Construct an isosceles triangle with two equal sides of length 7 cm and angles of 30°, 75° and 75°. Measure the shortest side of the triangle.

5 (a) Construct a triangle with sides of length 6 cm, 7 cm and 8 cm.

(b) By constructing the perpendicular bisectors of two of the sides, construct the circle which passes through all the vertices of this triangle.

6 (a) Construct a triangle with sides 8 cm, 10 cm and 11 cm.

(b) By constructing two angle bisectors, construct the circle which lies inside the triangle and touches each of its sides.

7 (a) Construct a triangle with sides 6 cm, 7 cm and 8 cm.

(b) Drop perpendiculars from the vertices of the triangle on to the opposite sides.

(c) What do you notice about the three perpendiculars you have drawn?

S14 UNITS OF MEASUREMENT, CONVERSIONS AND COMPOUND MEASURES, INCLUDING SPEED AND DENSITY

METRIC MEASURES

Length
1 km	= 1000 m	
1 m	= 100 cm	= 1000 mm
1 cm	= 10 mm	

Mass or weight
1 tonne	= 1000 kg
1 kg	= 1000 g

Capacity or volume
1 litre	= 1000 ml	= 1000 cm^3
1 m^3	= 1000 litres	
1 cm^3	= 1 ml	

IMPERIAL MEASURES

Length
1 mile	= 1760 yards	
1 yard	= 3 feet	= 36 inches
1 foot	= 12 inches	

Mass or weight
1 pound (lb)	= 16 ounces (oz)
14 pounds	= 1 stone

Capacity or volume
1 gallon	= 8 pints

RELATIONSHIP BETWEEN METRIC AND IMPERIAL UNITS

Length
1 mile is about 1.6 km
1 foot is about 30 cm
1 metre is a bit more than a yard

Mass or weight
1 kilogram is about 2.2 lb
1 ounce is about 30 g

Capacity or volume
1 litre is about $1\frac{3}{4}$ pints
1 gallon is about 4.5 litres

> Also remember: 1 cm^3 of water weighs 1 g.

SPEED

Speed = distance ÷ time

DENSITY

Density = mass ÷ volume

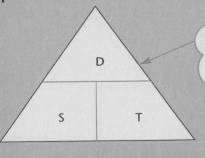

These triangles may help you to remember the three formulae connected with speed and density

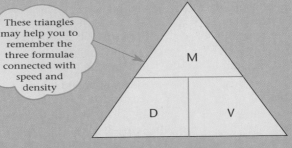

Do not use a calculator for Questions 1 to 8.

1 This sign can be seen outside French towns, warning of a 50 k.p.h. speed limit.

Is 30 m.p.h. slower, or faster, than this? Show your working.

2 Estimate how much longer a metre is than a yard. Give your answer in inches.

3 A car holds 6 gallons of petrol when full. If it is filled up from empty with petrol costing 52.3p per litre, estimate how much it will cost to the nearest pound.

4 One weighing scale gave my weight as 56.00 kg.
   Another gave is as 58.20 kg.
   What was the difference in weight in pounds?

5 An aeroplane's average speed is 360 m.p.h.
   How far will it travel at this speed
   (a) in 2 hours?
   (b) in 20 minutes?
   (c) in 3 hours 10 minutes?
   (d) in 1 hour 8 minutes?

6 A spacecraft is travelling at 12.4 km per second.
   Write this speed
   (a) in kilometres per minute
   (b) in metres per second

7 Iron has a density of 7900 kg/m^3.
   (a) What is this in
      (i) kg/cm^3?
      (ii) g/cm^3?
   (b) What is the mass of 0.8m^3 of iron?

8 A piece of cork with a volume of 4 cm^3
   weighs 3.5 g.
   What is the density of the cork?

9 The density of the planet Mercury is 5 400 kg/m^3
   and its mass is 3.3×10^{23} kg.
   What is the planet's volume?

10 A car starts from rest and reaches a speed of
   50 m.p.h. in 11 seconds.
   What is the average acceleration of the car in
   miles/second^2?

S15 UPPER AND LOWER BOUNDS OF MEASURED AND CALCULATED VALUES

Something might be measured as 19 cm to the **nearest centimetre**. This means that
- the upper bound for its length is 19.5 cm, and
- the lower bound for its length is 18.5 cm.

Another way of writing this is 19 cm ± 0.5 cm.

Something might be measured as 18.3 cm to the **nearest millimetre**. This means that
- the upper bound for its length is 18.35 cm, and
- the lower bound for its length is 18.25 cm.

Another way of writing this is 18.3 cm ± 0.05 cm.

Something might be measured as 85 g to the **nearest 5 grams**. This means that
- the upper bound for its mass (weight) is 87.5 g, and
- the lower bound for its mass is 82.5 g.

Another way of writing this is 85 g ± 2.5 g.

When an answer is calculated, you have to think carefully about how to obtain the upper and lower bounds.
Someone travels 10 miles (to the nearest mile) in 15 minutes (to the nearest minute).
Upper bound of speed is 10.5 miles ÷ 14.5 minutes = 0.724 miles per minute = 43.4 m.p.h.

> Use *upper* bound of distance   Use *lower* bound of time

Lower bound of speed is 9.5 miles ÷ 15.5 minutes = 0.613 miles per minute = 36.8 m.p.h.

> Use *lower* bound of distance   Use *upper* bound of time

So, the speed is somewhere between 36.8 m.p.h. and 43.4 m.p.h.

1 The population of a town is estimated to be 26 800 to the nearest 100. The town covers an area of 130 km² correct to the nearest 10 km². Find upper and lower bounds for

(a) the population of the town

(b) the area of the town

(c) the population of the town per square metre.

2 (a) The winning time for a 100-metre race was given as 10.34 seconds to the nearest 0.01 seconds.
What are the upper and lower bounds for this time?

(b) The 100 metres was measured correct to the nearest 5 cm.
Find the upper and lower bounds for the average speed of the winner.

3 (a) A car is travelling at a speed of 66 m.p.h. measured to the nearest 2 m.p.h.
What are the upper and lower bounds for the speed?

(b) It travels at this speed for 1 hour 50 minutes to the nearest 5 minutes.
What are the upper and lower bounds for the distance covered?

4 The area of a rectangle is 56 cm² to the nearest cm². The length of the rectangle is 8.4 cm to 2 significant figures.
Find the upper and lower bounds for the width of the rectangle.

5 (a) The sides of a rectangle have dimensions 20 cm and 30 cm each measured to the nearest centimetre.
Calculate the smallest possible area of the rectangle.

(b) The sides of a square have length x cm measured to the nearest centimetre.
Write down and simplify an expression, in terms of x, for the difference between the largest and smallest possible areas of the square.

SEG 1998

6

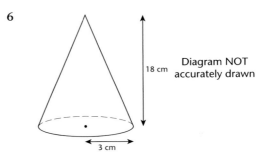

18 cm   Diagram NOT accurately drawn

3 cm

A cone has a height of 18 cm and the radius of its base is 3 cm.

(a) Calculate the volume of the cone.

The measurements of the cone are correct to the nearest millimetre.

(b) Write down the lower bound of the radius of the cone.

(c) Calculate the difference between the upper and lower bounds of the volume of the cone expressed as a percentage of the volume of the cone found in part (a).

Edexcel 1997

AREAS AND PERIMETERS OF TRIANGLES, QUADRILATERALS AND CIRCLES, INCLUDING SEGMENTS AND SECTORS

AREA OF A TRIANGLE

The area of any triangle is $\frac{1}{2} \times$ **base** $\times$ **height**.
The height must always be measured at right angles to the base.
The base may be in any orientation.
Area $= \frac{1}{2} \times 5\,\text{cm} \times 4\,\text{cm} = 10\,\text{cm}^2$

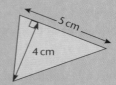

> In this triangle, the base is 5 cm and the height is 4 cm.

AREA OF A PARALLELOGRAM

All these parallelograms have the same area, because they have the same base and height.

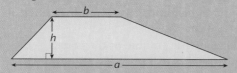

Area $= 3\,\text{cm} \times 2\,\text{cm} = 6\,\text{cm}^2$
The area of any parallelogram is **base** $\times$ **height**.

AREA OF A TRAPEZIUM

Area of trapezium is half the sum of the parallel sides × height.
$A = \frac{1}{2}(a + b)h$

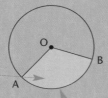

AREA OF A CIRCLE

Area of a circle $= \pi \times$ radius $\times$ radius
$= \pi r^2$

PERIMETER

The **perimeter** of a shape is the distance around its boundary.

CIRCUMFERENCE OF A CIRCLE

Circumference of a circle $= \pi \times$ diameter
$= \pi d$
$= 2\pi r$

SECTORS AND SEGMENTS

> The area of a **sector** OAB can be found by finding the appropriate fraction of the area of the circle.

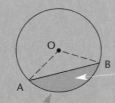

> The area of a **segment** can be found by finding the area of the sector OAB and subtracting the area of the isosceles triangle OAB.

> The length of the **arc** AB can be found by finding the appropriate fraction of the circumference of the circle.

Do not use a calculator for Questions 7, 8 and 9.

1 Find the areas of these shapes.

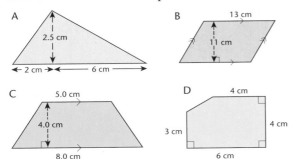

2 Calculate the area of this sign.

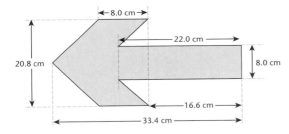

3 The wheel of a child's bicycle rotates 12 times as it moves along 10 m.
Find the diameter of the wheel to the nearest centimetre.

4 A window is made up of a semicircle and a rectangle.

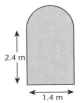

(a) Find the area of the window.

(b) Find the perimeter of the window.

5 A disc of radius 2.36 cm is fitted on to a square of side 4.72 cm as shown.

Find the shaded area.

6 A circle has a circumference of 28.4 cm. Find its area.

7 In the diagram, *ABCD* is a parallelogram. Calculate the area of this parallelogram.

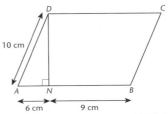

OCR 2000 specimen

8 (a) A circle has a diameter of 5 cm.
Find its circumference and area in terms of π.

(b) The area inside a circle is 36π cm^2.
Find the radius of the circle.

9 (a) These circles have the same centre and their radii are 4 cm and 6 cm.
Find the blue area in terms of π.

(b) In this diagram, the area of the red circle is 4 times the area of the blue circle.
The diameter of the outer circle is 10 cm.

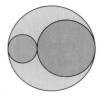

Find the green area in terms of π.

10 This 60° sector is cut from a circle of radius 5.4 cm.

    (a) Find the area of the sector.

    (b) Find the perimeter of
         the sector.

11 Find the area of the blue segment.

12 The diameter of this circle is 10 cm.
    The length of the chord is 7 cm.

    Find the area of the red segment.

13

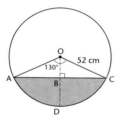

The diagram shows the circular cross-section of
a cylindrical oil storage tank.

The radius of the tank is 52 cm and angle
AOC = 130°.

(a) Calculate the area of the sector OADC.

(b) The length of the tank is 1.5 m.
     How many litres of oil are lying in
     the tank?

(c) Calculate the external surface area of the
     cylindrical tank.

CCEA 1996

14 The diagram shows the cross-section of the
framework for a railway station.

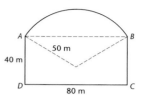

The roof is an arc of a circle, radius 50 m.

(a) Calculate the arc length AB of the roof.

(b) Calculate the area of the cross-section.

SEG 1995

15

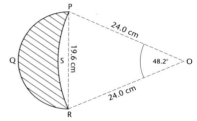

The crescent, shaded in the diagram, is like
that found on many flags.

PSR is an arc of a circle, centre 0 and radius 24.0 m.

Angle POR = 48.2°.

PQR is a semicircle on PR as diameter,
where PR = 19.6 cm.

Calculate, correct to 3 significant figures,

(a) the perimeter of the crescent,

(b) the area of the sector POR.

CCEA 1996

VOLUME AND SURFACE AREA OF PRISMS, PYRAMIDS, CONES AND SPHERES

VOLUME AND SURFACE AREA OF A CUBOID

The volume of a cuboid is
length × width × height

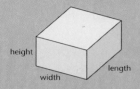

To find the surface area of a cuboid,
find the areas of the six rectangular faces,
and add them.

VOLUME OF A CYLINDER

A **cylinder** is a prism with a circular cross-section.
Volume of a cylinder
= area of circular base × height
= $\pi r^2 h$

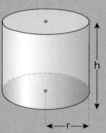

SURFACE AREA OF A CYLINDER

Curved surface area of a cylinder
= circumference of circular end × h
= π × diameter × h
= $2\pi r h$

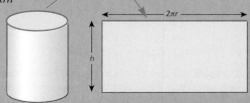

If the cylinder has a base, you need to add πr^2 for the
area of the base.
If it has both ends closed, you need to add another πr^2.
So, the total surface area of a closed (or solid)
cylinder = $2\pi r h + 2\pi r^2$.

VOLUME OF A PRISM

Volume of a prism
= area of base × height

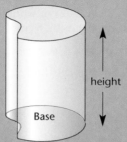

VOLUME OF A PYRAMID

Volume of a pyramid = $\frac{1}{3}$ × area of base × height

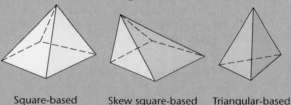

Square-based   Skew square-based   Triangular-based
pyramid   pyramid   pyramid or
                                            tetrahedron

VOLUME AND SURFACE AREA OF A SPHERE

Volume of a sphere = $\frac{4}{3}\pi r^3$
Surface area of a sphere = $4\pi r^2$

VOLUME AND SURFACE AREA OF A CONE

Volume of a cone = $\frac{1}{3}$ × area of base × height = $\frac{1}{3}\pi r^2 h$

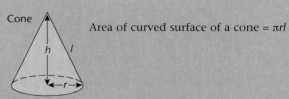

Cone   Area of curved surface of a cone = $\pi r l$

Do not use a calculator for Questions 1, 2, 6, 8 and 12.

1 The volume of a cuboid is 168 cm^3.
   Its length is 7cm and its height is 4 cm.

   (a) Find its width.

   (b) Find its surface area.

2 How many cuboids 5 cm by 3 cm by 2 cm would fit into a cuboid box 12 cm by 10 cm by 8 cm? Describe how they would fit in.

3 160 litres of liquid are poured into this tank. How deep is the liquid?

4 A cuboid has two square ends with edge length 7 cm. Its surface area is 238 cm^2. Find the volume of the cuboid.

5 This cylindrical can has a diameter of 7.4 cm and a height of 11.6 cm.

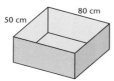

   (a) Calculate the volume of the can.

   (b) This label goes round the can with an overlap of 1 cm.

   What are the dimensions of the label?

6 Look at this wedge.

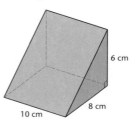

   Find its volume and surface area.

7 The water in this swimming pool has a cross-section in the shape of a trapezium. The water is 1 m deep at the shallow end and 1.8 m deep at the deep end.

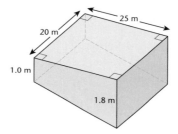

   Find the volume of water in the pool in

   (a) m^3

   (b) litres

8

   A cylindrical can of orange juice has an internal base radius of 3 cm and a volume of 310 ml.

   Taking $\pi = 3.1$, calculate the internal height of the can, giving your answer correct to the nearest centimetre.

   OCR 2000 specimen

9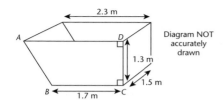

2.3 m

Diagram NOT
accurately
drawn

1.3 m

1.5 m

A   *D*

B   1.7 m   *C*

A skip is in the shape of a prism with
cross-section *ABCD*.
AD = 2.3 m, *DC* = 1.3 m and *BC* = 1.7 m.
The width of the skip is 1.5 m.

(a) Calculate the area of the shape *ABCD*.

(b) Calculate the volume of the skip.

The weight of an empty skip is 650 kg.
The skip is full to the top with sand.
1 m³ of sand weighs 4300 kg.

(c) Calculate the total weight of the skip
and the sand.

Edexcel 1998

0 A square-based pyramid has a volume of 26 cm³
and a height of 3.7 cm.
Find the perimeter of its base.

1 A spherical ball bearing has a volume of 35.0 mm³.
Find its surface area.

2 A sphere has a volume of 36π cm³.
Find its surface area in terms of π.

3 (a) Find the volume of a cone with a base of
diameter 5.6 cm and a height of 9.4 cm.

(b) This conical container has a depth of
12.8 cm and holds 174 cm³.

12.8 cm

What is the radius of the top of the
container?

(c) The container is filled with water to a
depth of 6.4 cm.
The water in it is poured into a cylinder
with diameter 4 cm.
How deep is the water in this cylinder?

14 A circular cone of paper is made by joining the
two radii of this yellow sector.

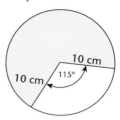

10 cm

10 cm

115°

Find the volume of the cone.

15 A container is in the shape of a truncated cone.
The diameter of its base is 12 cm and the
diameter of its top is 24 cm.
The container is 10 cm high.

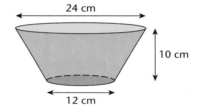

24 cm

10 cm

12 cm

Find the volume of the container.

LENGTH

In formulae for **length**, each term consists of just one length.

- $2(l + w)$ = perimeter of a rectangle
- $2\pi r$ = circumference of a circle
- $\dfrac{2A}{h}$ = base of a triangle given its area and height

r = radius	A = area
h = height	V = volume
l = length	
w = width	

AREA

In formulae for **area**, each term consists of two lengths multiplied together.

- lw = area of a rectangle
- πr^2 = area of a circle
- $2\pi rh + 2\pi r^2$ = surface area of a cylinder
- $\dfrac{V}{h}$ = cross-section of a prism, given its volume and height

VOLUME

In formulae for **volume**, each term consists of three lengths multiplied together.

- lwh = volume of a cuboid
- $\pi r^2 h$ = volume of a cylinder
- Ah = volume of a prism, given its cross-sectional area and length

---

1 In these formulae, each of the letters represents a length.
Which formulae could be for a length?
Which could be for an area?

$$\pi d \qquad a + 2c \qquad \pi ab$$

$$r\sqrt{p^2 + q^2} \qquad \pi(a + b) \qquad \frac{ab}{2}$$

2 In these formulae, each of the letters represents a length.
Which of the formulae could be for a volume?

$$2ab + d \qquad a(a + c) \qquad 4p^2q \qquad xy\sqrt{u^2 + v^2}$$

3

> In Question 3, r and h are lengths,
> A is an area and V is a volume.

Pick which formulae are for length, which for area and which for volume. One is for none of these.

$$\frac{V}{h} \qquad \pi r^2 A \qquad \sqrt[3]{\frac{3V}{4\pi}}$$

$$2\pi r(r + h) \qquad \sqrt{\frac{V}{\pi h}}$$

4 The letters a and b represent lengths.
State whether the following formulae could represent areas.
Write YES or NO for each formula.

(a) $\dfrac{a^2}{\pi}$ (b) $\pi(a^2 + b^2)$

(c) $\dfrac{(a^3 + 3a^2b^2 + b^3)}{(a + b)}$ (d) $a(a + b)$

NEAB 1996

5 The diagram represents a solid shape.

From the expressions below, choose the one that represents the volume of the solid shape.
π and $\frac{1}{3}$ are numbers which have no dimensions.
a, b and h are lengths.

$\frac{1}{3}\pi(b^2 - ab + a^2)$, $\frac{1}{3}\pi h(b^2 + ab + a^2)$,

$\frac{1}{3}\pi h^2(b^2 - a^2)$, $\frac{1}{3}\pi(a^2 + b^2)$, $\frac{1}{3}\pi h^2(b^2 - ab + a^2)$.

Write down the correct expression.

Edexcel 1997

SIMILAR FIGURES AND SIMILAR SOLIDS

SIMILARITY

In Mathematics, two shapes are **similar** if they are the same shape; they can be a different size.

Two similar rectangles

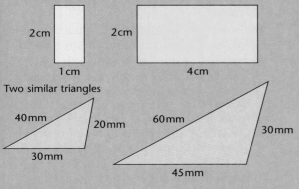

Two similar triangles

If two shapes are similar their sides are in the same ratio.

This result can be used to calculate missing lengths.

Example

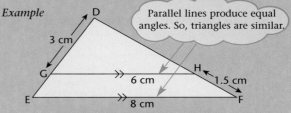

Parallel lines produce equal angles. So, triangles are similar.

The lengths in triangle DEF are $\frac{8}{6}$ times those in triangle DGH.

So, length of DE = $\frac{8}{6} \times 3$cm = 4 cm

So, GE is 4 cm – 3 cm = 1 cm, which is $\frac{1}{3}$ of GD.

Hence, FH is $\frac{1}{3}$ of DH. So, DH is 3 × 1.5 cm, i.e. 4.5 cm.

SIMILAR TRIANGLES

A pair of triangles are similar when

- their angles are equal
- all three of the sides of one are in the same ratio to the corresponding sides of the other (the ratio is the 'scale factor of the enlargement')
- two pairs of sides are in the same ratio and the included angles are equal.

AREAS AND VOLUMES OF SIMILAR SHAPES

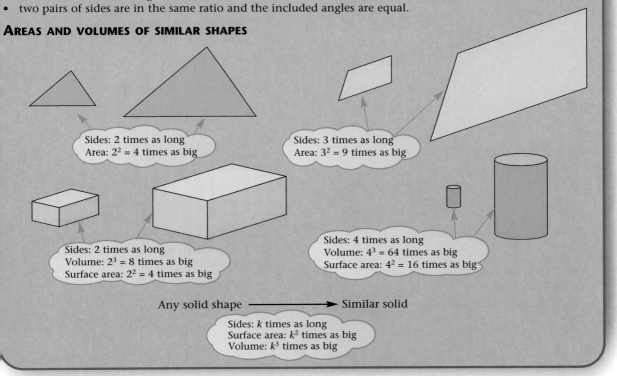

Sides: 2 times as long
Area: 2^2 = 4 times as big

Sides: 3 times as long
Area: 3^2 = 9 times as big

Sides: 2 times as long
Volume: 2^3 = 8 times as big
Surface area: 2^2 = 4 times as big

Sides: 4 times as long
Volume: 4^3 = 64 times as big
Surface area: 4^2 = 16 times as big

Any solid shape $\longrightarrow$ Similar solid

Sides: k times as long
Surface area: k^2 times as big
Volume: k^3 times as big

1 (a) Explain why these are similar triangles.

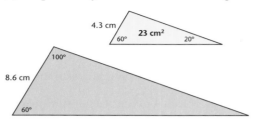

(b) Find the area of the larger triangle.

2

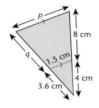

Diagram NOT accurately drawn

$AB : AC = 1 : 3$

(i) Work out the length of CD.

(ii) Work out the length of BC.

Edexcel 1998

3 Calculate the lengths marked p and q in this diagram.

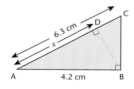

4 Look at this diagram.

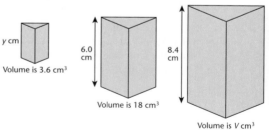

(a) Explain why triangles ABC and ADB are similar.

(b) Calculate the length of AD.

5 A soap powder manufacturer is proposing to market its soap in packets of three new sizes.

Small: 3 cm by 12 cm by 18 cm

Medium: To contain 8 times as much powder as small

Economy: Two of the dimensions are 9 cm and 54 cm

All the packets are to be similar.

(a) Find the dimensions of the medium size packet.

(b) How many small packets contain the same amount of soap as the economy packet?

(c) The size of the printing on each packet means that the printing covers the same percentage of the area on all three packets. A letter, O, on the small packet encloses an area of $2.2\,cm^2$. What area does the corresponding letter O on the economy size enclose?

6 The capacity of a railway truck is $12\,m^3$. A scale model of it has a capacity of $0.0015\,m^3$. The length of the model is 11 cm. What is the length of the real truck?

7 On a map drawn to a scale of 1:25 000, a park covers an area of $1.6\,cm^2$. What is the real area of the park

(a) in m^2?

(b) in km^2?

8 These prisms are similar.

Calculate the values of y and V to an appropriate degree of accuracy.

9   Everything for a doll's house is made to a scale
    of $\frac{1}{12}$th.
    Copy and complete this table.

	Real	Model
Area of dining room floor to be tiled	12.5 m²	
Area of bedroom rug		53.3 cm²
Length of stair carpet rod	38 cm	
Number of treads on stairs between 1st and 2nd floor	18	
Capacity of wardrobe		610 cm³

10 Two cones are similar.
    The ratio of their height is 3:2.
    Calculate the ratio of

    (a) their base areas

    (b) their volumes

11 The diagram below represents a rolling pin
    made from three pieces of wood.
    The central part of the rolling pin is a cylinder
    of length 20.5 cm and radius 2.5 cm.
    The handles are cylindrical with
    hemispherical ends.
    The cylindrical handles and their hemispherical
    ends each have a radius of 0.5 cm.
    The total length of the rolling pin is 40.5 cm.

    (a) Calculate the total volume of the rolling pin.

    (b) Another wooden rolling pin is **similar** to
         this rolling pin but all its dimensions are
         1.2 times larger. Using the answer to (a),
         calculate the volume of the larger rolling pin.
         WJEC 1998

12 The sloping sides of a flower bowl are part of a
    cone as shown.

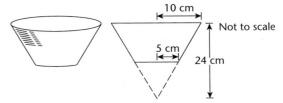

    The radius of the top of the bowl is 10 cm and
    the radius of the bottom of the bowl is 5 cm.
    The height of the full cone is 24 cm.

    (a) Calculate the volume of the full cone.

    (b) **By using similar figures**, calculate the
         volume of the flower bowl.
         NEAB 1996

COMBINING VECTORS

If $\mathbf{u} = \binom{4}{2}$ and $\mathbf{v} = \binom{3}{-5}$ then $\mathbf{u} + \mathbf{v} = \binom{7}{-3}$ and $\mathbf{v} - \mathbf{u} = \binom{3}{-5} - \binom{4}{2} = \binom{-1}{-7}$

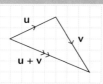

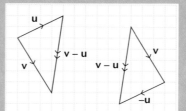

RESULTANT VELOCITIES

A boat being steered across a river 80 m wide at 5 m/s in a current of 2 m/s.

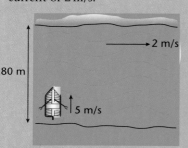

Distance triangle
Boat ends up 32 m downstream on the opposite bank.

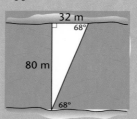

Velocity triangle
Boat travels at 5.4 m/s at 68° to the downstream bank.

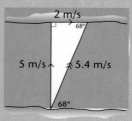

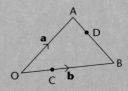

Resultant forces can be found in the same way.

VECTOR GEOMETRY

$\overrightarrow{OA} = \mathbf{a}$, $\overrightarrow{OB} = \mathbf{b}$. $\overrightarrow{AB} = \mathbf{b} - \mathbf{a}$

C is a point one-third of the way along OB. So $\overrightarrow{OC} = \frac{1}{3}\mathbf{b}$.

D is a point one-third of the way along AB. $\overrightarrow{AD} = \frac{1}{3}\overrightarrow{AB} = \frac{1}{3}(\mathbf{b} - \mathbf{a})$

$\overrightarrow{OD} = \overrightarrow{OA} + \overrightarrow{AD} = \mathbf{a} + \frac{1}{3}(\mathbf{b} - \mathbf{a}) = \frac{2}{3}\mathbf{a} + \frac{1}{3}\mathbf{b}$

$\overrightarrow{CD} = \overrightarrow{CO} + \overrightarrow{OA} + \overrightarrow{AD} = -\frac{1}{3}\mathbf{b} + \mathbf{a} + \frac{1}{3}(\mathbf{b} - \mathbf{a}) = \frac{2}{3}\mathbf{a}$

This tells you that CD is parallel to OA and $\frac{2}{3}$ of its length.

1 If $\mathbf{a} = \binom{-2}{4}$ and $\mathbf{b} = \binom{1}{-3}$, find column vectors for

  (a) $2\mathbf{a}$ (b) $-3\mathbf{b}$ (c) $\mathbf{a} + 2\mathbf{b}$

2 In this diagram,
$\overrightarrow{OA} = \mathbf{a}$, $\overrightarrow{OB} = \mathbf{b}$,
$\overrightarrow{OC} = \frac{1}{4}\overrightarrow{OB}$ and $\overrightarrow{AD} = \frac{1}{4}\overrightarrow{AB}$.

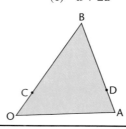

(a) Express $\overrightarrow{OC}$ in terms of $\mathbf{b}$.

(b) Express $\overrightarrow{AB}$ and $\overrightarrow{AD}$ in terms of $\mathbf{a}$ and $\mathbf{b}$.

(c) Express $\overrightarrow{CD}$ in terms of $\mathbf{a}$ and $\mathbf{b}$.

(d) What do your results tell you about triangle BCD?

3 In parallelogram OACB, $\overrightarrow{OA} = \mathbf{a}$ and $\overrightarrow{OB} = \mathbf{b}$.

$\overrightarrow{OP} = \frac{3}{4}\overrightarrow{OC}$

$\overrightarrow{BQ} = \frac{2}{3}\overrightarrow{BC}$

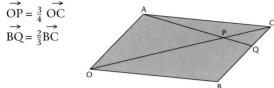

(a) Find $\overrightarrow{OP}$ and $\overrightarrow{OQ}$ in terms of $\mathbf{a}$ and $\mathbf{b}$.

(b) Show that A, P and Q lie on a straight line and state the ratio AP:PQ.

4 *ABCD* is a parallelogram. The diagonals of the parallelogram intersect at *0*.

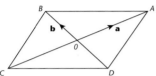

$\overrightarrow{OA} = \mathbf{a}$ and $\overrightarrow{OB} = \mathbf{b}$.

(a) Write an expression, in terms of $\mathbf{a}$ and $\mathbf{b}$, for

    (i) $\overrightarrow{CA}$,   (ii) $\overrightarrow{BA}$,   (iii) $\overrightarrow{BC}$.

X is the point such that $\overrightarrow{OX} = 2\mathbf{a} - \mathbf{b}$.

(b) (i) Write down an expression, in terms of $\mathbf{a}$ and $\mathbf{b}$, for $\overrightarrow{AX}$.

    (ii) Explain why B, A and X lie on the same straight line.

Edexcel 1997

5 A pilot wishes to fly to a point West of his starting position. The plane's speed relative to the air is 250 km/h. There is a wind of 35 km/h from the South West.
In which direction should the pilot head?

6 Two forces are acting on an object, as shown.

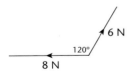

Find the magnitude of the resultant force and the angle it makes with the 6N force.

7 A boat sets from a pier, P, to travel to a landing at a tree. T, across a straight river.
The river is 40 metres wide and the tree is 20 m downstream from a point directly opposite the pier, P.
In still water the boat can travel at 1.5 m/s.
The river flows at 0.9 m/s.

(a) Show that if the boat steers in a perpendicular direction to the bank it will end up 4 metres past the tree.

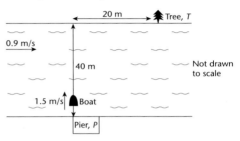

(b) What angle, θ, relative to the river bank should the **boat steer** to cross to the tree, T?

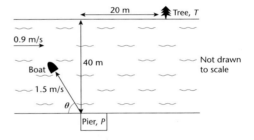

NEAB 1999

8 A ship, whose speed in still water is 20 km per hour, sets course due West.

The ship is driven off course by a current flowing due South-West at 5 km per hour.

(a) Draw an accurate vector diagram to show the resultant speed and direction of the ship. [Use a scale of 1 cm to represent 2 km per hour.]

(b) (i) What is the resultant speed of the ship? Give your answer to the nearest 0.1 km per hour.

    (ii) What is the resultant direction of the ship? Give your answer as a 3 figure bearing correct to the nearest degree.

Edexcel 1995

1 The inside lane of a race track consists of two straights, 110 m long, and two semicircles (as shown).

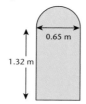

(a) Does a 400-m race need *more* than, or *less* than, one lap of this track?

(b) Calculate the area inside the track.

2 This diagram shows a design for a window in the shape of a semicircle above a rectangle. What area of glass is needed for it?

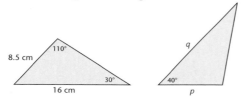

3 (a) These triangles are congruent.

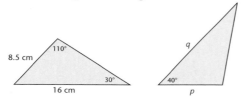

Find the lengths marked *p* and *q*.

(b) Explain why triangles ABC and ADE are similar.

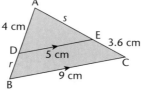

Find the lengths marked *r* and *s*.

4 ABC is an equilateral triangle with sides of length 7 cm.

(a) Construct ABC accurately.

(b) By accurate construction shade the set of points inside the triangle that are nearer to A than to B, nearer to BC than AB and more than 4 cm from A.

5 Here are some expressions.

$\pi r^2 l$	$2\pi r^2$	$4\pi r^3$	$abrl$	$\dfrac{abl}{r}$	$3(a^2 + b^2)r$	$\pi r l$

The letters *r*, *l*, *a* and *b* represent lengths. π, 2, 3 and 4 are numbers that have no dimensions.

Three of the expressions represent volumes. Which ones are they?

Edexcel 199

6 Mr and Mrs Snow travelled to Mrs Snow's mother for the weekend.

They travelled 83 miles, correct to the nearest mile and the journey took 2 hours and 10 minutes, correct to the nearest five minutes. Find upper and lower bounds for the average speed of the journey.

7 This diagram shows the net of a pyramid. Square A has sides of length 3.6 cm and the triangles B and C are isosceles.

(a) Calculate the surface area of the pyramid.

(b) Calculate the volume of the shape formed by three of these pyramids stuck together.

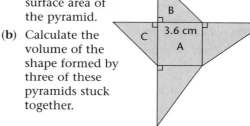

8 (a) Draw a triangle LMN in which LM is 5.6 cm MN is 7.3 cm and LN is 8.4 cm. Measure ∠LMN.

(b) Find ∠LMN by calculation.

9

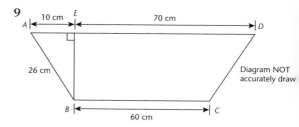

In triangle *ABE*, *AB* = 26 cm, *AE* = 10 cm and angle *AEB* = 90°.

(a) Calculate the length of *BE*.

(b) Calculate the area of the trapezium *ABCD*.

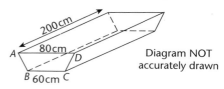

ABCD is the cross section of a trough used in a village competition.
The trough is a prism of length 200 cm.

(c) Calculate the volume of the trough.

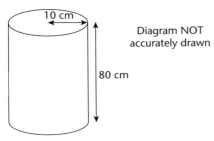

Diagram NOT
accurately drawn

Cylindrical containers are also used in the competition.
Each cylindrical container has radius 10 cm and height 80 cm.

(d) Calculate the volume of one cylindrical container.

In the competition the cylinders are filled with water and emptied into the trough.

(e) What is the least number of cylinders that must be emptied into the trough so that the trough is full?

Edexcel 1996

10 (a) Two litres of liquid are poured into a cylindrical container whose base has a diameter of 12.4 cm.
How deep will the liquid be?

(b) A heavy metal ball with radius 4.3 cm is now placed in the container.
By how much does the level of liquid rise?

11 A farmer's storage container is in the shape of a cylinder with a hemisphere on top.

The height of the cylinder is 9.5 m.

The radius of both the cylinder and the hemisphere is 2.4 m.

(a) Calculate the volume of the farmer's storage container.

(b) The volume of a similar storage container is half the volume of the farmer's container
Calculate the radius of this new container.

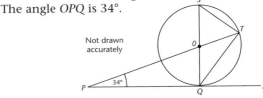

SEG 1996

12 A minor sector *AOB* is cut from a circle of radius 20 cm. Angle *AOB* = 45°.

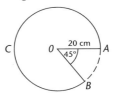

(a) Calculate the length of the arc *ACB*.

The radii *OA* and *OB* are joined without overlap so that a cone is formed, as shown in the diagram.

(b) Calculate

    (i) the base radius of the cone,

    (ii) the volume of the cone.

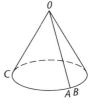

NEAB 1998

13 The line *PQR* is a tangent to a circle with centre *O*.
QS is a diameter of the circle.
T is a point on the circumference of the circle such that *POT* is a straight line.
The angle *OPQ* is 34°.

Not drawn accurately

Calculate the size of angle *TQR*.

NEAB 1998

14 (a) Find the values of *x* between 0 and 360 for which $\frac{1}{2} \tan x° = 1$.

(b) Draw *x*- and *y*-axes for values of *x* from 0 to 360 and for values of *y* from −1 to +1.
Use a scale of 1 cm to 30 units on the *x*-axis, and a scale of 5 cm to one unit on the *y*-axis.

On these axes draw
    (i) the graph of *y* = −cos *x*°, plotting points at intervals of 30°;
    (ii) the graph of $y = \frac{1}{2} \tan x°$.

(c) Write down the solutions of the equation
$$\cos x° + \frac{1}{2} \tan x° = 0$$
for $0 \le x \le 360$.

MEG 1996

QUESTIONNAIRES AND SAMPLING METHODS

D1

SAMPLING METHODS

A sample needs to be as **representative** as possible of the population.
If it is not representative then it is a **biased sample**.

In **simple random sampling**, every item has the same chance of being chosen.
Each item in the population is assigned a number and these numbers are then
drawn out of a hat or selected in some other way through the use of **random numbers**.

> Random numbers can be generated
> using the random number key on a calculator.
> Tables of random numbers
> can also be used.

In **systematic sampling**, each item in the population is assigned a number and then every 10th or 20th
(or whatever) item is chosen.

In **stratified sampling**, the population is divided into subgroups which *do not overlap*, called **strata**. One way
of obtaining a representative sample of a population is to take a separate random sample of each stratum.

> The size of the random sample for
> each stratum needs to be proportional
> to the size of the stratum.

QUESTIONNAIRES

Questions need to be

- clear and unambiguous
- free from bias
- easy to answer and analyse
- not too open ended

TYPES OF DATA

Qualitative data – e.g. hair colour
Discrete data (counting) – e.g. number of children in a family
Continuous data (measuring) – e.g. height in centimetres

---

1   A bus company attempted to estimate the
    number of people who travel on local buses in
    a certain town. They telephoned 100 people in
    the town one evening and asked 'Have you
    travelled by bus in the last week?'

    Nineteen people said 'Yes'. The bus company
    concluded that 19% of the town's population
    travel on local buses.

    Give 3 criticisms of this method of estimation.
    OCR 2000 specimen

2   After plans for a by-pass to a large town were
    announced, the local newspaper received twelve
    letters on the subject. Eleven were opposed to it.
    The newspaper claimed:

    > 'OVER 90% ARE AGAINST NEW BY-PASS'

    (a) Give **two** reasons why the newspaper could
        be criticised for making this claim.

    (b) The local council is to carry out a survey to
        find the true nature of local opinion.
        Give **two** factors that should be taken into
        account when selecting the sample.

    NEAB 1997

3 (a) You wish to take a sample of a population.
Give **two** factors that you should consider when selecting your sample.

Jenny wants to test this hypothesis:

> Among car drivers with more than 5 years' experience, women drivers are less likely than men to have had an accident.

Jenny questions a random sample of 100 people.

(b) Why might this sample not be suitable?

(c) Design a questionnaire which Jenny could use.
NEAB 1996

4 A head teacher wants to survey his pupils' opinions about a new catering system.
There are eight hundred pupils in the school, of whom two hundred are in the sixth form.

How should the headteacher select a sample of fifty pupils for his survey?
MEG 1998

5 You have been asked to do a survey of the eating habits of the students in a Sixth Form College.

The grid below shows the number of students.

	Year 12	Year 13
Boys	253	198
Girls	201	222

You want your results to give a reliable representation of the students in the college. Explain how you will choose your sample, giving reasons.
NEAB 2000 specimen

6 (a) A random sample of 100 adults from a particular residential area of a city is required. One suggested method was to select at random 100 households from the area and then to select at random one adult from each household. Explain briefly why this method will not produce a random sample.

(b) Use the following extract from a table of random digits to obtain a random sample of size 5 from a group of 47 people. Describe your method.

29975   55493   07248   33929   17032
03027   51025   54854   29533   03451
WJEC 2000 specimen

D2 FREQUENCY POLYGONS AND PIE CHARTS

FREQUENCY POLYGON

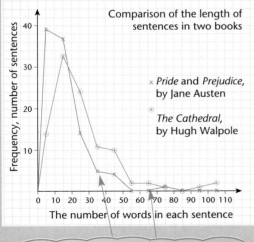

Comparison of the length of sentences in two books

x *Pride* and *Prejudice*, by Jane Austen

⊙ *The Cathedral*, by Hugh Walpole

Frequency, number of sentences

The number of words in each sentence

The points are plotted against the mid-points of the class intervals

PIE CHART

Type of transport	Number of children	Size of angle in pie chart
Car	13	$13 \times 12° = 156°$
Bus	5	$5 \times 12° = 60°$
Train	1	$1 \times 12° = 12°$
Cycle	2	$2 \times 12° = 24°$
Walk	9	$9 \times 12° = 108°$
Total	30	$360°$

How do you get to school?

☐ Car
☐ Bus
☐ Train
☐ Cycle
☐ Walk

There are 30 students altogether. So, each student is represented by $360° \div 30 = 12°$

1 Megtown Villa played 36 matches last season. They were watched by crowds of the following sizes.

11462	17584	8470	13460	21230	12464
18471	15000	14964	17852	19701	21400
12956	8465	12842	7465	9740	10061
7407	18560	17004	9846	17046	8470
23742	15642	9470	3900	16420	14710
19407	9649	18729	11214	12473	16872

(a) Copy and complete this table.

Size of crowd	Tally	Number of matches
0 to 4999		
5000 to 9999		
10000 to 14999		
15000 to 19999		
20000 to 24999		

(b) Using axes like this, draw a frequency polygon to show this information.

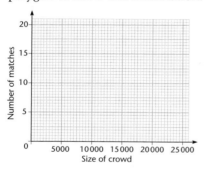

MEG 1996

2 A gardener tests a fertiliser.
He grows some tomatoes with the fertiliser and some without.
He records the weights of all the tomatoes grown.

weight (grams)	frequency with fertiliser	without fertiliser
$50 < W \leq 100$	10	2
$100 < W \leq 150$	15	42
$150 < W \leq 200$	55	46
$200 < W \leq 250$	53	41
$250 < W \leq 300$	17	34
$300 < W \leq 350$	8	1

(a) Draw a frequency polygon for each distribution on a grid like this, clearly indicating which is **with fertiliser**, and which is **without fertiliser**.

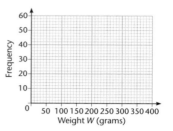

(b) Use the frequency polygons to compare the effects of the fertiliser.

NEAB 1996

3 (a) The pie chart shows the nutritional content of **white** bread.

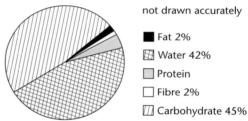

not drawn accurately

■ Fat 2%
▨ Water 42%
▢ Protein
☐ Fibre 2%
▥ Carbohydrate 45%

(i) What percentage of the nutritional content is protein?

(ii) What size of angle should represent carbohydrate in an accurate diagram?

(b) The nutritional content of **wholemeal** bread may be represented in a pie chart using the following angles:

Fat	11°
Water	151°
Protein	36°
Fibre	
Carbohydrate	137°

(i) What size of angle represents fibre?

(ii) What percentage of the total nutritional content of wholemeal bread is carbohydrate?

(c) Draw a pie chart showing the nutritional content of **wholemeal** bread.

(d) A diet that is high in fibre and low in carbohydrate is said to be good for people who are watching their weight. Compare the content of each of the 2 kinds of bread and decide which type of bread these people should eat. Give **two** reasons for your answer.

CCEA 1998

4 The length of a new born baby is partly its head, partly its body and partly its legs. This pie chart shows the proportion of the length contributed by each. The size of each angle at the centre of the pie chart is marked.

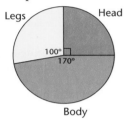

(a) What percentage of the baby's length is contributed by the baby's legs?

(b) The baby's head is 12.5 cm long. How long are the baby's legs?

5 This pie chart shows the distribution of types of land use within a country park.
The grass area is 1.6 times the area consisting of rocks and bare ground.

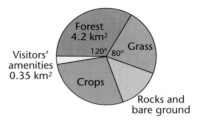

(a) Find the angle of the visitors' amenities sector.

(b) Find the area which is rocks and bare ground.

(c) Find the percentage of land devoted to crops.

EQUAL CLASS INTERVALS

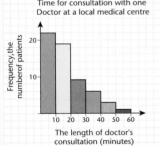

Time for consultation with one Doctor at a local medical centre

Frequency, the number of patients

The length of doctor's consultation (minutes)

> The **area** of each bar represents the frequency.

UNEQUAL CLASS INTERVALS

Time taken to complete test (*t* secs)	Frequency (*f*)	Class width (*w*)	Frequency density (*f* ÷ *w*)
$0 \le t < 10$	1	10	0.1
$10 \le t < 30$	4	20	0.2
$30 \le t < 45$	3	15	0.2
$45 \le t < 50$	2	5	0.4
$50 \le t < 60$	3	10	0.3

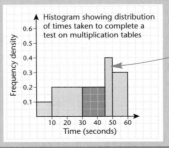

Histogram showing distribution of times taken to complete a test on multiplication tables

Frequency density

Time (seconds)

> The **modal group** is 45–50 seconds, because it has the tallest bar. It is *not* 10–30 seconds (which has the highest frequency in the table).

1 Kim sowed some seeds in her greenhouse. 10 weeks later she measured the heights of the plants. Some of the results are shown in the table and the histogram.

Height (*h*) in cm	Number of plants
0 < *h* ≤ 5	0
5 < *h* ≤ 20	30
20 < *h* ≤ 30	120
30 < *h* ≤ 35	
35 < *h* ≤ 40	
40 < *h* ≤ 50	96
Over 50	0

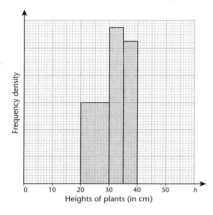

(a) Use the information to copy and complete the table and the histogram.

Kim had sown 500 seeds.

(b) Calculate the number of seeds that had not produced plants.

Edexcel 1997

2 The unfinished histogram and table show information about the salaries, in pounds, of the teachers at Mathstown High School.

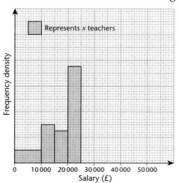

Salary (*s*) in pounds	Frequency
0 ≤ *s* < 10 000	4
10 000 ≤ *s* < 15 000	6
15 000 ≤ *s* < 20 000	5
20 000 ≤ *s* < 25 000	.....
25 000 ≤ *s* < 30 000	8
30 000 ≤ *s* < 50 000	4

(a) Calculate the value of *x*.

(b) Use the information in the histogram to copy and complete the table.

(c) Use the information in the table to copy and complete the histogram.

Edexcel 199

3 As the 124 members of sixth form handed over the money they had raised by taking part in a sponsored walk along the coastal path, one of the prefects made a tally chart which sorted the sixth-formers into groups.

The following frequency table was produced from the tally chart, where *C*(£) is the amount raised by an individual sixth-former.

Amount Collected *C*(£)	Number of Sixth-Formers
0 < *C* ≤ 10	20
10 < *C* ≤ 15	21
15 < *C* ≤ 20	32
20 < *C* ≤ 25	28
25 < *C* ≤ 37.5	23

Illustrate this table by constructing a histogram on graph paper.
Use a scale of 2 cm to represent £5, and an area of 1 cm² to represent 1 sixth-former.

CCEA 199

4 Students finishing a word-processing course had their speeds measured in characters per minute (ch/min) with the following results.

Speed (in ch/min)	Number of students
100 –	20
300 –	34
350 –	40
400 –	32
450 –	28
500 –	12
600 and over	0

Using axes like these, draw a histogram to display these data.

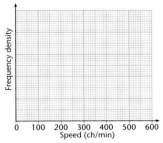

MEG 1996

5   A company manufactures various types of light bulbs. One type of bulb manufactured by the company is considered to be environmentally friendly since bulbs of this type have a long lifetime. The lifetimes, in thousands of hours, of a sample of 50 bulbs of this type are measured and the results are summarised in the grouped frequency distribution below.

Lifetime, x (1000 s hours)	Number of bulbs, f	Frequency density
$6 \leq x < 10$	4	
$10 \leq x < 12$	15	
$12 \leq x < 14$	19	
$14 \leq x < 16$	8	
$16 \leq x < 20$	4	

   (a) Work out the frequency density column in the table and draw a histogram of the data in the table using axes like those in (b).

(b) Another company also manufactures an environmentally friendly light bulb. The lifetimes, in thousands of hours, of a sample of these bulbs are also measured. The results are shown in the histogram below.

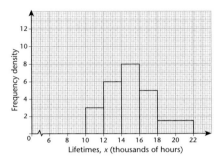

Estimate the proportion of the light bulbs manufactured by the second company that last longer than 15 000 hours.

(c) **By comparing the two histograms**, and giving a reason for your answer, comment on which of the two companies manufactures the most environmentally friendly light bulbs.
WJEC 1998

D4   **SCATTER DIAGRAMS AND LINES OF BEST FIT**

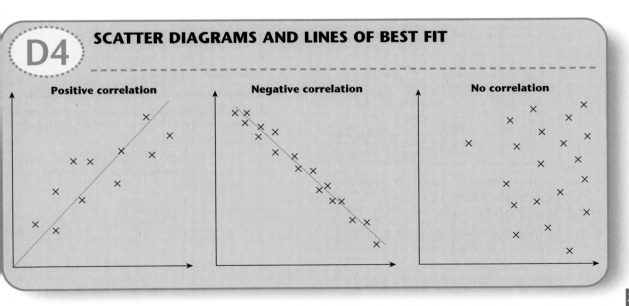

Positive correlation   Negative correlation   No correlation

1 These pairs of test results were gained by students in Geography and History. The Geography test was out of 70 and the History test out of 40.

Geog.	Hist.
58	30
54	31
61	33
37	24
30	24
43	31
65	34
51	30
27	20
48	28

Geog.	Hist.
41	27
37	26
44	35
54	33
43	27
56	29
56	33
36	27
66	37
34	23

(a) Plot the results on a scatter diagram.

(b) A student obtained 60 marks in the Geography test but was absent for the History test.
Estimate the History mark for this student.

(c) Comment on this statement.

Students who are poor at Geography are good at History.

2 This table shows the price and age of some second-hand cars.

Age	Price
2	3500
3	2400
1	5450
4	2000
5	1750
2	3050
3	3000
6	1500
2	3750
3	3950

(a) Plot the points on a scatter diagram and describe the correlation.

(b) Draw a line of best fit.

(c) Estimate the cost of a second-hand car which is 3 years 6 months old.

(d) A second-hand car costs £3250.
What age would you expect it to be?

3 The table shows the results of an analysis of the performance of 7 cricketers.

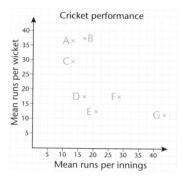
Cricket performance

(a) What evidence is there to support this statement?

Good bowlers are poor batsmen.

(b) Which cricketer is the worst bowler in the group?

(c) Which cricketer bowls very well and is giving a good performance at batting?

4 Nine students of different ages were set the same mental Mathematics test.
Here are the results.

Student	A	B	C	D	E	F	G	H	I
Age (years and months)	12y 9m	10y 11m	13y 10m	14y 2m	11y 10m	14y 5m	12y 8m	13y 2m	14y 1m
Test score (percentage)	80	45	65	87	58	63	69	60	80

(a) Plot this data on a scatter diagram.

(b) Describe the correlation between the ages and the test scores.

(c) Draw a line of best fit on your diagram.

(d) Use your diagram to decide what a typical student aged 13 years 6 months might be expected to score.

(e) Taking age into account, to which student would you award a prize for the best performance?

5 This table shows the number of hours of sunshine and the maximum temperature in ten British towns one day in February.

Town	Hours of sunshine	Maximum temperature (°C)
Aberdeen	0.8	10
Anglesey	0.4	9
Bournemouth	3.6	12
Bristol	0.4	10
Clacton	0.9	11
Colwyn Bay	0.2	11
Fishguard	1.1	7
Hunstanton	0	8
Saunton	1.8	11
Southsea	3.9	12

(a) Plot this data on a scatter diagram.

(b) Describe the correlation between hours of sunshine and maximum temperature.

(c) Plot the point that represents the mean number of hours sunshine and the mean maximum temperature.

(d) Which towns were above the mean for both sunshine and temperature?

(e) Which town was colder than you might expect from considering the number of hours of sunshine?

D5   MEANS OF FREQUENCY DISTRIBUTIONS

MEAN OF A FREQUENCY DISTRIBUTION

Example: Find the mean number of children in the families of this Y10 class.

Number of children	1	2	3	4	5
Frequency	6	12	4	2	1

> This means that there are four families with 3 children.

Number of children	Frequency of children	Total number
1	6	6 × 1 = 6
2	12	12 × 2 = 24
3	4	4 × 3 = 12
4	2	2 × 4 = 8
5	1	1 × 5 = 5
Total	25	55

> 55 ÷ 25 = 2.2
> So, the mean number of children is 2.2 children.

MEAN OF GROUPED FREQUENCY DISTRIBUTION

Example: Find the mean hand span of students in this Y10 class.

Hand span (*h*cm)	Frequency	Middle value	Frequency × middle value
$16 \leq h < 17$	3	16.5	3 × 16.5 = 49.5
$17 \leq h < 18$	2	17.5	2 × 17.5 = 35
$18 \leq h < 19$	1	18.5	1 × 18.5 = 18.5
$19 \leq h < 20$	4	19.5	4 × 19.5 = 78
$20 \leq h < 21$	4	20.5	4 × 20.5 = 82
$21 \leq h < 22$	2	21.5	2 × 21.5 = 43
$22 \leq h < 23$	4	22.5	4 × 22.5 = 90
$23 \leq h < 24$	2	23.5	2 × 23.5 = 47
Total	22		443

> The mean hand span is 443 cm ÷ 22 = 20.1 cm (to 1 d.p.)

Nelson GCSE Maths   REVISION GUIDE: HANDLING DATA (HIGHER)

1 A survey was carried out to find out how much time was needed by a group of pupils to complete homework set on a particular Monday evening.

The results are shown in the table below.

Time, t hours, spent on homework	Number of pupils
0	3
$0 < t \leq 1$	14
$1 < t \leq 2$	17
$2 < t \leq 3$	3
$3 < t \leq 4$	1

Calculate an estimate for the mean time spent on homework by the pupils in the group.

Edexcel 1997

2 These are the diameters of a sample of bolts.

Diameter (cm)	2.737–2.739	2.740–2.742	2.743–2.745	2.746–2.748	2.749–2.751	2.752–2.754	2.755–2.757	2.758–2.760
Frequency	4	12	16	30	36	24	8	2

Estimate the mean diameter.

3 The first 500 words of a book were examined to find the number of letters in each word.

Number of letters in each word	Number of words
1	25
2	24
3	44
4	76
5	109
6	93
7	78
8	42
9	5
10	2
11	2

(a) Calculate the mean number of letters in a word.

(b) Write down the median and the modal number of letters in a word.

(c) Another 5 books are analysed in a similar way.

This table shows the results.

	Median	Range
Book 1	5	7
Book 2	4	12
Book 3	7	14
Book 4	6	12
Book 5	5	13

Explain why these statements might be true.

(i) Book 1 is easier to read than Book 5 because the range is smaller.

(ii) Book 2 is easier to read than Book 4 because the median is smaller.

4 Some women walked one mile.

The time taken by each was recorded.

The results are as follows.

Time t minutes	$12 \leq t < 16$	$16 \leq t < 20$	$20 \leq t < 24$	$24 \leq t < 28$	$28 \leq t < 32$
Number of women	1	9	43	22	5

(a) (i) What is the modal class for the time taken?

(ii) Calculate an estimate of the mean time taken.

One mile is approximately 1.6 km.

(b) Use the data to calculate an estimate of the mean time taken by these women to walk one kilometre.

SEG 1998

5 This table shows the heights of the Y10 students in two Maths classes.

(a) Work out an estimate for the mean height.

(b) Calculate an estimate for the mean height in feet and inches.

Height (cm)	Frequency
155–159	1
160–164	8
165–169	19
170–174	9
175–179	9
180–184	7
185–189	1

WJEC 1998

There are more questions on means of frequency distributions on page 277.

MEDIAN AND QUARTILES FOR SMALL DATA SETS

These are the marks obtained by 13 students in a test.

14, 12, 22, 34, 23, 61, 49, 27, 31, 43, 27, 33, 62

List the marks in order of size.

12, 14, **22**, 23, 27, 27, **31**, 33, 34, **43**, 49, 61, 62

Lower quartile (median of data below the median)

Median (middle number)

Upper quartile (median of data above the median)

Interquartile range = upper quartile – lower quartile
= 46 – 22.5
= 23.5

This measures how spread out the results are.

MEDIAN AND QUARTILES FOR LARGE DATA SETS: CUMULATIVE FREQUENCY

These are the ages of people in a sports club.

Age (years)	Frequency	Cumulative frequency
$10 \leq y < 20$	4	4
$20 \leq y < 30$	33	37
$30 \leq y < 40$	60	97
$40 \leq y < 50$	41	138
$50 \leq y < 60$	22	160
Total	160	

To work out the numbers in this column: add up the frequencies as you go along e.g. 4 + 33 = 37.

These should be the same.

Use the upper bound of the class interval and the cumulative frequency for plotting points. So, plot (20,4), (30, 37), (40, 97), (50, 138) and (60, 22).

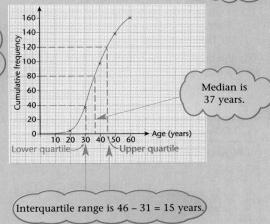

Median is 37 years.

Interquartile range is 46 – 31 = 15 years.

---

1 This cumulative frequency curve shows the distribution of heights among adult men.

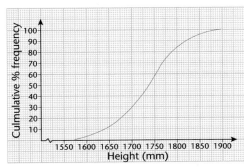

(a) Use the graph to find the median height for adult men.

(b) Find the 5th and 95th percentiles.

(c) The doorway to a garden shed is 1.63 m high. What percentage of men would have to duck their heads when going into this shed?

(d)
FRANKIE'S NIGHT CLUB
....
Bouncer needed
Must be at least 6 feet tall

What percentage of men are tall enough for the job?

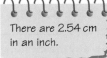

There are 2.54 cm in an inch.

2 This graph shows the population survival rates in a 'developed' country and a 'developing' country.

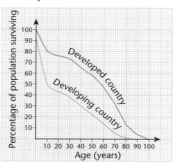

(a) Estimate the median age of death for each country.

(b) Estimate the interquartile range of ages of death for each country.

(c) Estimate the percentage of the population surviving beyond 15 years of age in each of the countries.

(d) Estimate the percentage of the population surviving beyond 65 years of age in each of the countries.

3 A secretary conducted a survey of the weights of 500 letters posted one week.

Weight in grams (w)	Frequency
$0 \leq w < 10$	52
$10 \leq w < 20$	157
$20 \leq w < 30$	125
$30 \leq w < 40$	71
$40 \leq w < 50$	51
$50 \leq w < 60$	44

(a) Construct a cumulative frequency table.

(b) Draw a cumulative frequency graph.

(c) Find the median weight of the letters.

(d) How many letters weighed more than 45 grams?

4 A tele-sales manager monitored the length of telephone calls made by the team.
This data was the result.

Length of call (t minutes)	$0 < t \leq 1$	$1 \leq t < 2$	$2 \leq t < 3$	$3 \leq t < 4$	$t \geq 4$
Frequency	52	204	109	33	2

(a) Draw a cumulative frequency graph for this data.

(b) From the graph estimate the median length of the telephone calls.

(c) The manager wishes to avoid calls that are longer than necessary.
A policy statement is published.

At present 25% of calls are longer than 3 minutes, and company employees should make efforts to reduce the time of calls.

Explain why this statement is inaccurate.

5 The table below shows a grouped frequency distribution of the ages, in complete years, of the 80 people taking part in a carnival in 1997

Age in years	0 to 29	30 to 39	40 to 49	50 to 59	60 to 69	70 to 89
Frequency	2	18	27	18	12	3

(a) Copy and complete this cumulative frequency table.

Age (less than)	30	40	50	60	70	90
Cumulative frequency						

(b) On graph paper, draw a cumulative frequency diagram to show these results.

(c) Copy this table which shows the median, lower quartile, upper quartile and inter-quartile range for the ages of the people taking part in the carnival for the years 1995 and 1996.

Year	Median	Lower quartile	Upper quartile	Inter-quartile range
1995	60	50	75	25
1996	52	46	60	15
1997				

Use your graph to complete your table for 1997.

(d) One year the local newspaper stated:

"Twenty-five percent of the people taking part in the carnival this year are aged 60 or more."

Which of the three years was it?
Give a reason for your answer.

WJEC 1998

STANDARD DEVIATION

Standard deviation measures how spread out the data is.

FOR SMALL SETS OF DATA
- Find the mean.
- Find the difference between each item of data and the mean.
- Square these differences.
- Add up all these squared differences.
- Divide by the number of items of data.
- Square root the answer.

This method gives a standard deviation of 12.1 for these ten GCSE mock exam marks.

63, 64, 63, 38, 64, 44, 81, 60, 44, 61

> You can also use the statistical functions on your calculator to find means and standard deviations.

FORMULAE
These formulae are given on your GCSE paper.

$$s = \sqrt{\frac{\Sigma(x - \bar{x})^2}{n}}$$

> This is the formula for the method explained on the left.

$$s = \sqrt{\frac{\Sigma x^2}{n} - \left(\frac{\Sigma x}{n}\right)^2}$$

> This alternative form might be easier to use in some circumstances.

FOR A FREQUENCY DISTRIBUTION
This shows the earnings of staff working at a hotel.

An estimate for the mean wage is £98 and for the standard deviation is £63. Check that you agree.

Wage (£w)	Frequency
$0 \leq w < 50$	18
$50 \leq w < 100$	22
$100 \leq w < 150$	28
$150 \leq w < 200$	6
$200 \leq w < 300$	2
$300 \leq w < 500$	1

FINDING THE MEAN AND STANDARD DEVIATION WHEN THE DATA IS CHANGED

	Mean	Standard deviation
Original data	m	s
Add 5	$m + 5$	s
Subtract 10	$m - 10$	s
Multiply by 3	$3m$	$3s$
Divide by 2	$\frac{m}{2}$	$\frac{s}{2}$
Multiply by 4 and subtract 3	$4m - 3$	$4s$

Nelson GCSE Maths   REVISION GUIDE: HANDLING DATA (HIGHER)

---

1 Mary plants 12 seedlings. She plants 6 in one tray and 6 in another.

She treats the second tray with 'MightyGro' fertiliser.
After a month she measures the plants.
The treated plants have heights of

12.6 cm,   13.1 cm,   11.4 cm,   12.0 cm,
11.6 cm,   11.9 cm.

(a) Calculate the mean and standard deviation of the treated plants.

(b) She finds the heights of the untreated plants have a mean of 11.5 cm and a standard deviation of 1.3 cm.
On the side of the 'MightyGro' packet is a label.

> *MightyGro will increase the height of your plants by 10%.*
>
> *MightyGro will give you plants of a more consistent height.*

Comment on these claims.

NEAB 1998

2 Rashmi recorded the temperature at 12 noon on nine days.
He measured the temperature in degrees Celsius (°C). Here are his results.

18°C, 18°C, 17°C, 22°C, 23°C, 16°C, 19°C, 18°C, 20°C

The mean of these temperatures is 19°C.

(a) Calculate the standard deviation of these temperatures.

To change a temperature from degrees Celsius to degrees Kelvin you add 273.

(b) (i) Write down the mean of Rashmi's data in degrees Kelvin.
(ii) Write down the standard deviation in degrees Kelvin.

Edexcel 1998

3 A set of examination scores has a mean of 27.2 marks and standard deviation of 7.82 marks.

(a) If 5 marks are added to each score, what are the mean and the standard deviation?

(b) If all the original examination scores are doubled, what are the mean and the standard deviation?

SEG 1996

4 In an experiment, Cathy has to take readings of radioactive emissions from six pieces of rock. Her reading are 490, 497, 511, 500, 479 and 484.

(a) Calculate the mean and standard deviation of her readings.

(b) Cathy is told that the electronic counter she was using was faulty and each reading was 10 emissions too high.
Cathy used her original answers for the mean and standard deviation to write down their true values.
Explain how she did this.

(c) Cathy took samples from two sites. The higher the radioactive emissions the more dangerous is the site; 500 is considered to be dangerous. She recorded the following data from the sites A and B.

	Mean	Standard deviation
Site A	485	15
Site B	480	68

Which site is the more dangerous?
Give clear reasons for your answer.

NEAB 2000 specimen

5 The delivery times in days of a sample of 20 first class letters are shown.

1 1 3 1 1 1 1 1 2 1
1 2 4 1 1 1 1 1 2 1

(a) Calculate the mean and the standard deviation of the delivery times.

The delivery times of a sample of 20 second class letters have a mean of 3.1 days and a standard deviation of 1.2 days.

(b) Comment on the differences between the delivery times for first and second class letters.

During bad weather delivery times for second class letters are increased by one day.

(c) How does bad weather change the mean and the standard deviation of the delivery times for second class letters?

SEG 1998

6 There are seven brothers. The oldest is Doc and then, in order of age, there are Bashful, Grumpy, Happy, Dopey, Sneezy and Sleepy. The age gaps are all exactly two years and Sleepy was born today.

(a) (i) Which brother's age is the median age?
(ii) Which brother's age is the mean age?
(iii) Which brother's age is the range of the ages?
(iv) Which brother's age is the standard deviation of the ages?

(b) How will your answers to part (a) change when Sleepy is as old as Dopey is now?

7 The percentage of nitrogen in a new product is being tested. 70 tests produced these results.

Nitrogen (%)	Frequency
4.20	2
4.30	4
4.40	9
4.50	12
4.60	17
4.70	14
4.80	7
4.90	4
5.00	0
5.10	1

(a) Calculate the mean percentage of nitrogen and the standard deviation.

(b) In a subsequent series of tests, it was concluded that the percentage of nitrogen had doubled.
What might the mean and standard deviation have been for these tests?

8 This table shows the quantity of electricity used per week by an office during a period of 52 weeks.

Electricity used (kWh)	Frequency
141–160	1
161–180	4
181–200	6
201–220	9
221–240	12
241–260	7
261–280	6
281–300	4
301–320	3

(a) Estimate the mean and standard deviation for the quantity of electricity used per week.

(b) The office workers are told that they must reduce their consumption of electricity by 10%. What might the mean and standard deviation be if they achieved this target?

9

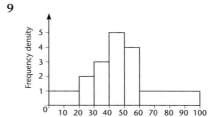

(a) Calculate the standard deviation of the set of data represented in the histogram above. The mean of the data is 47.

(b) Which of the three histograms below represents data with standard deviation nearest to the standard deviation calculated in (a)?

A
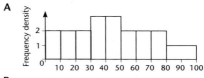

B
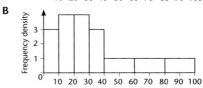

C
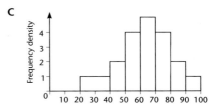

CCEA 1995

BASIC PROBABILITY

EQUALLY LIKELY OUTCOMES

Equally likely outcomes are when all the outcomes have the same chance of happening. To calculate the probability, list all the equally likely outcomes and find how many times the event you want occurs in the list.

$$\text{Probability} = \frac{\text{number of times the event occurs}}{\text{total number of outcomes}}$$

Example: If a dice is thrown, there are six outcomes: 1, 2, 3, 4, 5, 6.
If the event you want is to throw an even number, this occurs three times in the list: 2, 4, 6.
So, the probability of throwing an even number is $\frac{3}{6} = \frac{1}{2}$.

PROBABILITIES OF COMBINED EVENTS

Listing all the possible outcomes is often the quickest method.
Example: What is the probability of obtaining 7 when two dice are thrown and the scores added?

Second dice

	1	2	3	4	5	6
First dice +	1	2	3	4	5	6
1	2	3	4	5	6	7
2	3	4	5	6	7	8
3	4	5	6	7	8	9
4	5	6	7	8	9	10
5	6	7	8	9	10	11
6	7	8	9	10	11	12

There are 36 possible outcomes and six of them are 7.
So, the probability of obtaining 7 is $\frac{6}{36} = \frac{1}{6}$.
For other problems a **tree diagram** is more helpful. See card D10.

---

1 A lorry contains 232 boxes of crisps.
   Each box has either plain crisps or cheese and onion flavour crisps.
   The probability that a box selected at random holds plain crisps is $\frac{1}{3}$ of the probability that the box holds cheese and onion flavour crisps.

   (a) Calculate the number of boxes of plain crisps.

   Each box holds 48 packets of crisps.
   One in every 8 packets of plain crisps has a prize in it. One in every 16 packets of cheese and onion flavour crisps has a prize in it.

   A packet is to be selected at random from the lorry.

   (b) Calculate the probability that the packet will have a prize in it.

   Edexcel 1998

2 A "Lucky Dip" contains some biscuits wrapped in coloured paper.
   The biscuits have different flavours.
   When a biscuit is chosen at random the probability of each flavour is shown in the table.

Flavour	Probability
Mint	0.4
Lime	0.3
Raspberry	0.2
Coffee	0.1

   Half the biscuits are wrapped in green paper.
   All the lime flavoured biscuits are wrapped in green paper, and all the coffee flavoured biscuits are wrapped in brown paper.
   A biscuit is chosen at random.

   (a) What is the probability that it is coffee flavoured **or** wrapped in green paper?

   (b) The probability of getting a biscuit wrapped in green paper is 0.5.
        Explain why the probability of getting a lime flavoured biscuit or a biscuit wrapped in green paper is **not** 0.8.

   (c) There are 50 biscuits in the "Lucky Dip".
        How many of these are lime flavoured?

   SEG 1996

3   What are the probabilities of these events occurring?

   A: Drawing a King from a complete pack of playing cards

   B: Drawing a red ball from a bag containing 5 red and 35 blue balls

   C: Throwing a number greater than 2 with a dice numbered 1 to 6

   D: Winning the first prize in a raffle if you have bought 5 tickets out of the two hundred tickets sold

   E: Picking an odd numbered card from a pack numbered 1 to 12

   F: Drawing a picture card (Jack, Queen or King) from a complete pack of playing cards

4   On a square spinner, each of the numbers 3, 4, 5 and 6 is equally likely to be obtained.

   (a) What is the probability that when this spinner is used the number obtained is
       (i)   even?
       (ii)   prime?
       (iii) even but *not* square?

   (b) This spinner is used twice. What is the probability that
       (i)   the sum of the two numbers obtained is 8?
       (ii)   the difference between the two numbers obtained is greater than 1?
       (iii) the product of the two numbers obtained is a multiple of 4?

D9   ESTIMATING PROBABILITY

Probability can sometimes be estimated from the results of an experiment.

$$\text{Probability} = \frac{\text{number of times the event occurs}}{\text{number of times the experiment takes place}}$$

This is also called **relative frequency**.

Example: If 40 drawing pins are dropped on to a table, and 26 of them land point up, the probability of the drawing pin landing point up is estimated to be $\frac{26}{40}$ (or 0.65 or 65%).

1   400 people were surveyed and asked how many times they had had their hair cut in the last month. Here is the result.

Response	Frequency
Twice or more	98
Once	247
Not had their hair cut	55

If one of these 400 people is chosen at random, what is the probability that in the last month this person

   (a) did not have their hair cut?

   (b) did have their hair cut at least once?

2   Harmeet and Tracey were investigating how often short words were used in English. Tracey counted 200 words and found 43 words with 3 letters or less. Harmeet counted 1000 words and found 272 words with 3 letters or less.

   Each used their results to estimate the probability that, if a word was picked at random from a passage in English, it would have 3 letters or less.

   (a) What estimate did each of them produce?

   (b) State with reasons whose estimate is likely to be more reliable.

3 A bag contains 600 counters. Jason took a counter from the bag, noted its colour and then replaced it. He did this 45 times.
Paula took a counter from the bag and then replaced it. She did this 350 times.
These are their results.

Results	Total number of counters	Number of red counters	Number of blue counters	Number of yellow counters
Jason	45	22	13	10
Paula	350	137	121	92

(a) Use Jason's results to estimate the probability of taking a yellow counter from the bag.

(b) Use Paula's results to estimate the probability of taking a blue counter from the bag.

(c) Use Jason's results to estimate the number of red counters in the bag.

(d) Use Paula's results to estimate the number of red counters in the bag.

(e) Which of your answers to parts (c) and (d) is likely to give a more reliable estimate of the number of counters in the bag? Explain why.

(f) Darren says 'I will obtain a better estimate. I will do the experiment 1000 times.'
Is it sensible for Darren to do the experiment more than 600 times?

4 Two fair spinners are used for a game. The scores from each spinner are added together.

For example: The total score from these two spinners is 4 + 5 = 9.

Tom played the game 500 times and kept a record of how many times he scored a total of 7. He recorded his results in this table.

Number of spins	Total number of 7s	Relative frequency
first 50	13	0.26
first 100	23	0.23
first 150	27	
first 200	38	
first 500	105	

(a) Copy and complete the table by calculating the relative frequencies for 150 spins, 200 spins and 500 spins.

(b) Which of these relative frequency results gives the best estimate of the probability of scoring a total of 7?
Give a reason for your answer.

NEAB 1998

5 Two dice are thrown and the result is obtained by adding the two numbers shown.
Two sets of dice are available.
Set A: one dice has 4 faces numbered 1 to 4 and the other 8 faces numbered 1 to 8.
Set B: each dice has 6 faces numbered from 1 to 6.

(a) Copy and complete a table to show the possible results for each set of dice.

Set A

+	1	2	3	4	5	6	7	8
1								
2								
3								
4								

Set B

+	1	2	3	4	5
1					
2					
3					
4					
5					
6					

(b) In an experiment with one of the sets of dice, these results were obtained.

Dice score	Frequency
2	15
3	25
4	44
5	54
6	68
7	87
8	66
9	54
10	43
11	30
12	14

Calculate the relative frequency for each score.

(c) Which set of dice were being used?
Give reasons for your answer.

PROBABILITY OF COMBINED EVENTS INCLUDING CONDITIONAL PROBABILITY

INDEPENDENT EVENTS

If a red dice and a blue dice are thrown, getting a six on the red dice is **independent** of getting a six on the blue dice.

The probability of a six on both dice is

$\frac{1}{6} \times \frac{1}{6} = \frac{1}{36}$

> When events are independent, the probability of *both* of them happening is found by *multiplying* the probabilities.

MUTUALLY EXCLUSIVE EVENTS

If a dice is thrown, getting a six and getting an odd number are **mutually exclusive** events.

The probability of a six or an odd number is

$\frac{1}{6} + \frac{1}{2} = \frac{2}{3}$

> When events are mutually exclusive, the probability that either one *or* the other happens is found by *adding* the probabilities.

TREE DIAGRAM

Example: A bag contains two red cubes, one blue cube and one yellow cube. One cube is drawn and then replaced. Another cube is drawn.

First draw	Second draw	Outcome	Probability
R	R	RR	$\frac{2}{4} \times \frac{2}{4} = \frac{4}{16}$
	B	RB	$\frac{2}{4} \times \frac{1}{4} = \frac{2}{16}$
	Y	RY	$\frac{2}{4} \times \frac{1}{4} = \frac{2}{16}$
B	R	BR	$\frac{1}{4} \times \frac{2}{4} = \frac{2}{16}$
	B	BB	$\frac{1}{4} \times \frac{1}{4} = \frac{1}{16}$
	Y	BY	$\frac{1}{4} \times \frac{1}{4} = \frac{1}{16}$
Y	R	YR	$\frac{1}{4} \times \frac{2}{4} = \frac{2}{16}$
	B	YB	$\frac{1}{4} \times \frac{1}{4} = \frac{1}{16}$
	Y	YY	$\frac{1}{4} \times \frac{1}{4} = \frac{1}{16}$

> The probability of drawing a red followed by a blue is $\frac{2}{16} = \frac{1}{8}$.

> The probability of drawing one red and one yellow is $\frac{2}{16} + \frac{2}{16} = \frac{4}{16} = \frac{1}{4}$.

CONDITIONAL PROBABILITY

Sometimes the outcome of one event affects the outcome of another.

For example, a card is drawn at random from a normal pack, and then a second card is drawn without replacing the first.

The probability that the second card is an ace depends on whether the first card is an ace. This is an example of **conditional probability**.

First card	2nd card	Outcome	Probability
Ace	Ace	Two aces	$\frac{4}{52} \times \frac{3}{51} = \frac{1}{221}$
	Not an ace	One ace	$\frac{4}{52} \times \frac{48}{51} = \frac{16}{221}$
Not an ace	Ace	One ace	$\frac{48}{52} \times \frac{4}{51} = \frac{16}{221}$
	Not an ace	No aces	$\frac{48}{52} \times \frac{47}{51} = \frac{188}{221}$

> The conditional probability that the second card is an ace if the first card was an ace is $\frac{3}{51}$.

> The probability of one ace is $\frac{16}{221} + \frac{16}{221} = \frac{32}{221}$

> The conditional probability that the second card is an ace if the first card was not an ace is $\frac{4}{51}$.

1 Two counters are drawn at random from a bag containing 3 red, 5 blue and 10 yellow counters. The first counter is replaced before the second is selected.

(a) Copy and complete this tree diagram to show all the possible outcomes.

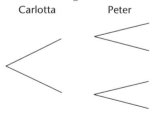

First counter	Second counter	Outcome	Probability
	Red	Red Red	$\frac{3}{18} \times \frac{3}{18} = \frac{9}{324}$
Red	Blue		
	Yellow		
Blue			
Yellow			

(b) What is the probability that
  (i) two blue counters will be drawn?
  (ii) one red and one yellow counter will be drawn?
  (iii) two counters of the same colour will be drawn?
  (iv) two counters of different colours will be drawn?

2 Carlotta and Peter are both members of a walking club. Carlotta goes to 60% of the club's meetings. If Carlotta goes to a meeting the probability that Peter will go is $\frac{2}{3}$. If Carlotta does not go to a meeting the probability that Peter will go is $\frac{1}{4}$.

(a) Use this information to copy and complete this tree diagram.

Carlotta   Peter

(b) Using your tree diagram, find the probability that, for a randomly chosen meeting,
  (i) both Carlotta and Peter will go,
  (ii) neither of them will go.

MEG 1998

3 In a bag, there are 5 red cubes, 3 blue cubes and 4 yellow cubes.
Two cubes are taken at random from the bag *without* replacement.
What is the probability that
(a) both cubes are yellow?
(b) both cubes are the same colour?
(c) neither cube is red?

4 A door has a latch lock, A, and a mortice lock, B, both locked. The porter has a key ring with three latch keys and four mortice keys on it.

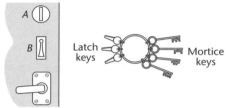

Latch keys   Mortice keys

The Porter does not know which latch key fits lock A or which mortice key fits lock B.
He is equally likely to choose any latch key for lock A and any mortice key for lock B.

(a) What is the probability that the first latch key he chooses will open lock A **and** the first mortice key he chooses will open lock B?

If he chooses a wrong key he will now select from the others.

(b) (i) What is the probability that the first latch key he chooses does not work and the second latch key he chooses will open lock A?
  (ii) What is the probability that he chooses exactly four keys to open both locks?
SEG 1996

5 A toddler is sitting beside some building blocks. Altogether there are three red blocks and six yellow blocks.

(a) The toddler picks up two blocks at random, one after the other without replacement. By using a tree diagram, or otherwise, find the probability that
  (i) the toddler's first choice is a red block and her second choice is a yellow block,
  (ii) the toddler's second choice is a red block.

(b) The toddler picks up a third block. Find the probability that she now has two blocks of one colour and one block of the other colour.
CCEA 1996

6 When a spinner is used, it produces either a 3 or a 4. The probability of obtaining 3 is 0.3 and the probability of obtaining 4 is 0.7. The spinner is spun several times and the numbers obtained are added to give the score.

(a) Calculate the probability of scoring a total of 6 when the spinner is spun twice.

(b) Calculate the probability of scoring a total of 15 when the spinner is spun four times.

(c) Two players each spin the spinner twice. To win, a player must score exactly 1 more than their opponent.
Calculate the probability that neither player wins.

7 Helen drives to work each day from Monday to Friday. There are two routes, A and B, to work. On Monday, she is equally likely to take either route. On other days, the probability that she takes the same route as the day before is $\frac{1}{3}$.
What is the probability that

(a) she takes route B on Monday and Tuesday?

(b) she takes route A on Wednesday?

(c) she takes the same route on Tuesday, Wednesday and Thursday?

(d) she does not use the same route all week?

MISCELLANEOUS EXERCISE

1 The graph gives information about the weight of cucumbers produced from 100 seeds of two different varieties, type x and type y.

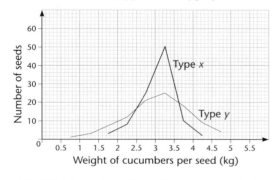

(a) Which variety of seed has more variation in the weight of cucumber produced?

(b) Give a reason for your answer.

SEG 1995

2 This table shows the results of a survey at a small building merchants. It shows the weekly wage in pounds and the age in years for the nine employees.

Age (in years)	Weekly wage (£)
21	164
22	205
25	125
28	210
36	167
39	660
43	143
55	805
57	564

(a) Calculate the mean age of all the employees.

(b) Calculate the mean weekly wage of all the employees.

(c) Draw a scatter diagram of wages against age for the nine employees.

(d) On the scatter diagram, plot the point which represents the mean age and the mean weekly wage.

(e) Make two comments about this data.

3 (a) Write down three positive whole numbers for which the median is 10, the mean is 8 and the range is 8.

(b) Write down five positive whole numbers for which the median is 3, the mean is 4 and the mode is 7.

Nelson GCSE Maths REVISION GUIDE: HANDLING DATA (HIGHER)

4 Sam was making a survey of pupils in his school. He wanted to find out their opinions on noise pollution by motor bikes.
The size of each year group in the school is shown below.

Year Group	Boys	Girls	Total
8	85	65	150
9	72	75	147
10	74	78	152
11	77	72	149
6th Form	93	107	200
			798

Sam took a sample of 80 pupils.

(a) Explain whether or not he should have sampled equal numbers of boys and girls in year 8.

(b) Calculate the number of pupils he should have sampled in year 8.

Edexcel 1995

5 The students at Loovilla College decided to have a biscuit eating competition.
A random sample of 25 students was taken. Copy this table which shows the number of students eating different numbers of biscuits in four minutes.

Number of Biscuits eaten in 4 minutes	Mid-point	Frequency (Number of students)	
1 – 5		2	
6 – 10		8	
11 – 15		7	
16 – 20		5	
21 – 25		2	
26 – 30		1	
		25	

(a) Calculate an estimate of the mean number of biscuits eaten in 4 minutes.

(b) Write down the modal class interval.

(c) 250 students entered the competition. Estimate how many of them will eat more than 20 biscuits in the four minutes.

Edexcel 1995

6 The waiting time for patients to be seen by a doctor after arriving at the accident department of a hospital during a weekend period were recorded. The histogram shows the results.

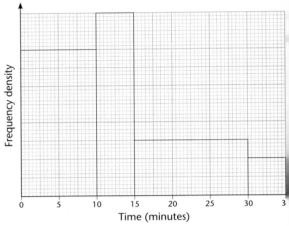

There were exactly 20 patients who were seen by a doctor in a time which was greater than or equal to 10 minutes and less than 15 minutes.

No patient had to wait 35 minutes or longer before being seen by a doctor.

Use the information in the histogram to copy and complete this frequency table.

Waiting time in minutes (t)	Frequency
$0 \le t < 10$	
$10 \le t < 15$	20
$15 \le t < 30$	
$30 \le t < 35$	
$35 \le t$	0

Edexcel 199

7 In a bag, there are 10 red cubes, 9 green cubes and 5 white cubes.
Two cubes are picked at random without replacement.
What is the probability that

(a) both cubes are green?

(b) one cube is red?

(c) the cubes are different colours?

8 This table shows how the weights of adult
women in the UK are distributed.

Weight (w kg)	Percentage
35 ≤ w < 40	2
40 ≤ w < 45	1
45 ≤ w < 50	7
50 ≤ w < 55	9
55 ≤ w < 60	13
60 ≤ w < 65	15
65 ≤ w < 70	17
70 ≤ w < 75	15
75 ≤ w < 80	10
80 ≤ w < 85	7
85 ≤ w < 90	4

(a) Find an estimate for the mean weight of
the women.

(b) Draw a cumulative percentage curve for the
data.

(c) Use your curve to find the median weight
for the women.
Compare this with the mean weight.

(d) Find the 5th and 95th percentiles.

(e) Find the interquartile range.

(f)
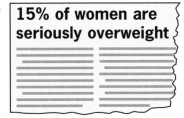

**15% of women are
seriously overweight**

A woman of average height should weigh
about 60 kg. Is the newspaper correct?

(g) Consider this statement:

Any woman weighing more than 11 stone
should go on a diet.

What percentage of women weigh more
than 11 stone?

There are 14lb
in a stone.

9 Claire did a survey on students' part time
weekly earnings. Some of her results are shown
in the table.

Number of students	59
Lowest earnings	£5
Highest earnings	£37
Median	£15
Lower quartile	£12
Upper quartile	£21

(a) Use this information to draw a possible
cumulative frequency curve using axes
like these.

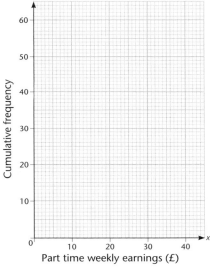

(b) Find the inter-quartile range.

(c) How many students' weekly earnings were
more than £20?

SEG 1995

10 (a) To test the ability of a mouse to find food, a maze of tunnels is set up as shown in the diagram. The tunnels are too narrow for the mouse to turn around. It is known that at any junction the probability that the mouse will carry straight on is 0.6.

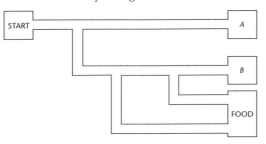

The mouse leaves the START area and moves until it reaches one of the areas marked A, B or FOOD. Calculate the probability that the mouse

(i) reaches B,   (ii) finds the food.

(b) The tunnels are widened so that a mouse can move freely along them in any direction. The test is carried out with one hundred and twenty mice. The distribution of the times taken to reach the food is given in the table below.

Time (t seconds)	Frequency
$0 < t \le 10$	18
$10 < t \le 15$	46
$15 < t \le 20$	35
$20 < t \le 30$	13
$30 < t \le 50$	8

On the grid like this, draw a histogram to represent this information.

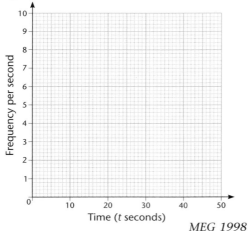

MEG 1998

11 'Smart' cards, such as cashcards to withdraw money from a cash machine, have four-digit PINs using the digits 0 to 9 exclusive.

(a) If you randomly punch four digits, what is the probability that you will produce the correct PIN?

(b) Someone knows his PIN consists of the digits 2, 6, 8 and 8, but has forgotten the order. How many different possibilities are there for him to try?

12 There are ten grown up brothers and sisters in a family. Five of these are called Chris, Adrian, Wendy, Jeremy and Margaret. Chris's age is the same as the median age of the brothers and sisters. Adrian's age is the same as the mean. Adrian is three years older than Chris, three years younger than Wendy, six years younger than Jeremy and nine years younger than Margaret. There are also some children in the family. Grace's age is the standard deviation of the age of the ten brothers and sisters. Rob's age is the range of the ages of the ten brothers and sisters. David is three years younger than Grace; Jan three years younger than Rob; Alan nine years younger than Grace, and Simon nine years older than Rob.
In three years' time, whose age will be

(a) the mean age of the ten brothers and sisters

(b) the median age of the ten brothers and sisters?

(c) the range of the ages of the ten brothers and sisters?

(d) the standard deviation of the ages of the ten brothers and sisters?

13 There are 8 balls in a box. 7 of the balls are yellow and 1 ball is red.
Jean selects balls at random, without replacement, from the box until she obtains the red ball.
When she obtains the red ball, then she stops selecting.
By copying and extending this tree diagram, or otherwise, calculate the probability that Jean selects the red ball on one of her first three selections.

Edexcel 1999

Type of operation	Number of operations	Cost per operation (£)
Plastic surgery	3	2000
Varicose veins	3	4500
Knee replacements	1	5200
Hip operations	3	7800

The table shows the number and costs of some operations in a hospital over one month.

The mean cost of an operation was £4810.

(a) Calculate the standard deviation of the cost of an operation.

Give your answer correct to the nearest £100.

The hospital later realised that each operation cost £200 more than originally thought.

(b) Write down

(i) the true mean cost of an operation,

(ii) the true standard deviation of the cost of an operation.

Edexcel 1995

5 Thirty 14-year old children are surveyed to find out how much television they watch in a week. The results are shown below.

Number of hours, x, per week	Frequency
$0 \le x < 10$	2
$10 \le x < 25$	12
$25 \le x < 30$	9
$30 \le x < 40$	7

(a) Draw a histogram to represent this information.

(b) Calculate an estimate of the mean number of hours of television watched per week.

(c) Calculate an estimate of the standard deviation of the number of hours watched per week.

(d) A similar survey of 16-year olds produced a mean of 18.5 hours and a standard deviation of 4.8 hours.

Comment on the differences in the amount of time these 14-year olds and 16-year olds spend watching television per week.

NEAB 1996

COURSE REVISION EXERCISES

1 (a) This is the mass of an electron.
$0.000\,000\,000\,000\,000\,000\,000\,000\,000\,91$ g
Find the mass of $60\,000$ electrons, in standard form.
(b) The 1971 Census recorded 48.8 million people in England and Wales. They lived in 16.5 million households.
Estimate the mean number of people per household in 1971.

2 $9801 = 11^2 \times a^4$
(a) Find the value of a.
(b) 9801 is a square number.
Find its square root.
(c) Write down the cube root of $2^6 \times 3^9$ as a product of its prime factors.

3 Change each of these to fractions in their simplest form.
(a) $0.1\dot{5}$ **(b)** $0.2\dot{6}\dot{7}$

4 Which of these numbers are rational?
Which are irrational?
(a) $\dfrac{\sqrt{8}}{\sqrt{2}}$ **(b)** $\dfrac{\sqrt{8}}{2}$
(c) $\sqrt{\dfrac{8}{2}}$ **(d)** $\dfrac{\pi}{\sqrt{2}}$
(e) $\dfrac{\pi}{2}$ **(f)** $(\sqrt{8}+\sqrt{2})^2$

5 (a) A school contains 240 students at Key Stage 4 and 320 in the Sixth Form.
A survey is being conducted about their use of the library and it is proposed to ask a sample of 100 students.
How many of these should be from Key Stage 4 and how many from the Sixth Form if the sample is to be representative?
(b) Suggest a method of selecting the sample of 100 students.

6 The relationship between d and a is given by this formula.
$d = \dfrac{3a - 15}{a + 1}$
(a) Find d when $a = 1.5$
(b) Make a the subject of the formula.

7 (a) Simplify these expressions.
   (i) $4a^{-3} \times 3a^4$ **(ii)** $t^5 \div t^{-2}$ **(iii)** $8^{\frac{5}{3}}$
   (iv) $27^{-\frac{1}{3}}$ **(v)** $\left(\dfrac{16}{9}\right)^{-\frac{3}{2}}$
(b) Factorise $3x^2 - 48y^2$.
(c) Simplify $\dfrac{(2b - 4)(3b + 6)}{b(b^2 + 3b - 10)}$.

8 (a) Draw graphs to find the solution to these simultaneous equations.
$3x + 2y = 12$
$2y = x - 6$
(b) Shade the region in which $3x + 2y < 12$ and $2y > x - 6$ are both true.

9 (a) Jenny measured up to see how many 10 cm square tiles she would need and thought that it was 200 tiles. When she got to the shop, she decided she preferred some that were 20 cm squares. She thought that, because they were twice as long she would need half the number and so she bought 100. Was she right?
(b) A toy manufacturer packs a large ball in the same size box as 8 smaller balls which each have half the diameter of the larger one. Explain why the larger ball takes up the same proportion of the space in the box as the 8 smaller ones.

10 (a) In this part of the question, express your answer in its simplest form in terms of π.
A symmetrically shaped timer is made from hollow hemispheres, cylinders and cones joined together as shown in the diagram. It contains sand just sufficient to fill the top cone and cylinder sections.

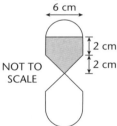

Calculate the volume of sand.
(b) When all the sand has run through, it collects as shown in the diagram.
Calculate the height, h cm, of sand in the cylindrical part of the timer.

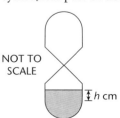

OCR 2000 specimen

1 The relationship between p, q and r is given by this formula.
$$r = (4p - q)^{\frac{3}{2}}$$
   (a) Find r when $p = 4.5 \times 10^6$ and $q = 6.82 \times 10^5$, giving your answer in standard form correct to 3 significant figures.
   (b) Find p when $r = 0.125$ and $q = -0.63$.

2 The length of a rectangle is 8.4 cm and its width is 5.8 cm, each measurement being correct to the nearest millimetre. Find the upper and lower bounds for
   (a) the perimeter of the rectangle
   (b) the area of the rectangle

3 Solve these.
   (a) $4(x - 3) > 28$
   (b) $2x^2 < 18$
   (c) $x^2 - 3x - 28 = 0$

4 A fair coin and a fair dice are thrown together.
   (a) List all the possible outcomes.
   (b) What is the probability of obtaining a head with an even number?
   (c) What is the probability of obtaining a tail with a score of 5 or more?

5 This diagram shows the shape of the inside of a garage which is a trapezium prism.

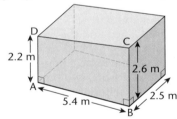

   (a) Calculate the angle between the vertical edge CB and the sloping edge CD.
   (b) Find the area of the sloping ceiling.
   (c) Find the volume of the garage.

6 At t hours after midnight, the height, h metres, of a tide is given by this formula.
$$h = 6 + 4\sin (30t°)$$
   (a) Copy and complete this table for values of h.

t	0	1	2	3	4	5	6
h	6	8			9.5		

   (b) Draw the graph of h against t for values of t between 0 and 6.
   (c) From your graph, find the times when the height of the tide is 9 m.

7 (a) Show that $2x^3 - 8x = 70$ has a solution between 3 and 4.
   (b) Use trial and improvement to find this solution correct to 2 decimal places.

8 (a) Construct this kite accurately, using ruler and compasses.

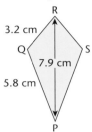

   (b) Construct the perpendicular from Q on to PR.
      Why does it pass through S?
   (c) Measure QS and work out the area of the kite.
   (d) Check your measurement for QS by calculating it.

9 (a) £3500 is invested at 7.5% per annum compound interest.
      Calculate the total amount in the account after three years.
   (b) After how many complete years will the amount invested have doubled?

10 The following grouped frequency table shows the maximum daily temperature, in °F, throughout the month of April.

Temperature, T	Frequency
$40 < T \le 50$	6
$50 < T \le 54$	6
$54 < T \le 58$	8
$58 < T \le 62$	5
$62 < T \le 70$	5

   (a) Calculate an estimate of the mean and the standard deviation of the distribution.
   (b) On graph paper, draw a histogram to represent your distribution in part (a).

For the month of June, the mean maximum daily temperature was 58.9°F and the standard deviation was 5.3°F.

   (c) Make two comments on the differences between these figures and the corresponding figures for April.

OCR 2000 specimen

EXERCISE 3

1 (a) Work out $2000 \div 0.04$

(b) Estimate this to 1 significant figure.
$$\frac{0.83 \times 57.1}{0.241 \times 2.9}$$

(c) Calculate each of these, giving your answer in standard form.
  (i) $(4.5 \times 10^{13}) \times (3 \times 10^{-24})$
  (ii) $(4.5 \times 10^{8}) \div (1.5 \times 10^{-12})$

2 A 550 g packet of cereal has been made 12% taller for a special offer of '15% extra free'.
(a) What is the new amount in the packet?
(b) The taller packet is 28 cm tall.
How tall is the usual packet?

3 Give an example of each of these.
(a) Two different irrational numbers whose *sum* is rational
(b) Two different irrational numbers whose *product* is rational
(c) Two different irrational numbers whose *difference* is rational

4 (a) The winning jump in a triple jump measured 14.93 m to the nearest 0.01 m. What is the smallest the jump could have been?
(b) The jump of the competitor coming second was given as 14.92 m to the nearest 0.01 m. Was the awarding of places correct?

5 (a) If y is directly proportional to x^2 and if $y = 6$ when $x = 2$, find
  (i) y when $x = 6$ **(ii)** x when $y = 1.5$
(b) Sketch the graphs of
  (i) y against x **(ii)** y against x^2

6 (a) Solve these simultaneous equations.
$$2x + 5y = 21$$
$$3x - 2y = -16$$
(b) Find the positive whole numbers x for which
$$1 \leq \frac{12}{x} \leq 4.$$

7 (a) Simplify these expressions.
  (i) $(5t)^3$ **(ii)** $\dfrac{w^8 \times w^5}{w^4}$

  (iii) $\dfrac{3^5 \times 3^{-2}}{3^{-7}}$ **(iv)** $27^{-\frac{2}{3}}$

  (v) $(4^{\frac{1}{2}})^6$
(b) By factorising, solve $x^2 - 14x + 45 = 0$.

8 (a) Sketch the graph of $y = \cos x$ for values of x between 0° and 360°.
(b) Cos 42° = 0.743 to 3 significant figures. State another angle between 0° and 360° whose cosine is 0.743 to 3 significant figures.

9 (a) ABCD is a parallelogram and BC = BE.

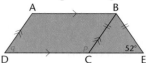

Calculate the values of the angles marked with letters. Give reasons for your answers.
(b) PT is a tangent to this circle whose centre is O.

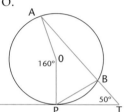

Calculate angle OAB, giving reasons.

10 In a bag, there are 12 coloured beads, of which 5 are red and the rest are white.
(a) One bead is taken out at random and its colour noted. The bead is replaced. Another bead is taken out.
What is the probability that
  (i) the first bead is red and the second bead is white?
  (ii) both beads are the same colour?
(b) In a different experiment, two beads are taken from the bag without replacement. What is the probability that these beads are the same colour?

EXERCISE 4

1 (a) What is the highest common factor of $2^3 \times 3^2$ and $2^2 \times 3^5$?
(b) What is the lowest common multiple of the numbers in part **(a)**?

2 The average distance between the Sun and the asteroid Juno is 247 800 000 miles.
(a) Write this distance in standard form.
(b) The orbit of Juno round the Sun is roughly circular.
Find the distance Juno travels in one orbit. Give your answer in standard form, correct to 3 significant figures.

3 Rewrite these, replacing each box by a number.
Do not use any number twice.
(a) $\square \div \square = 0$
(b) $\square + \square = 0$
(c) $\sqrt{\square} \times \sqrt{\square} = 6$

4 When you look out to sea, the distance of the
visible horizon is proportional to the square
root of your height above sea level.
From a height of 200 feet, you can see 17.2
miles. How far will you be able to see
(a) from a height of 100 feet?
(b) if your eyes are 5 feet above your feet and
you stand on the sea shore?

5 Use trial and improvement to find, correct to
one decimal place, the solution of $x^3 = 5x - 8$
which is close to −3.

6 Here are two sequences. The first sequence is
linear and the second is quadratic.
3, 7, 11, 15, ...
3, 8, 15, 24, 35, ...
(a) Write down the next two numbers in each
sequence.
(b) Work out an expression for the nth number
in each sequence.
(c) The number 575 appears in both sequences.
Which term is it in each sequence?
(d) The number 1000 does not appear in either
sequence.
Prove this.

7 (a) Draw the graph of $y = x^2 + 5$ for values of x
between −2 and 2. Use 1 cm for one unit on
each axis.
(b) From your graph, find when $x^2 + 5 = 7$.
(c) Estimate the gradient of your graph
when $x = -1$.
(d) Use the trapezium rule and trapezia of
width 1 to estimate the area enclosed by
the graph, the x-axis and the lines $x = -2$
and $x = 2$.

8 In this square-based pyramid, each of the
triangular faces is right-angled.
(a) Sketch a net for
the pyramid.
(b) Calculate the lengths
of BE and AE.
(c) Calculate the surface
area of the pyramid.
(d) Calculate the volume
of the pyramid.

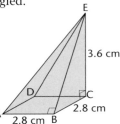

9 (a) The direct distance of Niton church from
the 'Pepper Pot' is 5.0 cm on the map.
The scale of the map is 1:25 000.
What is the actual distance between these
two buildings? Give your answer in
kilometres.
(b) The distance on the map between the
church and the Hoy monument is 9.0 cm.
The bearing of the Hoy monument from
the church is 333°. The bearing of the
'Pepper Pot' from the church is 294°.
Calculate
(i) the actual distance between the Hoy
monument and the 'Pepper Pot'
(ii) the bearing of the "Pepper Pot' from the
Hoy monument

10 This table shows the heights of some seedling
fir trees.

Height (h cm)	Frequency
$20 \leq h < 25$	3
$25 \leq h < 30$	17
$30 \leq h < 35$	24
$35 \leq h < 40$	30
$40 \leq h < 45$	22
$45 \leq h < 50$	23
$50 \leq h < 55$	11
$55 \leq h < 60$	5
Total	135

(a) Draw a cumulative frequency diagram for
this data.
(b) Estimate the median height of the seedlings.
(c) Estimate the interquartile range of the heights.
(d) What percentage of the seedlings were at
least 48 cm tall?
(e) Some seedling fir trees of another type were
at the same stage of maturity.
They had a median height of 42 cm and an
interquartile range of 10 cm.
Which type would make a better hedge
when planted side by side?
(f) Three seedlings of the first type were
ordered by a gardener.
Assuming the seedlings were picked at
random, estimate the probability that the
seedling are all at least 55 cm tall.
Give your answer to 2 significant figures.

1 (a) Simplify $(2 + \sqrt{3})^2 - 4(2 + \sqrt{3})$.
  (b) Hence, state a solution to the equation
      $x^2 - 4x + 1 = 0$.

2 (a) What is the cube root of 125?
      Hence, find the cube roots of 0.125 and
      125 000.
  (b) Express each of these expressions as a
      power of 5.
      (i) $(5^2)^3$
      (ii) $\dfrac{5^3 \times 5^{-4}}{5^{-2}}$
      (iii) $\sqrt{5^6}$
      (iv) $\sqrt[3]{5^6}$

3 Convert 0.18 and $0.\dot{1}\dot{8}$ to fractions in their
   lowest terms.

4 Simplify these expressions.
  (a) $\dfrac{\sqrt{50}}{5}$
  (b) $\sqrt{6} \times \sqrt{18}$
  (c) $\sqrt{10} \times \sqrt{80}$
  (d) $\dfrac{3 + \sqrt{18}}{6}$
  (e) $(\sqrt{6} + \sqrt{18})^2$

5 Find the exact value of $\cos x$ and $\sin x$.

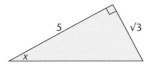

6 (a) A mistake has been made in this table of
      values for a straight-line graph. Find and
      correct the mistake.

x	−2	−1	1	2
y	−5	−4	4	7

  (b) Find the gradient of the line.
  (c) Find the equation of the line.

7 (a) Simplify these expressions.
      (i) $\dfrac{a^2b^3 \times ab^5}{a^4b^4}$ **(ii)** $\sqrt{12t^3} \times \sqrt{3t^5}$
      (iii) $\dfrac{3}{x^2y} + \dfrac{4}{xy^2}$ **(iv)** $\dfrac{3}{x^2y} \div \dfrac{4}{xy^2}$
  (b) A relationship between R, S and T is given
      in this equation.
      $$\frac{1}{R} = \frac{1}{S} + \frac{1}{T}$$
      (i) What is the value of S when $R = 6$
          and $T = 8$?
      (ii) Express T in terms of R and S.

8 (a) Copy this diagram.

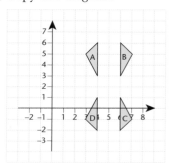

  (b) B is obtained from A by a reflection.
      Draw the mirror line and state its equation.
  (c) C is obtained from B by a reflection.
      Draw the mirror line and state its equation.
  (d) Describe the transformation which maps
      B to D.
  (e) Translate shape A by $\begin{pmatrix} -5 \\ 0 \end{pmatrix}$.
      Label the image E.
  (f) What transformation maps B to E?

9 (a) What is the size of each exterior angle of
      a regular decagon?
  (b) An octagon has interior angles $x°$, $3x°$, $1.5x°$,
      $2x°$, $1.5x°$, $2x°$, $4x°$ and $x°$.
      Find the sizes of the two largest angles.

0 A bag contains 20 cubes. Jenny carried out an experiment a large number of times.
Each time one cube was taken a random from the bag, its colour was noted and then it was replaced in the bag.
These are her results.

Colour	Blue	Yellow	Purple
Frequency	205	94	201

(a) Estimate the number of blue, yellow and purple cubes in the bag.

(b) If the experiment had been carried out 200 times, how many times would you estimate the yellow might have appeared?

(c) Using your answer to part **(a)**, write down the probability that if the experiment is carried out twice, a blue cube is obtained on both occasions.

EXERCISE 6

1 (a) A 12% deposit is being paid when ordering a sofa. The amount paid is £84. What is the full cost of the sofa?

(b) A restaurant bill comes to £32.70 including VAT at $17\frac{1}{2}$%. What was the amount of the bill before VAT was added?

2 (a) The Jurassic period lasted from 204 million years ago to 130 million years ago. Write how long this was, in standard form.

(b) A town with a population of 30 000, to the nearest hundred people, covers an area of 26.0 km^2 to the nearest 0.1 km^2. What is the smallest that the number of people per km^2 could be?

3 The frequency of radio waves is inversely proportional to the wavelength. When the frequency is 111 Hz the wavelength is 2700 m.

(a) Find the frequency for a wavelength of 1000 m.

(b) Find the wavelength for a frequency of 250 Hz.

(c) Sketch the graph of frequency against wavelength.

4 Here are some instructions.

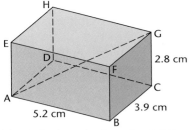

(a) If you start with 27, what is your answer?

(b) If the answer is 17, what are the possible starting numbers?

(c) If the answer is A, write an expression for the possible starting numbers.

5 By plotting y against x^2, find the relation between y and x.

x	1	1.6	2	2.8	3.2	3.6
y	11	16.5	21.5	34.9	43.4	52.9

6 ABCDEFGH is a cuboid.

(a) Calculate the length of AG, correct to 2 significant figures.

(b) Calculate the angle between AG and the base ABCD to the nearest degree.

7 A small factory has 200 employees. The annual wages are shown in this table.

Wage(£)	Number of employees
6000 – 8400	112
8400 – 10 800	35
10 800 – 13 200	15
18 000	24
24 000	9
36 000	4
60 000	1

(a) Calculate an estimate for the mean wage.

(b) State the mode.

(c) In which group does the median lie?

(d) Which form of average would you use if you were
  (i) a union official bargaining for a pay rise?
  (ii) the managing director?

8 Solve these equations.

(a) $\dfrac{x + 4}{2} - \dfrac{x - 5}{3} = \dfrac{53}{12}$

(b) $2x^2 + 5x + 1 = 0$
(correct to 2 decimal places)

(c) $\dfrac{2}{x} + \dfrac{3}{x + 2} = 1$

9 Copy this grid and triangle ABC and vectors **a** and **b** as shown here.

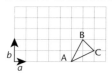

(a) Draw the position of the triangle ABC after translation by the vector **b** – 2**a**.

(b) (i) Write the vector $\overrightarrow{AB}$ in terms of **a** and **b**.

(ii) Write the vector $\overrightarrow{BC}$ in terms of **a** and **b**.

(c) D is an unmarked point on the grid.
$\overrightarrow{BD} = \frac{2}{3} \overrightarrow{BC}$.
$\overrightarrow{AD} = x\mathbf{a} + y\mathbf{b}$.

Use your answers to **(b)** to **calculate** the values of x and y.

You **must** show all your working.

SEG 1998

10 A ladder, *AB*, of length 18.5 feet, leans against a vertical wall and across a barrel of diameter 5 feet.
The barrel touches the wall at *D*, the horizontal ground at *E* and the ladder at *F*.
$AE = x$ feet and $BF = y$ feet.

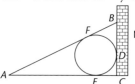

Not drawn to scale

(a) Explain why $x + y = 18.5$.

(b) Show that
(i) $BD = (18.5 – x)$ feet,
(ii) $BC = (21 – x)$ feet.

(c) Using Pythagoras' theorem on the triangle *ABC*, find the greatest height that the ladder can reach up the wall while still touching the barrel.

SELECTED ANSWERS

1 EXTENDING NUMBER SYSTEMS

Exercise 9   Page 12

1   $\sqrt{25 + 100 + 225} = \sqrt{350} = \sqrt{25 \times 14} = 5\sqrt{14}$

2   **(a)**   AB = $\sqrt{2}$, DE = $4\sqrt{2}$ using similarity
        and $\sqrt{32} = \sqrt{16 \times 2} = 4\sqrt{2}$; or $\sqrt{4^2 + 4^2} = 4\sqrt{2}$,
        using Pythagoras' theorem

3   **(a)**   PQ = $\sqrt{13}$
      (b)   UV = $5\sqrt{13}$ using similarity
           Using Pythagoras' theorem,
           UV = $\sqrt{325} = \sqrt{25 \times 13} = 5\sqrt{13}$

4   Each is $\frac{5}{4}$

5   $\frac{3}{\sqrt{3}} = \sqrt{3}$, $\frac{6}{\sqrt{2}} = 3\sqrt{2}$, $2\sqrt{3} = \frac{6}{\sqrt{3}}$

6   **(a)** $2\sqrt{3}$ **(b)** $5\sqrt{2}$ **(c)** $5\sqrt{3}$
      (d) $3\sqrt{3}$ **(e)** $4\sqrt{3}$ **(f)** $20\sqrt{2}$
      (g) $40\sqrt{5}$ **(h)** $30\sqrt{3}$

7   **(a)** $3\sqrt{2}$ **(b)** $7\sqrt{3}$ **(c)** $\sqrt{5}$
      (d)   18   **(e)**   30   **(f)**   30

     (Here there is the opportunity to discuss whether,
     e.g. $\sqrt{12} \times \sqrt{75} = \sqrt{900} = 30$, or $\sqrt{12} \times \sqrt{75} = 2\sqrt{3} \times 5\sqrt{3} = 10 \times 3$
     is the preferred approach)

8   **(a)**   3   **(b)** $\frac{\sqrt{5}}{\sqrt{3}}$ **(c)** $\sqrt{5} - 2$
      (d) $\frac{3}{\sqrt{2} + \sqrt{5}}$

9   **(a)** $\sqrt{32} = 4 \times 1.414 = 5.656$
      (b)   **(i)**   8.484   **(ii)**   7.07   **(iii)**   17.32
             (iv)   6.708   **(v)**   14.14   **(vi)**   44.72

Exercise 10   Page 13

1   **(a)** $\frac{5\sqrt{6}}{6}$ **(b)** $\sqrt{2}$
      (c) $4\sqrt{3}$ **(d)** $2\sqrt{5}$

2   $\frac{2}{\sqrt{3}}$

3   **(a)** $8 + 2\sqrt{2}$ **(b)** $8\sqrt{3} + 3$
      (c) $2 + 4\sqrt{2}$ **(d)** $-4\sqrt{3} - 11$
      (e) $9 + 4\sqrt{2}$ **(f)** $8 - 10\sqrt{3}$
      (g) $10 + 5\sqrt{5} + 6\sqrt{2} + 3\sqrt{10}$ **(h)** -1
      (i) $19 + 8\sqrt{3}$ **(j)** $16 - 6\sqrt{7}$
      (k) $43 - 30\sqrt{2}$

4   **(a)** $5 + 7\sqrt{2}$ **(b)** $5 - 5\sqrt{2}$
      (c) $-3 - 9\sqrt{5}$
      (d) $\sqrt{2}$; the difference of squares pattern needs to be
           spotted here

5   $x = 12$, $y = 9$; appreciate that $\sqrt{x}$ must contain $\sqrt{3}$ and then
     use a trial and error approach

6   **(a)** $(\sqrt{2} + \sqrt{3})^2 = 5 + 2\sqrt{6}$; $\left(\sqrt{2 + 3}\right)^2 = 5$;
           hence, $\sqrt{2} + \sqrt{3} > \sqrt{2 + 3}$
      (b) $(\sqrt{a} + \sqrt{b})^2 = a + b + 2\sqrt{ab}$; $\left(\sqrt{a + b}\right)^2 = a + b$;
           hence, $\sqrt{a} + \sqrt{b} > \sqrt{a + b}$

7   $(\sqrt{10} - 2)^2 + 4(\sqrt{10} - 2) = 14 - 4\sqrt{10} + 4\sqrt{10} - 8 = 6$

8   $x^2 = \frac{1}{4}(1 + \sqrt{5})^2 = \frac{1}{4}(6 + 2\sqrt{5}) = \frac{1}{2}(3 + \sqrt{5})$
     $x + 1 = \frac{1 + \sqrt{5}}{2} + 1 = \frac{3 + \sqrt{5}}{2}$

Exercise 11   Page 14

1   **(a)** $6(\sqrt{2} + 1)$
      (b) $\frac{5}{7}(3 - \sqrt{2})$
      (c) $-\frac{1}{7}(\sqrt{3} + 2)(\sqrt{2} - 3)$ or $\frac{1}{7}(6 + 3\sqrt{3} - 2\sqrt{2} - \sqrt{6})$
      (d) $17 - 12\sqrt{2}$

2   **(a)**   2   **(b)**   16

3   $\frac{4}{\sqrt{6} + 2} = 2\sqrt{6} - 4$; all the others equal $2\sqrt{6} + 4$

2 TRANSFORMATIONS AND VECTORS

Exercise 12   Page 39

1   486 km/h, 278°

2   295 km/h, 352°

3   **(a)**   5.4 m/s, 68° to downstream bank
      (b)   32 m

4   **(a)**   4.3 m/s, 69° to downstream bank
      (b)   7.5 m

5   5.7 m/s, 84° to upstream bank

6   348° or 349°, 255 km/h

7   **(a)**   71° to upstream bank
      (b)   11 seconds

8   **(a)**   53° to upstream bank
      (b)   10 seconds

9   **(a)**   097°   **(b)**   305 km/h

10   15 or 16 knots on 040° or 039°

Exercise 13   Page 41

1   10 N at 53°

2   14.8 N at 36°

3   10.4 N at 16°

4   **(a)**   12 N   **(b)**   67°

3 QUADRATIC EQUATIONS

Exercise 5   Page 50

1   **(a)** $x = 1$, or $x = 2$ **(b)** $x = 0$, or $x = -5$
      (c) $x = -4$, or $x = 9$ **(d)** $x = -3$
      (e) $x = -1$, or $x = -\frac{1}{3}$ **(f)** $x = -\frac{1}{2}$
      (g) $x = -2$, or $x = -\frac{1}{2}$ **(h)** $x = \frac{1}{3}$, or $x = 3$

2   **(a)** $x = 1$, or $x = 4$ **(b)** $x = -2$, or $x = 6$
      (c) $x = 5$ **(d)** $x = -4$, or $x = 1$
      (e) $x = -\frac{7}{6}$, or $x = 5$ **(f)** $x = -\frac{1}{3}$ or $x = \frac{20}{11}$
      (g) $x = -1$, or $x = 11$ **(h)** $x = 8$, or $x = 12$

3   (a) $x = -36$, or $x = -1$ (b)   Not possible

    (c) $x = -1$, or $x = 36$ (d) $x = -4$, or $x = 9$

    (e)   Not possible   (f) $x = 6$

    (g) $x = -36$, or $x = 0$ (h)   Not possible

Exercise 6   Page 51

1   (a) $x = -1 \pm \sqrt{2}$; $x = 0.41$, or $x = -2.41$

    (b) $x = -2 \pm \sqrt{3}$; $x = -3.73$, or $x = -0.27$

    (c) $x = 3 \pm \sqrt{6}$; $x = 0.55$, or $x = 5.45$

    (d) $x = 4 \pm \sqrt{21}$; $x = -0.58$, or $x = 8.58$

2   (a) $x = 1.5 \pm \sqrt{7.25}$; $x = -1.19$, or $x = 4.19$

    (b) $x = -0.5 \pm \sqrt{1.25}$; $x = -1.62$, or $x = 0.62$

    (c) $x = 2.5 \pm \sqrt{3.25}$; $x = 0.70$, or $x = 4.30$

    (d) $x = -3.5 \pm \sqrt{8.25}$; $x = -6.37$, or $x = -0.63$

3   (a) $x = 2$, or $x = 6$

    (b) $x = -18$, or $x = -2$

    (c) $x = -3$, or $x = 25$

    (d) $x = -18$, or $x = 4$

4   (a) $x = 2 \pm \sqrt{2}$; $x = 0.59$, or $x = 3.41$

    (b) $x = 1 \pm \sqrt{5}$; $x = -1.24$, or $x = 3.24$

    (c) $x = -3 \pm \sqrt{11}$; $x = -6.32$, or $x = 0.32$

    (d) $x = -4 \pm \sqrt{6}$; $x = -6.45$, or $x = -1.55$

5   (a) $x = 1.5 \pm \sqrt{9.25}$; $x = -1.54$, or $x = 4.54$

    (b) $x = 2.5 \pm \sqrt{4.25}$; $x = 0.44$, or $x = 4.56$

    (c) $x = 9 \pm \sqrt{74}$; $x = 0.40$, or $x = 17.60$

    (d) $x = 25 \pm \sqrt{725}$; $x = -1.93$, or $x = 51.93$

6   (a) $x = -4 \pm \sqrt{24.5}$; $x = -8.95$, or $x = 0.95$

    (b) $x = 2 \pm \sqrt{\left(\frac{8}{3}\right)}$; $x = 0.37$, or $x = 3.63$

    (c) $x = -10 \pm \sqrt{80}$; $x = -1.06$, or $x = -18.94$

    (d) $x = 1.5 \pm \sqrt{5.75}$; $x = -0.90$, or $x = 3.90$

Exercise 7   Page 52

1   (a) $x = -7$, or $x = -2$; sum $= -9$, product $= 14$

    (b) $x = 3$, or $x = 5$; sum $= 8$, product $= 15$

    (c) $x = -9$, or $x = 4$; sum $= -5$, product is -36

    (d) $x = -1$, or $x = 6$; sum $= 5$, product $= -6$

2   (a) $x = 6 \pm \sqrt{26}$; sum $= 12$, product $= 6^2 - 26 = 10$

    (b) $x = 1 \pm \sqrt{13}$; sum $= 2$, product $= 1^2 - 13 = -12$

    (c) $x = -3 \pm \sqrt{5}$; sum $= -6$, product $= 3^2 - 5 = 4$

    (d) $x = -5 \pm \sqrt{33}$; sum $= -10$, product $= 5^2 - 33 = -8$

3   (a)   For equation $x^2 + bx + c = 0$; the sum of the roots is $-b$, and the product is c

    (c)   For equation $ax^2 + bx + c = 0$; the sum of the roots is $-\frac{b}{a}$, and the product is $\frac{c}{a}$

4   (a) $x = -3 \pm \sqrt{2}$; $x = -4.41$, or $x = -1.59$

    (b) $(x - 1)^2 = -2$; not possible

    (c) $(x + 2)^2 = -1$; not possible

    (d) $x = 2$, or $x = 8$

    (e) $(x + 5)^2 = -9$; not possible

    (f) $x = 5 \pm \sqrt{59}$; $x = -2.68$, or $x = 12.68$

5   (a) $(x - 1)^2 = -2 \Rightarrow x - 1 = \pm i\sqrt{2} \Rightarrow x = 1 \pm i\sqrt{2}$

    (b) $x^2 + 4x + 5 = 0 \Rightarrow x = -2 \pm i$;

        $x^2 + 10x + 34 = 0 \Rightarrow x = -5 \pm 3i$

Exercise 8   Page 5

1   (a) $x = -9.44$, or $x = 2.44$

    (b) $x = 2.27$, or $x = 16.73$

    (c) $x = -0.41$, or $x = 4.08$

    (d) $x = -1.84$, or $x = -0.76$

    (e) $x = 0.79$, or $x = 2.35$

    (f) $x = -2.20$, or $x = 1.08$

2   (a) $x = -10.60$, or $x = 1.60$

    (b) $x = -0.75$, or $x = 4.25$

    (c) $x = -3.12$, or $x = 2.46$

    (d) $x = 0.24$, or $x = 4.09$

    (e) $x = 0.31$, or $x = 1.22$

    (f) $x = -4.33$, or $x = 11.33$

3   (a) $(x - 3)(x - 48)$ (b) $(x + 37)(x - 15)$

    (c) $(x - 24)(x - 42)$ (d) $(5x - 8)(4x + 9)$

    (e) $(8x - 15)((25x - 12)$ (f) $(8x + 27)(9x + 16)$

4   $a = -3$; $b = 2$

5   $a = \frac{6}{5}$; $b = \frac{1}{5}$

6   (a) $x = 2.26$ or $x = 0.74$

    (b) $y = 0 \pm 1.50$ or $y = \pm 0.86$

7   (a) $y = \pm 2$ or $y = \pm 3$ (b) $y = \pm 0.5$ or $y = \pm 5$

    (c) $x = \pm 2$ (d)   No solutions

    (e) $y = 1.44$ or $y = 1$ (f) $y = 1.44$ or $y = -1.26$

    (g) $z = \pm 1.73$ (h) $x = -1.71$

8   (a)   4   (b)   4   (c)   2   (d)   0

    (e)   2   (f)   2   (g)   2   (h)   1

Exercise 10   Page 55

1   6.18 cm and 16.18 cm

2   24 and 26

3   7 and 17; or −15 and −5

4   15 years old and 36 years old

5   2.83 cm

6   7.2 cm and 27.8 cm

7   1.86 cm, 3.86 cm, 4.28 cm; or 2.21 cm, 3.58 cm and 4.21 cm

8   Dimensions of rectangle are $2r$ m and $(1 - r)$ m

    $r = 0.57$

    Perimeter is $(2 + \pi r)$ m or 3.79 m

9   Dimensions of remaining rectangle are 1 and $\phi - 1$

    These are still in the ratio ϕ:1

    Hence $\frac{1}{\phi - 1} = \frac{\phi}{1}$

    $\phi = 1.618$ to 3 d.p.

10   $(1 + 0.01r)^2 = 1.12$; 5.83%

4 STATISTICS AND PROBABILITY

Exercise 7   Page 72

1   (a)   1976: mean = 66.7 mm; s.d. = 46.3 mm
          1980: mean = 82.0 mm; s.d. = 32.0 mm

    (b)   E.g. 1976: less rainfall, but more variable (September,
          October)
          Big difference between June 1976 and June 1980

2   Mean = 2.1 children; s.d. = 1.1 children

3   Mean = 1.67 m; s.d. = 0.53 m

4   (a)   Mean = 13 days, s.d. = 13 days
    (b)   Mean = 12 days, s.d. = 8 days

5   (a)   (i)   Mean = 174.8 cm; s.d. = 6.1 cm
          (ii) Mean = 167.0 cm; s.d. = 5.3 cm
    (b)   E.g. males taller and heights more variable

6   (a)   Mean = 95 mins; s.d. = 64 mins
    (b)   Mean = 85 mins; s.d. = 64 mins

Exercise 8   Page 74

1   C

2   (a)   Mean = m + 10; s.d. = s (b)   Mean = $2m$; s.d. = $2s$
    (c)   Mean = $2m$ – 10; s.d. = $2s$

3   (a)   Mean = 63; s.d. = 14   (b)   Mean = 94.5; s.d. = 21

4   (a)   270 mm
    (b)   280 mm – 261 mm = 19 mm
    (c)   245 mm
    (d)   4%

5   (b)   285 mm
    (c)   295 mm – 275 mm = 20 mm
    (d)   255 mm

6   (a)   (i)   4%   (ii)   36%
    (b)   Surprisingly low figures; presumably chairs are designed
          to accommodate children from 5 up to 7 years old, so
          many five–year–olds are too small for them

7   (a)   (ii) Median = 84 cm (approx.)
                IQR = 95 cm – 71 cm = 24 cm (approx.)
    (b)

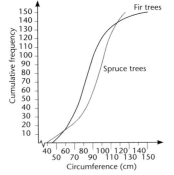

    (c)   Spruce trees tend to have thicker trunks (96 > 84)
          Same IQR, but smaller range, so more very thin-
          trunked and thick-trunked fir trees compared to
          spruce trees

8   (a)

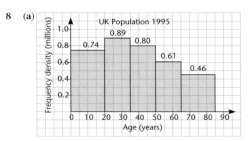

    (b)   38 years (taking mid–points as 10, 27.5, 42.5, 57.5, 75)
    (c)   22 years
    (d)

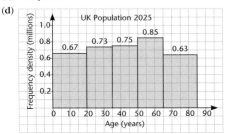

    (e)   Mean = 42 years; s.d. = 23 years
    (f)   Aging population predicted for 2025,
          compared to 1995
          People living longer, lower birth rate;
          not much change in spread of ages

9   Beech trees: $\dfrac{6.460 - 7}{0.899} = -0.60$

    Oak trees: $\dfrac{7.125 - 8}{1.029} = -0.85$

    Negative signs show mean is less than mode;
    oak trees show more skewness

10 (a)   Mean = 41 secs, s.d. = 17 secs
    (c)   Median = 38, IQR = 54 – 28 = 26
    (d)   Good (< 24 secs) 14 students; poor (> 58 secs)
          14 students; average 47 students
    (e)   Good (< 22 secs) 11 students; poor (> 62 secs)
          11 students; average 53 students

5 ALGEBRAIC MANIPULATION

Exercise 1   Page 81

1   (a) $\frac{2}{3}$ (b) $\frac{3}{5}$ (c) $\frac{13}{12}$ (d) $\frac{3}{4}$
    (e) $\frac{a}{b}$ (f) $\frac{3}{4}$ (g) $\frac{c}{2d}$ (h) $\frac{2a}{b}$

2   (a) $\frac{b}{c}$ (b) $\frac{b}{a}$ (c) $\frac{qr}{mn}$ (d) $\frac{y}{2z}$
    (e) $\frac{3r}{4s}$ (f) $\frac{2ab}{5de}$

3   (a) $\frac{a}{b}$ (b) $\frac{x}{y}$ (c) $\frac{ab}{2}$ (d) $\frac{n^2}{m^2}$
    (e) $\frac{2ab}{3c^2}$ (f) $\frac{2c^2}{5a^2}$

4   (a) $\frac{3x}{4}$ (b) $\frac{a}{2}$ (c) $\frac{7}{n}$ (d) $\frac{c}{8}$
    (e) $\frac{p}{30}$ (f) $\frac{3}{2x}$

5 (a) $\dfrac{3x + 2}{6}$ (b) $\dfrac{3a}{4}$

   (c) $\dfrac{-2c - 7}{15}$ (d) $\dfrac{-a + 9b}{24}$

   (e) $\dfrac{9p + 8q}{7}$ (f) $\dfrac{5a + 9b}{12}$

6 (a) $\dfrac{a + b}{ab}$ (b) $\dfrac{3y - 2x}{xy}$

   (c) $\dfrac{6 - 2q}{pq}$ (d) $\dfrac{9 - 5x}{x}$

   (e) $\dfrac{n^2 - 9}{3n}$ (f) $\dfrac{a^2 - b^2}{ab}$

7 (a) $\dfrac{xy}{6}$ (b) $\dfrac{a}{c}$ (c) $\dfrac{2r}{q}$ (d) $\dfrac{1}{2}$

   (e) 5   (f) $\dfrac{x^2}{z^2}$ (g) pqr (h) $\dfrac{wz}{y^2}$

Exercise 2   Page 82

1 (a) $\dfrac{3n + 9}{n + 2}$ (b) $\dfrac{-3y - 3}{y + 3}$

   (c) $\dfrac{8x}{(x - 1)(x + 1)}$ (d) $\dfrac{4}{(y - 1)(y + 1)}$

   (e) $\dfrac{c + 17}{(c - 1)(c + 5)}$ (f) $\dfrac{2x + 8}{x(x + 2)}$

2 (a) $\dfrac{10n + 25}{2(n + 2)}$ (b) $\dfrac{x^2 - 6x + 5}{2(x - 3)}$

   (c) $\dfrac{p^2 - 2pq - q^2}{(p + q)(p - q)}$ (d) $\dfrac{4xy}{(x - y)(x + y)}$

3 (a) £$\dfrac{60}{x}$ (b) £$\dfrac{30}{x - 2}$

   (c) £$\dfrac{30x - 120}{x(x - 2)}$

4   $\dfrac{300}{s(s - 5)}$

Exercise 3   Page 83

1 (a) $x + 2$ (b) $\dfrac{1}{2 - 3a}$

   (c) $\dfrac{x + 1}{x}$ (d) $\dfrac{1}{x + 2}$

   (e) $\dfrac{x - 1}{x}$ (f) $\dfrac{x + 2y}{x - 2y}$

2 (a) $\dfrac{2a + 1}{a - 2}$ (b) $\dfrac{3z + 5}{z + 4}$

   (c) $\dfrac{3 + 2x}{3 - 2x}$ (d) $\dfrac{2p - 3q}{p - 3q}$

   (e) $\dfrac{2a^2}{3a + 8}$ (f) $\dfrac{a - 12b}{3a + 8b}$

3 (a) $\dfrac{(x + 2)(x + 1)}{3(x - 1)}$ (b) 1

   (c) $\dfrac{x + 1}{2(x - 2)}$ (d) $\dfrac{2x + 3}{3}$

4 (a) $\dfrac{3 + 2x}{x(x - 3)}$ (b) $\dfrac{1}{(x - 1)(x + 1)}$

   (c) $\dfrac{3x - 1}{(x - 1)^2(x + 1)}$ (d) $\dfrac{9x + 41}{(2x - 7)(x + 1)(3x + 4)}$

   (e) $\dfrac{-2x^2 - 31}{(x + 2)(x + 3)(x - 4)}$

5 (a) $\dfrac{2}{x + 1} + \dfrac{3}{x + 2}$

   (b) (i) $\dfrac{6}{a + 1} + \dfrac{6}{a - 1}$ (ii) $\dfrac{3}{p - 5} + \dfrac{5}{p + 3}$

      (iii) $\dfrac{1}{x + 1} + \dfrac{3}{(x + 1)^2}$

Exercise 4   Page 84

1 (a) $x = -\dfrac{8}{3}$ (b) $x = -\dfrac{1}{3}$

   (c) $x = -\dfrac{5}{3}$ (d) $x = -1.2$

   (e) $x = 7$ (f) $x = -3$

2 (a) $x = 2$ (b) $x = -3$, or $x = 4$

   (c) $x = 2$, or $x = 12$ (d) $x = -\dfrac{1}{4}$, or $x = 4$

   (e) $x = -4\dfrac{1}{2}$, or $x = 5$ (f) $x = -3$, or $x = 3\dfrac{1}{2}$

3 (a) $x = 1$, or $x = 3\dfrac{3}{4}$ (b) $x = -2\dfrac{1}{2}$, or $x = 5$

   (c) $x = -5\dfrac{2}{3}$, or $x = 7$

6 FURTHER TRIGONOMETRY

Exercise 1   Page 99

1 (a) 8.24 cm   (b) 176 cm³

   (c) 64.1°   (d) 55.6°

2 (a) 5 cm   (b) 90°, 36.9°, 53.1°

3 (a) 12.4 cm   (b) 66.3°, 55.8°, 43.7°

4   Two edges are of length 12.8 cm, at an angle of 38.7° to the base

   The other edge is of length 16.2 cm, at an angle of 29.5° to the base

5 (a) 10.6 cm   (b) 45°

   (c) 70.5°   (d) 109.5°

6   1 in 6

7 (a) Long faces 26.6°; end faces 45°

   (b) 4.90 m

8 (a) 4.77 cm   (b) 11.1 cm

   (c) 25.5°   (d) 62.4°

9 (a) 6.93 cm   (b) 9.80 cm

   (c) 204 cm³   (d) 54.7°

   (e) 70.5°

10 (a) $\dfrac{1}{6}$ m³ or 167 000 cm³

   (b) 100 cm, 86.6 cm (4 of each)

   (c) 45°

11 (a) 102 cm³   (b) 35.3°

   (c) 60°, 60°, 90°   (d) No

12 (a)

   (b) $\dfrac{1}{6}$ (c) $\dfrac{1}{3}$

   (d) $\sqrt{2}$ units   (e) $2\sqrt{3}$ square units

Exercise 4 — Page 108

1. A: 25.8 cm^2 B: 22.1 cm^2 C: 3 810 mm^2

2. A: $x = 30°$ B: $x = 72.2°$ C: $x = 21.7°$

3. 15.6 cm^2

4. 8 cm^2

5. (a) 90°   (b) 30°

6. (a) Triangles ABC, CDE and EFA are all congruent (sides 2 cm and 3 cm, included angle 120°)
   (b) 4.36 cm
   (c) 8.23 cm^2
   (d) Area of triangle ABC = 2.60 cm^2; total area of hexagon is 16.0 cm^2

Exercise 5 — Page 109

1. (a) 9.40 cm   (b) 9.85 cm

2. 29.5 km

3. (a) Jim   (b) 13.4 km
   (c) 11.4 km

4. (a) 9.60 km   (b) 025°

5. 3.4 km

6. (a) 580 m   (b) 180 m

7. (a) Andy   (b) 690 m

8. 115 m

9. (a) 26.5 m   (b) 25.6 m, 27.4 m

10. (a) 4.48 cm, 4.65 cm   (b) 6.79 cm^2, 7.19 cm^2

11. 28.2 km, 30.9 km

12. (a) 23 m   (b) 20.2 m, 25.7 m

Exercise 6 — Page 112

1. (a) −0.57   (b) 0.82   (c) −0.94
   (d) 0.34   (e) −0.64   (f) −0.77
   (g) 0.64   (h) −0.77

2. (a) 0.5   (b) −0.87   (c) −0.91
   (d) −0.42   (e) 0.77   (f) 0.64
   (g) −0.77   (h) 0.64

3. (a) (i) −0.866   (ii) −0.866   (iii) 0.985
      (iv) −0.174   (v) 0.342   (vi) −0.866

Exercise 7 — Page 113

1. (a) −1.4, −0.4, 1.2, −1.2
   (b) −1.428, −0.364, 1.192, −1.192

2. (a) −1.7, 0.5, 0.8, −0.8
   (b) −1.732, 0.466, 0.839, −0.839

3. (a) (i) 0.839   (ii) −1.732   (iii) −5.671
      (iv) 5.671   (v) 11.430   (vi) 1.732

Exercise 8 — Page 114

1. (a) −1   (b) 0   (c) 0   (d) 1
   (e) 0   (f) 0   (g) 0   (h) −1
   (i) 1

2. (a) 0.545
   (b) (i) 0.545   (ii) 0.545
      (iii) 0.545   (iv) 0.545

3. (a) $\frac{5}{13}$ (b) $\frac{12}{13}$ (c) $\frac{12}{5}$ (d) $-\frac{5}{13}$
   (e) $-\frac{12}{13}$ (f) $-\frac{12}{5}$ (g) $-\frac{5}{12}$

Exercise 9 — Page 115

1. (b) 23.6°   (c) 156.4°

2. (a) $p = -110°$ (b) $p = \pm145°$

3. (a) 45°, 225°, 405°   (b) −45°, 135°, 315°
   (c) −43°, 137°

4. (a) 17.5°, 162.5°   (b) 116.6°, 296.6°

5. (a) −66.4°, 66.4°, 293.6°, 426.4°
   (b) −23.6°, 203.6°, 336.4°

6. 40°, 140°

7. (a) 40°, 220°, −140°, −320°   (b) 125°, 305°, −235°, −55°

8. ±0.8

9. −0.8

10. (a) 70°, 110° and these values with multiples of 360° added or subtracted
    (b) 200°, 340° and these values with multiples of 360° added or subtracted

11. (a) 15.9 cm
    (b)

OP − ON = (15.9 − 15.9 cos θ) cm
    (c) 121° or 239°
    (d) 57 cm

12. (a) 7   (b) 4.5, 22.5
    (c) 0.97, 8.03

13. (a) 5 m   (b) 7.6 m
    (c) 8 m   (d) 6.5 m

14. (a) 5 m   (b) 1.14 m
    (c) Up to 2 p.m.

Exercise 12   Page 114

1   (a)   4   (b)   −2
     (c)   (2, 4)   (d)   (4, 0)
     (e) $x > 2$

2   (b)   Line of symmetry is $x = 2$ (c) $m = 1$
     (d) $(1, -1\frac{1}{2})$ (e) $n = -4$
     (f)   (6, 6)   (g)   (2, −2)

3   (a)   At $x = 1$, gradient is 5; at $x = -2$, gradient is −1
     (b) $x < -1\frac{1}{2}$

4   (a)   At $x = 1$, gradient is 3; at $x = -2$, gradient is 12
     (b)   None

5   (a)   Rotational symmetry of order 2 about origin
     (b)   8
     (c)   (−2, 0)
     (d)   At about (−1.2, 3.1) and (1.2, −3.1)
     (e)   At (1, −3)
     (f) $x < -1.2$ or $x > 1.2$

6   (a)   (2, 7)   (b)   (4, 4)
     (c)   (−2, −4)   (d)   (1, 2)

Exercise 13   Page 143

1   (a)   Acceleration in ft/sec²
     (b)   Speed in km/hr
     (c)   Rate of change of volume in litres/sec
     (d)   Rate of change of temperature in °C/min

2   (a)   At about 8.53 a.m, about 8–9 m.p.h
     (b)   At about 8.56 a.m, about 2 m.p.h
     (c)   3.6 m.p.h.

3   (a)   About 7 ft/sec   (b)   About 16 ft/sec
     (c)   0.75 seconds   (d)   12 ft/sec

4   (a)   80 m   (b)   4 m/s²

5   (a)   60 m.p.h.   (b)   Zero
     (c)   12–15 minutes   (d)   11 miles

6   (a)   2–3 m/s²   (b)   0.5–0.6 m/s²
     (c)   About 120 m   (d)   About 10 m/s

7   (a)   15 m/s   (b)   2 m/s
     (c)   950 m – 1000 m   (d)   About 0.1 m/s²
     (e)   About 0.1 m/s²

8   (b)   −2 m/s²   (c)   3 seconds
     (d)   21 m (using 4 strips)

9   (a)   5 miles
     (b)

10   (b)   Approximate speeds (in cm/s): 0, 12, 24, 36, 48, 60
      (d)   Constant, at just over 20 cm/s²

Answers to Revision Guide Exercises

N1: EQUIVALENCE OF FRACTIONS, DECIMALS AND PERCENTAGES

1 $\frac{25}{64}$; all the rest are equal to $\frac{5}{8}$

2 (a) and (b)
$\frac{4}{7} = 0.57$, $\frac{7}{11} = 0.64$, $\frac{9}{13} = 0.69$, $\frac{7}{10} = 0.7$, $\frac{3}{4} = 0.75$,
$\frac{7}{5} = 1.4$, $\frac{13}{9} = 1.44$, $\frac{5}{3} = 1.67$

3 22%, 0.227, $\frac{7}{27} = 0.259$, 27%, $\frac{2}{7} = 0.285$, $\frac{7}{22} = 0.318$, 77%,
$2\frac{2}{7} = 2.286$, 2.7, $\frac{22}{7} = 3.14$

4 $5\frac{1}{3} = 5.33$, $8\frac{1}{6} = 8.17$, $12\frac{5}{6} = 12.8$, $7\frac{2}{3} = 7.67$,
$14\frac{1}{12} = 14.1$, $1\frac{7}{12} = 1.58$

N2: RATIONAL AND IRRATIONAL NUMBERS

1 (a) $\sqrt{18} = 3\sqrt{2}$; irrational
   (b) 17, rational
   (c) 2, rational
   (d) $9 - 2\sqrt{18} = 9 - 6\sqrt{2}$, irrational
   (e) 27, rational

2 (a) 2.5, rational   (b) Irrational
   (c) 6, rational   (d) 0.5, rational
   (e) Irrational   (f) Irrational
   (g) 3, rational   (h) $\frac{7}{11}$, rational

3 (a) =   (b) >
   (c) >   (d) =
   (e) =   (f) <

4 (a) One that can be written in the form $\frac{a}{b}$, where a and b are integers
   (b) $(\sqrt{2} + \sqrt{8})^2 = (\sqrt{2})^2 + 2\sqrt{2}\sqrt{8} + (\sqrt{8})^2$
        $= 2 + 2\sqrt{16} + 8 = 18$
        Or $(\sqrt{2} + \sqrt{8})^2 = (\sqrt{2} + 2\sqrt{2})^2 = (3\sqrt{2})^2 = 18$
   (c) E.g. $(\sqrt{2} + 1)^2 = 3 + 2\sqrt{2}$, which is irrational

5 (a) E.g. $5 + \frac{\sqrt{2}}{2}$ or $\sqrt{30}$ (b) E.g. $\sqrt{5.5}$
   (c) E.g. $\frac{1}{3} = 0.3$ (d) E.g. $\sqrt{2}$
   (e) E.g. $\sqrt[3]{2}$

6 (a) 0.875   (b) 0.857 142
   (c) $0.4\dot{5}$ (d) 0.504

7 (a) $36.\dot{3}\dot{6}$, $\frac{4}{11}$
   (b) (i) $\frac{7}{36}$ (ii) $\frac{17}{37}$
        (iii) $\frac{9}{110}$

8 (a) E.g. 3, 4, 5   (b) E.g. 1, 1, $\sqrt{2}$
   (c) E.g. $\sqrt{3}$, $\sqrt{6}$, 3   (d) E.g. $\sqrt{2}$, $\sqrt{3}$, $\sqrt{5}$

9 (a) E.g. $\sqrt{2}$ and $2\sqrt{2}$ (b) E.g. $\sqrt{2}$ and $\sqrt{3}$
   (c) E.g. $\sqrt{2}$ and $2 - \sqrt{2}$ (d) E.g. $\sqrt{2}$ and $2 + \sqrt{2}$
   (e) E.g. $\sqrt[3]{2}$ and $2 \times \sqrt[3]{2}$ (f) E.g. $\sqrt[3]{2}$ and $2 \times \sqrt[3]{2}$

10 (a) $x = 3$ (b) $x = -0.5$
   (c) $x = 3.5$ (d) $x = 2.5$

11 (a) Irrational; if $x + 2 = \frac{p}{q}$, then $x = \frac{p - 2q}{q}$
   (b) Cannot tell; e.g. $(\sqrt{2})^2 = 2$ is rational, but $(\sqrt[3]{2})^2 = 2^{\frac{2}{3}}$ is irrational
   (c) Irrational; $\frac{1 - x}{1 - x^2} = \frac{1}{1 + x}$
        If $\frac{1}{1 + x} = \frac{p}{q}$, then $x = \frac{q - p}{q}$
   (d) Rational; -3

12 (a) $4\sqrt{3}$; irrational   (b) $3(\sqrt{2} + 1)$; irrational
   (c) 4; rational

N3: MULTIPLES, FACTORS AND PRIMES

1 (a) 72   (b) 1001

2 (a) $36 = 2^2 \times 3^2$; $56 = 2^3 \times 7$; $54 = 2 \times 3^3$
   (b) 4   (c) 2

3 (a) 14   (b) 140

4 $224 = 2^5 \times 7$; $280 = 2^3 \times 5 \times 7$
   Highest common factor is $2^3 \times 7 = 56$
   Lowest common multiple is $2^5 \times 5 \times 7 = 1120$

5 (a) $9800 = 2^3 \times 5^2 \times 7^2$
   (b) Smallest square number is $2^4 \times 5^2 \times 7^2 = 19\,600$

6 (a) 3   (b) $90X$

7 (a) $220 = 2^2 \times 5 \times 11$; $284 = 2^2 \times 71$
        Factors of 220: 1, 2, 4, 5, 10, 11, 20, 22, 44, 55, 110, 220
        Factors of 284: 1, 2, 4, 71, 142, 284
   (b) $1 + 2 + 4 + 5 + 10 + 11 + 20 + 22 + 44 + 55 + 110 = 284$
        $1 + 2 + 4 + 71 + 142 = 220$

N4: POWERS, ROOTS AND RECIPROCALS

1 (a) $27a^{12}$ (b) $\frac{a^4}{b^4}$ (c) a^3b^2
2 (a) x (b) x^2 (c) $x^{\frac{2}{3}} = \sqrt[3]{x^2}$
3 (a) $x = 0.5$ (b) $x = 1.5$ (c) $x = 2$
4 (a) 8   (b) 81   (c) $\frac{16}{9}$ (d) $\frac{1}{27}$
5 (a) $5^{-7.5}$ (b) 9
6 (a) $11^3 = 1331$; $12^3 = 1728$; $1331 < 1500 < 1728$
        So $\sqrt[3]{1500}$ lies between 11 and 12
   (b) $x = 107$
7 $y = 2^{-2.25}$
8 $\frac{1}{a^5}$, a^{-2}, $\sqrt{\frac{1}{a}}$, a^0, $a^{\frac{1}{3}}$

N5: STANDARD FORM

1 (a) 5.73×10^4 (b) 9.056×10^{-3} (c) 2.5×10^7
   (d) 1.5×10^5 (e) $6.435\,77 \times 10^2$ (f) 7.3×10^{-5}

2 (a) 6.9×10^5 (b) 6×10^5 (c) 3.5×10^{12}
   (d) 3×10^{10} (e) 1.6×10^{15} (f) 1.6×10^8
   (g) 3×10^3 (h) 5×10^3

3 (a) 1.5×10^9 (b) 7.2×10^{-1} (c) 7×10^1
  (d) 6×10^2 (e) 6.09×10^5 (f) 2.98×10^4
  (g) 5.23×10^{11} (h) 1.384×10^{-18}

4 (a) 1.14×10^9 litres (b) About 4×10^{11} litres

5 (a) 2.66×10^{17} (b) 9.30×10^{37} (c) 4.75×10^{-8}
  (d) 5.04×10^8 (e) 8.04×10^7 (f) 1.62×10^{12}

6 (a) 8.8×10^3 cm (b) 5.2×10^5 cm^2

7 1723

8 (a) 8.19×10^{13} (b) 2.7×10^8 seconds (c) 3100 days

9 (a) 3.62×10^8 (b) 5.12×10^8 km^2 (c) 71%

10 5.2×10^{-9} m.p.h.

N6: STRATEGIES FOR MENTAL ARITHMETIC

1 (a) 12 000 months
  (b) 2 592 000 seconds
  (c) 8760 hours

2 142 bottles

3 (a) 15 pieces (b) 25 cm

4 8 coaches

5 (a) 196 (b) 12 600 (c) 1.28 (d) 28.8

6 (a) 140 (b) 700 (c) 80 (d) 400

7 (a) 156 (b) 1722 (c) 2499 (d) 9991
  (e) 8281 (f) 3025

8 (a) 1598
  (b) (i) 1598 (ii) 0.047 (iii) 3400 (iv) 2.35

9 (a) 0.000 05 (b) 1.5625 (c) 0.81 (d) 0.5
  (e) 1.2 (f) 0.04

N7: THE FOUR RULES OF DECIMALS

1 (a) 12.96 (b) 8.47 (c) 7.66

2 (a) 1.035 (b) 33.02 (c) 24.054 (d) 14.44

3 (a) 6.1 (b) 0.75 (c) 16 (d) 0.26

N8: THE FOUR RULES OF FRACTIONS

1 $\frac{1}{4}$

2 (a) $13\frac{1}{2}$ (b) $6\frac{1}{2}$ (c) $3\frac{1}{2}$ (d) $2\frac{1}{7}$

3 (a) $4\frac{1}{12}$ (b) $7\frac{1}{2}$ (c) $2\frac{5}{8}$ (d) $1\frac{7}{12}$

4 (a) 8 (b) $21\frac{2}{3}$ (c) 3 (d) $1\frac{9}{10}$

5 $\frac{6}{11}$

N9: PERCENTAGES

1 5%

2 10.2%

3 £1470.05

4 12 years

5 40%

6 7.7%

7 (a) £418.30 (b) £424.68

8 1550 students

9 £12 500

10 (a) 17.9% (b) 7.89×10^8

11 1 gallon = 8×0.568 litres = 4.544 litres
   Error is 0.044; percentage error is 0.98%

12 19%

N10: RATIO AND PROPORTIONAL DIVISION

1 10 cm, 8 cm and 6 cm

2 7:13

3 £45 000 and £35 000

4 (a) 13.4 m^2 (b) 17.5 cm by 14 cm

5 (a) 37.5 cm (b) 25 cm

6 20 cm

N11: ORDER OF OPERATIONS AND EFFICIENT USE OF A CALCULATOR, INCLUDING ESTIMATION

1 (a) 7.25 (b) 0.406 593 4066
  (c) 0.440 926 9852

2 (a) $600 \times 5 \div 0.2 = 15\,000$ (b) 46.5

3 (a) 1.71 (b) 0.131
  (c) −437 (d) 123

4 (a) $900 \div 30 = 30$ (b) $4 \times 0.5 = 2$
  (c) $0.8 \div 0.2 = 4$ (d) $\sqrt{3^2 + 4^2} = 5$
  (e) $\frac{6}{12} + \frac{28}{56} = 1$ (f) $\frac{(0.3)^2 \times 400}{60 \times 0.01} = 60$

5 (a) $\frac{2 \times 20 - 3 \times 4}{20 - 4^2} = \frac{28}{4} = 7$ (b) 6.48

N12: DIRECT AND INVERSE PROPORTION

1 (a) $p = \frac{20}{q}$ (b) $p = 10$ (c) $q = 1$

2 (a) $d = 16t^2$ (b) 10.2 ft (c) 3.5 seconds

3
x	15	5	30	1.5
y	40	1080	5	40 000

4 (a) 500 metres (b) 356 kHz (c) 548 metres

5 (a) Multiplied by 4
  (b) Divided by 5
  (c) Increased by 21%
  (d) Decreased by 20%

6 (a) Halved (b) Multiplied by $\frac{7}{6}$
  (c) Decreased by 37.5%

7 A: W B: Z C: X

8 (a) $y = \frac{0.16}{x}$ or $y = \frac{0.032}{x^2}$
  (b) $x = 0.4 \Rightarrow y = 0.4$ using $y = \frac{0.16}{x}$
     $x = 0.4 \Rightarrow y = 0.2$ using $y = \frac{0.032}{x^2}$
     So $y = \frac{0.16}{x}$ looks more likely

MISCELLANEOUS EXERCISE

1 (a) 43 minutes
   (b) $(5 \times 10^8) \div (2 \times 10^5) \div 50 = 2.5 \times 10^3 \div 50 = 50$

2 (a) $dn = 50.4$ (b) $d = 1.6$ (c) 7:3

3 12.9%

4 (a) £7.40   (b) 14.75%

5 (a) 6.60 lies between 6.595 and 6.605, whereas 6.6 (the same number to two significant figures) lies between 6.55 and 6.65
   (b) No; 0.45 is the same to two decimal places and to two significant figures, with the same accuracy

6 At 2 m, the intensity is 9 times greater than at 6 m

7 (a) $\dfrac{0.4 \times 0.4 \times 500}{50 \times 0.04} = 40$
   (b) $\dfrac{1}{8} + \dfrac{1}{4} = \dfrac{3}{8} = 0.4$ to 1 d.p.

8 (a) $20 \times 40 \div 0.05 = 16\,000$
   (b) $2 \times 0.5 \times 3 + 2 \times 0.4 \times 3 + 2 \times 0.5 \times 0.4 = 5.8$
        So there is not enough

9 (a) $14\frac{14}{15}$ (b) 120

10 (a) $6\sqrt{3}$, irrational
    (b) $11 - 6\sqrt{2}$, irrational
    (c) $\frac{5}{9}$, rational

11 (a) 2   (b) $2\frac{1}{4}$ (c) 1   (d) 1

12 (a) $0.33333... = \frac{1}{3}$ and is rational
    (b) $\sqrt{4\frac{1}{4}} = \frac{\sqrt{17}}{2}$ is irrational
         $\sqrt{6\frac{1}{4}} = \frac{5}{2}$ is rational
         $(\sqrt{2} + \sqrt{3})^2 = 5 + 2\sqrt{6}$ is irrational
         $(\frac{1}{3}\sqrt{3})^2 = \frac{1}{3}$ is rational

13 (a) $\frac{3}{8}$ (b) $\frac{8}{11}$ (c) $\frac{49}{330}$

14 (a) 4, 25, 49, 121, 169, ...; each is the square of a prime
    (b) (i) $2^3 \times 3 \times 7$ (ii) $2 \times 3^2 \times 5 \times 7$
    (c) 2520
    (d) 42

15 (a) (i) 2.1×10^3 (ii) $2^2 \times 3 \times 5^2 \times 7$
    (b) 2

A1: LINEAR, QUADRATIC AND OTHER SEQUENCES

1 (a) $5n - 2$ (b) $7n - 11$
   (c) $61 - 11n$ (d) $a + b(n - 2)$

2 (a) n^2 (b) $n^2 - 1$
   (c) $3n^2$

3 (a) $n^2 + n$ (b) $2n^2 - 2n + 3$
   (c) $\dfrac{3n^2 - 3n + 8}{2}$ (d) $30 + \dfrac{n}{2} - \dfrac{n^2}{2}$

4 (a) 1, 5, 13, 25 squares
   (b) $2n^2 - 2n + 1$
   (c) 9 red and 16 blue squares
   (d) Square numbers
   (e) $n^2 + (n - 1)^2 = 2n^2 - 2n + 1$

5 (a) Red: 1, 4, 9, 16, 25
       Blue: 8, 12, 16, 20, 24
   (b) n^2, $4n + 4$
   (c) Total in Pattern $k - 2$ is $(k - 2)^2 + 4(k - 2) + 4$
        $= k^2 - 4k + 4 + 4k - 8 + 4 = k^2$

6 (a) $(n + 2)(n + 3)$
       Even because the product of consecutive integers, one of which must be even
   (b) $n(n + 1)(n + 2)$
       This is the product of three consecutive integers; one must be a multiple of 3 and at least one must be even
       $34 \times 35 \times 36 = 42\,840$

A2: GRAPHS OF REAL-LIFE SITUATIONS

1 (a) Red   (b) 4 m.p.h.   (c) 1 hour
   (d) 6 miles   (e) 3 m.p.h.   (f) 5 p.m.
   (g) 2 hours   (h) 6 m.p.h.   (i) 4 p.m.
   (j) 30 minutes

2 (a)
   (b) 12 km/h

3 (a)
   (b) 36 minutes

4

5 **(a)**

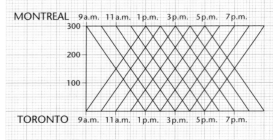

MONTREAL 9a.m. 11a.m. 1p.m. 3p.m. 5p.m. 7p.m.

300

200

100

TORONTO 9a.m. 11a.m. 1p.m. 3p.m. 5p.m. 7p.m.

   (b) **(i)** 3.30 p.m.   **(ii)** 7 trains

A3: LINEAR AND NON-LINEAR GRAPHS

1 **(a)** C: $x = -2$
   (b) A: $m = \frac{2}{3}, c = 2$ B: $m = -\frac{3}{5}, c = 3$
        D: $m = 0, c = 4$

2 **(a)** **(ii)** Because the values plotted lie in a straight line
   (b) **(i)** $a = 0.12, b = 850$ **(ii)** $P = 0.12S + 850$
   (c) **(i)** £850   **(ii)** 12%

3 **(a)** $3x + 2y = 60$
   (b) A(0, 20), B(30, 0), C(20, 0), D(0, 30), E(12, 12)
   (c) 240 square units

4 **(a)** **(i)** C   **(ii)** A   **(iii)** D
   (b)

$y = x^2 + p$

5 **(a)** A: $x^3 - 3x$ B: $x^2 - 3$ C: $\frac{3}{x^2}$
   (b)

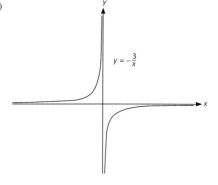

$y = -\frac{3}{x}$

A4: TRANSFORMATIONS OF GRAPHS

1 A: $y = x^2 + 2$ B: $y = (x + 1)^2$ C: $y = (x - 3)^2$
   D: $y = (x - 2)^2 + 1$ E: $y = (x + 4)^2 - 2$

2 **(a)**

$y = x^2$

(b)

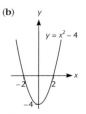

$y = x^2 - 4$

(c)

$y = (x - 2)^2$

(d)

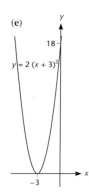

$y = 3x^2$

(e)

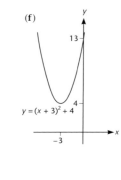

$y = 2(x + 3)^2$

(f)

$y = (x + 3)^2 + 4$

3 **(a)**

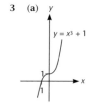

$y = x^3 + 1$

(b)

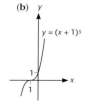

$y = (x + 1)^3$

(c)

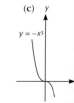

$y = -x^3$

4

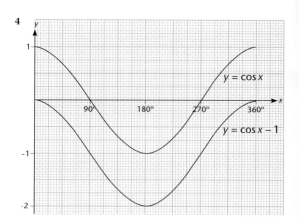

$y = \cos x$

$y = \cos x - 1$

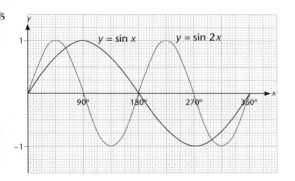

5 $y = \sin x$, $y = \sin 2x$

6 $y = -x^2$; $y = (x - 1)^2 - 1$; $y = (x + 1)^2 - 1$

7 (a)

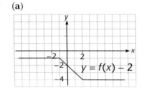
$y = f(x) - 2$

(b)

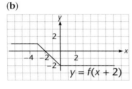
$y = f(x + 2)$

(c)

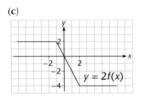
$y = 2f(x)$

(d)

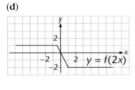
$y = f(2x)$

(e)

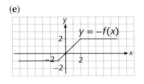
$y = -f(x)$

(f)

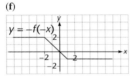
$y = -f(-x)$

A5: AREA UNDER A GRAPH AND TANGENTS TO CURVES

1 (a)

x	-3	-2	-1	0	1	2	3
y	-8	6	8	4	0	2	16

(b) 7 when $x = 2$; -2 when $x = -1$

2 26 seconds

3 (a)

Time in seconds (t)	0	1	1.5	2	3	4
Height in metres (h)	20	30	31.25	30	20	0

(c) 3.6 secs (d) Under the sea
(e) About -15 m/sec

4 (a) $2.6\,\text{ms}^{-2}$ (b) 38 metres

5 (a) About $1.7\,\text{ms}^{-2}$
(b) About 36 metres (using 2 steps for 0 to 4 seconds)

6 (b) $0.211\,\text{m}^2$ (c) Overestimate

A6: MANIPULATING ALGEBRAIC EXPRESSIONS

1 (a) $-2x^2 + 9xy$ (b) $-3p^3 - 7q^3 + 3pq^2$
(c) $12x^5$ (d) $35x^3y^4$
(e) $27a^6$ (f) $\dfrac{c^2}{3b}$
(g) $\dfrac{9a}{2b}$ (h) $6p^2q^2$

2 A: Perimeter $= (2x + 12)$ units; area $= 2x + 8$ square units
B: Perimeter $= (8x + 2)$ units; area $= 3x^2$ square units

3 (a) $\dfrac{x + 25}{x^2 + 5x - 14}$ (b) $\dfrac{8}{a^2 - 1}$
(c) $\dfrac{a^2 - b^2}{2a^2 + 5ab + 2b^2}$ (d) $\dfrac{p^2 + q^2}{p^2q + pq^2}$

4 (a) $\dfrac{x - y}{x + 2}$ (b) $\dfrac{2x - 1}{x + 3}$
(c) $\dfrac{a - 2}{a + 2}$ (d) $\dfrac{a - 2}{2a - 3}$

5 (a) $\dfrac{n - 1}{n - 2}$ (b) 1
(c) $\dfrac{3}{n^3 - 4n^2 - 5n}$ (d) $2n^2 + 18$

A7: ALGEBRAIC EXPRESSIONS USING BRACKETS

1 (a) $3a^3 - 7a$ (b) $6x + 35$
(c) $13a + 1$ (d) $x^3 - y^3$

2 (a) $2x^2 - 11x + 15$ (b) $2x^2 - 5x - 12$
(c) $6x^2 - 11x + 3$ (d) $6x^2 - x - 2$

3 (a) $x^2 - 4xy + 4y^2$ (b) $a^4 + 2a^2b^2 + b^4$
(c) $4ab$ (d) $5p^2 + 8pq + 5q^2$

4 (a) $a^2 + 2ab + b^2 + 2a + 2b + 1$
(b) $x^2 - y^2 + 3x - y + 2$
(c) $x^2 + 4y^2 + 9z^2 + 4xy - 12yz - 6xz$
(d) $3a^2 + 3b^2 + 3c^2 - 2ab - 2bc - 2ac$

5 (a) $(3 + x)^2\,\text{cm}^2$
(b) $9 + 6x + x^2 = 10 \Rightarrow x^2 + 6x = 1$

A8: FACTORISING INCLUDING COMPLETING THE SQUARE

1 (a) $4x(1 - 4x)$ (b) $2a(2a + 3b)$
(c) $4ab(b - 2a)$ (d) $4xyz(5xy - 9yz + 6xz)$

2 (a) $(a + 2)(a - 6)$ (b) $(a + 6b)(a - 3b)$
(c) $(a - 5b)(a + 5b)$ (d) $(a + 2b)^2$

3 (a) $(a - c)(b + d)$ (b) $(2x - y)(3x - 2)$
(c) $(a - d)(a + b + c)$ (d) $(2a - 3c)(3b + 4d)$

4 (a) $(3x - 4)(x - 5)$ (b) $(2x - 3)^2$
(c) $(3a - 2b)(2a - 3b)$ (d) $(6x - 5y)(4x + 3y)$

5 (a) $2(x - 2y)(x + 2y)$ (b) $3(2n - 1)(2n + 1)$
(c) $7(3x - 2y)(3x + 2y)$ (d) $3a(a - 5b)(a + 5b)$

6 $a = 3$, $b = 10$

7 (a) $(x - 4)^2 + 2$ (b) $(x + 2)^2 - 9$
(c) $2(x + 1)^2 - 1$ (d) $(x - 3.5)^2 - 5.25$

A9: CHANGING THE SUBJECT OF A FORMULA

1   $p = \dfrac{y + 49}{5}$

2   (a) $v = \dfrac{2s - ut}{t}$ (b) $u = \sqrt{v^2 - 2as}$

3   (a) $h = \dfrac{E - \frac{1}{2}mv^2}{mg}$ (b) $v = \sqrt{\dfrac{2(E - mgh)}{m}}$

4   $a = \dfrac{7b + 10}{3b + 2}$

5   (a) $R = \dfrac{ST}{S + T}$ (b) $T = \dfrac{SR}{S - R}$

6   (a)   32 000 coins   (b) $d = \sqrt{\dfrac{k}{N}}$
    (c)   4 cm

7   (a)   (i) $v = \dfrac{fu}{u - f}$ (ii)   120 cm

    (b)   (i) $R_2 = \dfrac{RR_1}{R_1 - R}$ (ii)   120 ohms

8   $x = \dfrac{3y}{7}$

9   (a) $b = \dfrac{a + 2a\sqrt{c}}{1 - \sqrt{c}}$ (b) $c = \left(\dfrac{b - a}{2a + b}\right)^2$

10 (a) $l = \dfrac{3d^2 + 8s^2}{3d}$ (b)   2.29 m

11 $m = \dfrac{M(16\pi^2 L - 3T^2 g)}{2T^2 g - 48\pi^2 L}$

12 (a) $V = \pi r^2 h = 2\pi r^3$; so, $r = \sqrt[3]{\dfrac{V}{2\pi}}$

    (b) $A = 2\pi r h + 2\pi r^2 = 6\pi r^2 = 6\pi\left(\dfrac{V}{2\pi}\right)^{\frac{2}{3}}$

    (c)   350 cm^2 (346.4 cm^2)

A10: LINEAR EQUATIONS

1   $x = 6$

2   (a) $x = \dfrac{4}{5}$ (b) $x = -\dfrac{3}{2}$

3   (a) $x = 18$ (b) $x = \dfrac{3}{20}$

4   (a) $x = -\dfrac{4}{5}$ (b) $x = -\dfrac{4}{7}$

5   $x = 45$

6   (a) $x = \dfrac{33}{10}$ (b) $x = \dfrac{8}{5}$ (c) $x = -\dfrac{22}{3}$

A11: INEQUALITIES AND LOCATING REGIONS BY LINES

1   (a) $x > -\dfrac{3}{2}$ (b) $y < -4$ (c) $x > 7$
    (d) $\dfrac{1}{2} < x < \dfrac{5}{2}$ (e) $-2 \leq x \leq 4$

2   (a)   7   (b)   −4   (c)   13

3   (a) $x < -9$ or $x > 5$ (b) $-4 < x < 0$
    (c) $x > -\dfrac{1}{2}$ (d) $x > \dfrac{3}{2}$

4   (a)
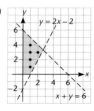

    (b)   (1, 1), (1, 2), (1, 3), (1, 4), (2, 3)

5   (a)
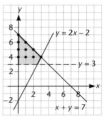

    (b)   (0, 4), (0, 5), (0, 6), (0, 7), (0, 8), (1, 4), (1, 5), (1, 6), (2, 4), (2, 5), (3, 4)

6   (a) $x > 3.5$
    (b) $x < -3.3$ or $0.7 < x < 2.6$
    (c) $x < -2.4$ or $-1 < x < 3.4$

7   (a)   (i) $15 \leq x + \dfrac{y}{2} \leq 24$ (ii) $x \leq y$
    (b)   Shaded region satisfies all four inequalities

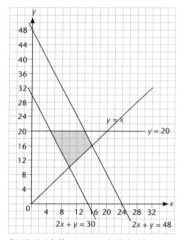

    (c)   2460 (14 full pages and 20 half pages)

8   (a) $50x + 50y \leq 4000$
    (b)   Hours worked by one employee = 5 × 9 + 5 = 50
          Hours worked by 12 employees = 600
          So, $6x + 10y \leq 600$, i.e. $3x + 5y \leq 300$
    (c)   (i) $x \geq 30$ (ii) $y \geq 20$

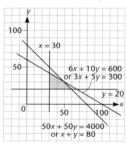

    (d) $P = 10x + 30y$
    (e)   30 Beechill; 42 Clary

A12: TRIAL AND IMPROVEMENT, INCLUDING SOLVING EQUATIONS

1   $x = 4.2$

2   (a) $x^3 - 16x = 300$ (b) $x = 7.49$

3   (a) $-3.1, 2.9$

    (b) $x = -0.8, x = 0.9$ or $x = 5.9$

4   (b) $(0, -5), (0.56, 0)$

5   (a)

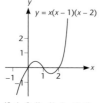

    $y = x(x - 1)(x - 2)$

    (b) $(0.4, 0.4), (1.6, -0.4)$

A13: QUADRATIC EQUATIONS

1   (a) $(3x - 8)(x + 2)$ (b) $x = 2\frac{2}{3}$ or $x = -2$

2   (a) $(x + 9)(x - 2)$ (b) $x = -9$ or $x = 2$

3   (a) $x = -7$ or $x = -5$ (b) $x = -1.5$ or $x = 5$

    (c) $x = -3.5$ (d) $x = \frac{7}{6}$ or $x = \frac{5}{2}$

4   (a) $x = -2.47$ or $x = 6.47$ (b) $x = -1.41$ or $x = 3.91$

    (c) $x = -0.62$ or $x = 1.62$ (d) $x = -1.47$ or $x = -0.39$

5   (a) $x^2 - 24x + 80 = 0$

    (b) $x = 20$ or $x = 4$; sides are $11\,\text{cm}, 60\,\text{cm}$ and $61\,\text{cm}$

    (c)   A triangle with sides $5\,\text{cm}, 12\,\text{cm}$ and $13\,\text{cm}$ (the other solution gives these but with one side negative)

6   $y = -5$ or $y = -1$

7   $y = 1.37$ or $y = 2.63$

8   (a) $11x^2 + 19x - 510 = 0$

    (b) $x = -\frac{85}{11}$ or $x = 6$

    Volume of cuboid $= 10\,\text{cm} \times 14\,\text{cm} \times 15\,\text{cm} = 2100\,\text{cm}^3$

9   $\dfrac{306}{x + 1} = \dfrac{272}{x} + 1$ so $x = 16$ or $x = 17$

    New values for mean are 17 or 18

0   (a)   Height is $\dfrac{210}{(x + 2)(2x - 1)}$

    Two vertical faces have area $\dfrac{210}{2x - 1}$ and the other two have area $\dfrac{210}{x + 2}$

    This gives the required equation

    (b) $x = 4$ or $x = -\frac{17}{26}$; $x = 4 \Rightarrow$ area of base $= 42\,\text{cm}^2$

1   (a) $2x^2 + 5x + 3$

    (b) $2x^2 + 5x + 3 = 66 \Rightarrow x = 4.5$ or $x = -7$

    Area of original lawn $= 40.5\,\text{m}^2$

    (c) $x = 8.2\,\text{m}$

2   (a) $x_2 = 3.316\,624\,79, x_3 = 3.211\,950\,309,$
    $x_4 = 3.195\,614\,23$

    (b) $x = 3.193$

A14: LINEAR SIMULTANEOUS EQUATIONS

1   (a) $x = 2, y = -1$ (b) $x = 2.5, y = 1.5$

2   (a) $x = 7, y = -1$ (b) $x = 8, y = -3$

    (c) $x = 5.5, y = 3.5$ (d) $x = 7, y = -4.5$

3   (a) $x = 2, y = 5$ (b) $x = 1, y = 1.5$

4   Dearer tickets are £13.50; cheaper are £8.75

5   Nightly fee is £2; season ticket is £11.50

6   5 packets and 2 cartons

A15: SOLVING EQUATIONS USING GRAPHS

1   (a) $x = -2.7$ or $x = 0.7$ (b) $x = -3.8$ or $x = 1.8$

    (c) $x = -1$

2   (b)   (i) $x = -2.6$ or $x = 1.6$

        (ii) $x = -2$ or $x = 1$

        (iii)   Draw $y = x + 4$; $x = -2.2$ or $x = 3.2$

3   (c) $x = -5$ or $x = 1$

    (d)   Draw $y = 3x + 3$; $x = -3.4$ or $x = 2.4$

4   (a)   Table of values

-3	-2	-1	0	1	2	3
-6	7	8	3	-2	-1	12

    (b)   (i)   Draw $y = 11$; $x = 2.95$

        (ii)   Draw $y = x + 2$; $x = -2.7, x = 0.1$ or $x = 2.6$

5   (a)   Table of values

-3	-2	-1	0	1	2	3
0.125	0.25	0.5	1	2	4	8

    (b)   Draw $y = x + 3$; solutions are $x = 2.4$ or $x = -2.9$

    (c)   Draw $y = \frac{1}{2}x^2$; solution is $x = -1$

6   (a)   Table of values

-2	-1	0	1	2	3
-6	4	4	0	-2	4

    (b) $x = -1.6, x = 1$ or $x = 2.6$

    (c) $p = 2, q = 5$

    (d) $x = 2.5$

7   (a)   Table of values

-2	-1.5	-1	-0.5	0.5	1	1.5	2	2.5	3
2.75	2.56	2	-1	-1	2	2.56	2.75	2.84	2.89

    (b)   If $3 - \dfrac{1}{x^2} = x$, then $3x^2 - 1 = x^3 \Rightarrow x^3 - 3x^2 + 1 = 0$

    $x = -0.5, x = 0.7$ or $x = 2.9$

    (c)   Use $y = x^2$; solutions are $x = -1.6, x = -0.6,$
    $x = 0.6$ or $x = 1.6$

A16: SELECTING FUNCTIONS TO FIT SETS OF DATA

1   $m = d^2 + 3$

2   $L = \dfrac{15}{R}$

3   (a) $k = 5$ (b) $n = 2$

    (c)   The value for 0.8 should be 3.2

4 **(a)** Because the points lie on a straight line

(b) $a = 15$, $b = 6000$ **(c)** £58 500

(d) 2600 items   **(e)** 600 items

5 **(a)** A straight–line graph

(b)

h (hours)	0.333	0.750	1.083	1.500	2.167
$(0.5)^h$	0.794	0.595	0.472	0.354	0.223
T (°C)	78	65	54	46	40

(c) $a = 65$, $b = 24$

(d) **(i)** 1   **(ii)** 89°C

6 $a = 40$, $b = -5$. $h = 40 - 5t^2$

MISCELLANEOUS EXERCISE

1 **(a)** $3n + 1$

(b) $n^2 + 3$

(c) **(i)** 4, 7, 14   **(ii)** 532 (17th term)

2 **(a)** $x = 0$ or $x = 9$ **(b)** $x = -1$ or $x = 10$

(c) $x = 4$ or $x = 5$ **(d)** $x = -0.5$ or $x = 5$

(e) $x = -\frac{1}{5}$ or $x = 2$

3 **(a)** $x = 3$, $y = -2$ **(b)** $x = 3.5$, $y = -1.5$

4 **(a)** **(i)** $7(p - 3)(p + 3)$ **(ii)** $(2n + 3)(n - 2)$

(b) **(i)** $\dfrac{x - 2}{x - y}$ **(ii)** $\dfrac{a^2 + b^2}{a^2 - b^2}$

(iii) $\dfrac{3}{y(y + 2)}$

5 **(a)** **(i)** $(x - 3)^2 + 1$; $p = -3$, $q = 1$

(ii)

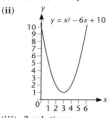

$y = x^2 - 6x + 10$

(iii) 2 solutions

6 **(a)** $p = 2$

(b) The given curve translated by $\begin{pmatrix} -2 \\ 0 \end{pmatrix}$

7 **(a)** $x + y \leq 80$ **(b)** $x \geq 20$, $y \geq 15$

(c) $5x + 8y \geq 240$

(d) Shaded area illustrates the four inequalities

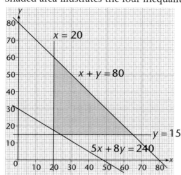

(e) **(i)** $x = 65$, $y = 15$ **(ii)** $x = 20$, $y = 18$

8 **(a)** $x = 1.1$ or $x = 3.7$ **(b)** $x = 1.6$ or $x = 2.8$

(c) $p = 2$, $q = 1$

9 **(b)** About -7

(c) 16.9, occurs when $x = 0.6$

(d) Draw $y = 5 - 2x$; $x = -0.7$, $x = 3.2$ or $x = 4.5$

10 **(a)** Passes through the origin

(b) Passes through (0, 1), (2, 0) and (−2, 0)

(c) Passes through (0, −3), (2, 0) and (−2, 0)

(d) Passes through (0, −1), (4, 0) and (−4, 0)

(e) Passes through (−2, −1), (−4, 0) and origin.

11 **(b)** About 35 000 m³

12 **(a)** **(i)**

d	0.50	0.75	1.00	1.25	1.50
t^2	1.74	2.56	3.35	4.20	5.06

(b) Points lie on a straight line

(c) $k = 0.3$

13 **(a)** Graph is a straight line through the origin

(b)

(c) **(i)** $d = \dfrac{t^2}{10}$ **(ii)** About 1.2 cm/s

14 **(a)** **(i)** $P = \dfrac{100A}{100 + TR}$ **(ii)** £2000

(b) $r = 4.32$

15 **(a)** $\dfrac{20}{x} + \dfrac{20}{x - 2} = 4$

(b) $20(x - 2) + 20x = 4x(x - 2)$

$\Rightarrow 4x^2 - 48x + 40 = 0$

$\Rightarrow x^2 - 12x + 10 = 0$

(c) $x = 0.9$ or $x = 11.1$

(d) Only one solution, 11.1, can be reduced by 2 and remain positive

S1: 3D OBJECTS AND THEIR 2D REPRESENTATION

1 C

2

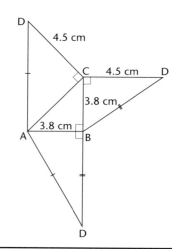

3 **(a)** 4 faces, 6 edges and 4 vertices

    (b) 7 faces, 15 edges and 10 vertices

4 11.7 cm

5 Here is one possible net for a tetrahedron with edge length 2 units

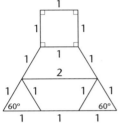

S2: CONGRUENT TRIANGLES

1 **(a)** and **(b)** E.g.

2 $y = 7.7$ cm

3 If they were congruent, the longest side of both triangles would be 8 cm which would make them isosceles with two angles of 100°!

4 AO = OB radii, ∠AOE = ∠BOE = 90°, EO is common
So, triangles are congruent
So, AE = BE and triangle AEB is isosceles

5 FY = AF (radii) = OF (because AOF is equilateral)
= OD (radii) = OX (radii)
∠AFY = ∠XOD = 30°
So triangles AFY and XOD are congruent (two sides and included angle equal)

6 **(a)** AD = AB (sides of equilateral triangle); AC = AE (sides of equilateral triangle); ∠DAC = ∠BAE (both angles are ∠BAC + 60°)
So, triangles are congruent (SAS)

    (b) So ∠ADC = ∠ABE, i.e. ∠ADX = ∠ABX

    (c) ∠BXC = ∠BDX + ∠DBX
= 60° − ∠ADX + 60° + ∠ABX = 120°

S3: ANGLE AND SYMMETRY PROPERTIES OF TRIANGLES AND QUADRILATERALS

1 **(a)** $u = 68°$ **(b)** $v = 44°$

2 **(a)** 40°   **(b)** 145°

3 **(a)**

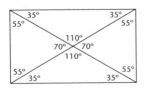

(b)

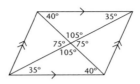

4 **(a)** Parallelogram

    (b) Rhombus or rectangle

5 A: No; it could be a kite

    B: Yes; at least two vertices do not lie on line of symmetry and the angles at these must be equal

    C: Yes; at least two sides do not intersect the line of symmetry at an internal point and these must be equal

    D: No; this is not true for an isosceles trapezium

S4: ANGLE AND SYMMETRY PROPERTIES OF POLYGONS

1 $j = 129°$

2 **(a)** 7 sides   **(b)** 140°

3 $p = 66°$

4 **(a)** 18 sides   **(b)** 20 sides

5 **(b)** Either none or one

6 36°, 36°, 108° (twice) and 36°, 72°, 72°

S5: CIRCLE THEOREMS

1 $e = 86°$, $f = 94°$, $g = 54°$

2 $h = 71°$

3 $i = 124°$

4 $j = 76°$, $k = 42°$

5 $l = 52°$

6 **(a)** Yes

    (b) Always: A and D
Never: B and C
Sometimes: E and F

7 **(a)** **(i)** Radius is perpendicular to tangent

        (ii) Triangles ATO and BTO are congruent (right–angle, side, hypotenuse)

        (iii) C is centre of circle passing through T, A, O

    (b) 20°

8 **(a)** 42°   **(b)** 144°

9 12 cm

10 4 cm or 44 cm

S6: PYTHAGORAS' THEOREM

1 $a = 2.5$ cm, $b = 2$ cm

2 13 units

3 **(a)** 7.3 cm   **(b)** 1.4 cm

4 5.7 cm

5   Lengths are √65, √65 and √26

6   Lengths are √14 and √28; √14:√28 = 1:√2

S7: TRIGONOMETRY

1   a = 3.8 cm; b = 7.4 cm; x = 58°; y = 62°; p = 8.8 cm; q = 20 m

2   (a)   3

    (b)   (i) $\frac{2}{\sqrt{5}}$ (ii) $\frac{2}{3}$ (iii) $\frac{5}{6}$

3   (a) $\frac{1}{2}$ (b)   √3   (c) $\frac{\sqrt{3}}{2}$

    (d) $\frac{1}{\sqrt{3}} = \frac{\sqrt{3}}{3}$ (e) $\frac{1}{\sqrt{2}} = \frac{\sqrt{2}}{2}$ (f)   1

4   28 km

5   (a)   No (66°)

    (b)   Between 0.78 m and 1.54 m

6   12 800 km

7   (a)   35°   (b)   68°

8   (a)   56°   (b)   47°

9   (a)   23.5 nautical miles

    (b)   9.7 nautical miles

    (c)   022°

10   (a)   4√2 cm = 5.66 cm

    (b)   109°

    (c)   90°

S8: SINE, COSINE AND TANGENT OF ANGLES OF ANY SIZE, INCLUDING TRIGONOMETRIC EQUATIONS

1   (a)   (i)   θ = 60° or θ = 300°

        (ii)   θ = 56° or θ = 236°

        (iii)   θ = 219° or θ = 321°

    (b)   E.g. 144°, 396°

2   y = 3 sin 2x

3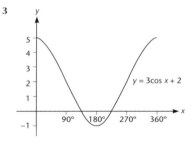

4   (a) x = 60° or x = 300°

    (b) x = 135° or x = 225°

    (c) x = 30° or x = 210°

5   (a)   (i)   13 m   (ii)   11.5 m

        (iii)   5.0 m

(b)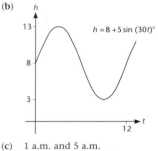

(c)   1 a.m. and 5 a.m.

S9: SINE AND COSINE RULES AND $\frac{1}{2}AB\sin C$

1   52.5°

2   (a)   31.8 cm²   (b)   8.0 cm

    (c)   71.8°

3   34.0°

4   (a)   32°   (b)   18.7 cm

5   24 m

6   (a)   40 cm²   (b)   77°

S10: TRANSFORMATIONS

1   (a) $\begin{pmatrix} -4 \\ -3 \end{pmatrix}$ (b)   (3, 9)

2   (a) and (b)

    (c)   Rotation of 90° clockwise about (1, 1)

3   (a) and (b)

    (c)   Reflection in $y = 1 - x$

4   (a)   2   (b)   (5, 1)

5   (b)   P′ is at (4, 2), Q′ at (8, 2) and R′ at (8, 8)

    (c)   P″ is at (7, –1), Q″ at (5, –1) and R″ at (5, –4)

    (d)   Half turn about (4.5, 0)

    (e)   Translation by $\begin{pmatrix} 3 \\ 0 \end{pmatrix}$

6   A: Two reflections in parallel lines

    B: Different centres of enlargement and scale factors k and $\frac{1}{k}$

    C: Rotations through equal and opposite angles about different centres

7 (a) (i) Translation by $\begin{pmatrix} 0 \\ -30 \end{pmatrix}$

(ii) Reflection in $y = 15$

(b)

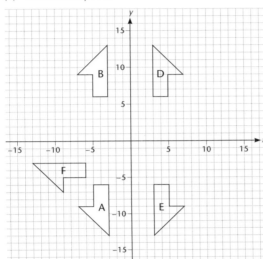

(c) E.g. Rotate 180° about origin and then reflect in y–axis

8 (a) Translation by $\begin{pmatrix} 3 \\ -6 \end{pmatrix}$

(b) Reflection in $y = -x$

(c) B $\underset{P}{\rightarrow}$ (1, –3), (3, –3), (1, –4) $\underset{Q}{\rightarrow}$ (–2, 0) (–2, 2), (–3, 0) = D

1 (a) (i) $\begin{pmatrix} 0 & 1 \\ 1 & 0 \end{pmatrix}$ **(ii)** $\begin{pmatrix} 3 & 0 \\ 0 & 3 \end{pmatrix}$

(b) $\begin{pmatrix} 0 & 3 \\ 3 & 0 \end{pmatrix}$

2 (a)

(b) Reflection in line $y = \frac{x}{3}$

3 (a) and (b)

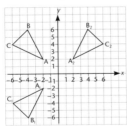

(c) (i) Reflection in y–axis

(ii) Half turn about origin or enlargement with centre origin and scale factor –1

4 (a) and (b)

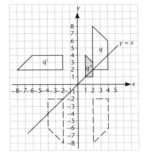

(a) (ii) Rotation about origin through 90° anticlockwise

(b) (ii) Enlargement with scale factor 2 and centre the origin

(iii) $\begin{pmatrix} 2 & 0 \\ 0 & 2 \end{pmatrix}$

5 (a) and (b)

(c) Rotation 45° clockwise about origin.
Enlargement with scale factor √2 and centre the origin.

1

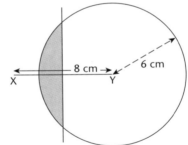

2

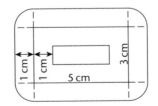

3
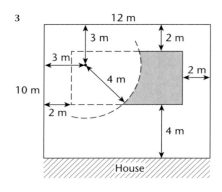

4 Quarter circle, radius √13, centre C

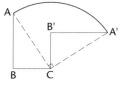

5

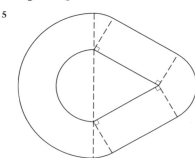

6 (a)

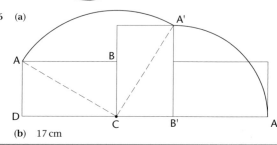

(b)   17 cm

S13: RULER AND COMPASS CONSTRUCTIONS

1   6 cm to 6.1 cm

2   (b)   3.4 cm to 3.5 cm

3   5.7 cm

4   3.6 cm

7   (c)   They all meet at a point

S14: UNITS OF MEASUREMENT, CONVERSIONS AND COMPOUND MEASURES, INCLUDING SPEED AND DENSITY

1   30 m.p.h. is slower (30 m.p.h. = 48 k.p.h.;
    50 k.p.h. = 31.25 m.p.h.)

2   4 inches

3   £14

4   4.84 lb

5   (a)   720 miles   (b)   120 miles
    (c)   1140 miles   (d)   408 miles

6   (a)   744 km/min   (b)   12 400 m/s

7   (a)   (i) 7.9×10^{-3} kg/cm³   (ii)   7.9 g/cm³
    (b)   6320 kg

8   0.875 g/cm³

9   6.1×10^{19} m³

10 1.26×10^{-3} miles/sec²

S15: UPPER AND LOWER BOUNDS OF MEASURED AND CALCULATED VALUES

1   (a)   26 750, 26 849   (b)   125 km², 135 km²
    (c)   198, 215

2   (a)   10.335 s, 10.345 s   (b)   9.66 m/s, 9.68 m/s

3   (a)   65 m.p.h., 67 m.p.h.
    (b)   116.5 miles, 125.6 miles

4   6.57 cm, 6.77 cm

5   (a)   575.25 cm²
    (b) $(x + 0.5)^2 - (x - 0.5)^2 = 2x$

6   (a)   170 cm³   (b)   2.95 cm
    (c)   Upper bound = 175.8 cm³; lower bound = 163.6 cm³; 7%

S16: AREAS AND PERIMETERS OF TRIANGLES, QUADRILATERALS AND CIRCLES, INCLUDING SEGMENTS AND SECTORS

1   A: 10 cm²   B: 143 cm²   C: 26 cm²   D: 23 cm²

2   356 cm²

3   27 cm

4   (a)   4.1 m² to 2 s.f.   (b)   8.4 m to 2 s.f.

5   4.78 cm²

6   64.2 cm²

7   120 cm²

8   (a)   Circumference = 5π cm; Area = 6.25π cm²
    (b)   Radius = 6 cm

9   (a)   20π cm²   (b) $\frac{100\pi}{9}$ cm²

10 (a)   15.3 cm²   (b)   16.5 cm

11 35.5 cm²

12 6.9 cm²

13 (a)   3070 cm²   (b)   305 litres   (c)   6.60 m²

14 (a)   92.7 m   (b)   4320 m²

15 (a)   51.0 cm   (b)   242 cm²

S17: VOLUME AND SURFACE AREA OF PRISMS, PYRAMIDS, CONES AND SPHERES

1 (a) 6 cm   (b) 188 cm²

2 32 cuboids, with the 5 cm along the 10 cm, the 3 cm along the 12 cm and the 2 cm along the 8 cm

3 40 cm

4 245 cm³

5 (a) 498.9 cm³ or 499 cm³ or 500 cm³
   (b) 11.6 cm by 24.2 cm

6 240 cm³; 288 cm²

7 (a) 700 m³   (b) 700 000 litres

8 11 cm

9 (a) 2.6 m²   (b) 3.9 m³   (c) 17 420 kg

10 18.4 cm

11 51.7 mm²

12 36π cm²

13 (a) 77.2 cm³   (b) 3.6 cm   (c) 1.7 cm

14 101 cm³

15 2640 cm³

S18: DISTINGUISH BETWEEN FORMULAE BY CONSIDERING DIMENSIONS

1 Length: πd, $a + 2c$, $\pi(a + b)$ Area: πab, $r\sqrt{p^2 + q^2}$, $\frac{ab}{2}$

2 $4p^2q$, $xy\sqrt{u^2 + v^2}$

3 Length: $\sqrt[3]{\frac{3V}{4\pi}}$, $\sqrt{\frac{V}{\pi h}}$

   Area: $\frac{V}{h}$, $2\pi r(r + h)$

   Volume: None of these

   $\pi r^2 A$ is not a formula for length, area or volume

4 (a) Yes   (b) Yes   (c) No   (d) Yes

5 $\frac{1}{3}\pi h(b^2 + ab + a^2)$

S19: SIMILAR FIGURES AND SIMILAR SOLIDS

1 (a) Same angles   (b) 92 cm²

2 (a) 12 cm   (b) 10 cm

3 $p = 4.5$ cm, $q = 7.2$ cm

4 (a) They have 90° and angle A in common
   (b) AD = 2.8 cm

5 (a) 6 cm × 24 cm × 36 cm   (b) 27 small packets
   (c) 19.8 cm² or 20 cm² (more sensibly)

6 2.2 m

7 (a) 100 000 m²   (b) 0.1 km²

8 $y = 3.5$, $V = 49$

9

	Real	Model
Area of dining room floor to be tiled	12.5 m²	868 cm²
Area of bedroom rug	0.767 m²	53.3 cm²
Length of stair carpet rod	38 cm	3.2 m
Number of treads on stairs between first and second floor	18	18
Capacity of wardrobe	1.05 m³	610 cm³

10 (a) 9:4   (b) 27:8

11 (a) 420 cm³   (b) 720 cm³

12 (a) 2500 cm³   (b) 2200 cm³

S20: VECTORS

1 (a) $\begin{pmatrix} -4 \\ 8 \end{pmatrix}$ (b) $\begin{pmatrix} -3 \\ 9 \end{pmatrix}$ (c) $\begin{pmatrix} 0 \\ -2 \end{pmatrix}$

2 (a) $\overrightarrow{OC} = \frac{1}{4}\mathbf{b}$ (b) $\overrightarrow{AB} = \mathbf{b} - \mathbf{a}$; $\overrightarrow{AD} = \frac{1}{4}(\mathbf{b} - \mathbf{a})$
   (c) $\overrightarrow{CD} = \frac{3}{4}\mathbf{a}$ (d) Similar to triangle BOA because $\overrightarrow{CD}$ is parallel to $\overrightarrow{OA}$

3 (a) $\overrightarrow{OP} = \frac{3}{4}\mathbf{a} + \frac{3}{4}\mathbf{b}$; $\overrightarrow{OQ} = \frac{3}{4}\mathbf{a} + \mathbf{b}$
   (b) $\overrightarrow{AP} = \frac{(3\mathbf{b} - \mathbf{a})}{4}$, $\overrightarrow{PQ} = \frac{3\mathbf{b} - \mathbf{a}}{12}$

   So $\overrightarrow{AP} = 3\overrightarrow{PQ}$ which means that APQ is a straight line and AP:PQ = 3:1

4 (a) (i) $2\mathbf{a}$ (ii) $\mathbf{a} - \mathbf{b}$ (iii) $-\mathbf{b} - \mathbf{a}$
   (b) (i) $\mathbf{a} - \mathbf{b}$
        (ii) Both $\overrightarrow{BA}$ and $\overrightarrow{AX}$ have same vector $\mathbf{a} - \mathbf{b}$

5 On a bearing of 264.3°

6 7.2 N at an angle of 74° with the 6 N force

7 (a) Distances will be in same ratio as speeds (0.9: 1.5)
        ⇒ distance is 24 m
   (b) 84° (scale drawing or sine rule in velocity triangle)

8 (b) (i) 23.8 kph   (ii) 261°

MISCELLANEOUS EXERCISE

1 (a) Perimeter is 408 m, race needs less than 1 lap
   (b) 9400 m²

2 1.02 m²

3 (a) $p = 8.5$ cm; $q = 16$ cm
   (b) Equal angles (parallel lines), $r = 3.2$ cm, $s = 4.5$ cm

4 (a) and (b)

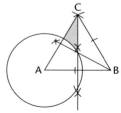

5 $\pi r^2 l$, $4\pi r^3$, $3(a^2 + b^2)r$

6 39.3 m.p.h., 37.4 m.p.h.

7 (a) 44.2 cm²   (b) 46.7 cm³

Nelson GCSE Maths   ANSWERS TO REVISION GUIDE EXERCISES (HIGHER)

8 (a) and (b) 80°

9 (a) 24 cm (b) 1680 cm²
(c) 336 000 cm³ or 336 litres (d) 25 100 cm³ or 25.1 litres
(e) 14 cylinders

10 (a) 16.6 cm (b) 2.8 cm

11 (a) 201 m³ (b) 1.9 m

12 (a) 15.7 cm
(b) (i) 2.5 cm (ii) 130 cm³

13 62°

14 (a) $x = 63.4$ or $x = 243.4$
(b)

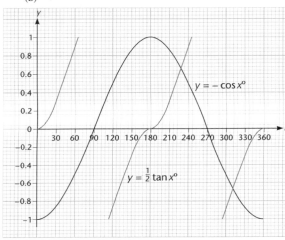

(c) $x = 231.3$ or $x = 308.7$ (calculated answers)

D1: QUESTIONNAIRES AND SAMPLING METHODS

1 Question only asks about last week; only accesses people with a telephone; likely to exclude children and old people in homes; sample small

2 (a) Biased sample (people will only write in if against); very small sample
(b) Randomly selected; needs to be a representative sample

3 (a) Representative sample (not biased); randomly selected
(b) Need to select people with more than 5 years' experience of driving; small sample
(c) Questionnaire needs to cover at least: gender; number of years of driving experience; number of accidents Questions need to have boxes for giving responses

4 12 or 13 sixth formers; 38 or 37 from rest of school

5 Select randomly, e.g. by numbering students and selecting random numbers
Size of sample should reflect size of groups;
e.g., for a 10% sample

	Y12	Y13
Boys	25	20
Girls	20	22

6 (a) Everyone is not equally likely to be selected (e.g. if you live in a house with a lot of other people you are less likely to be selected)
(b) Number the people 00 to 46; select digits in pairs; if number selected is between 47 and 93 subtract 47; if it is more than 93 reject; so, starting from the beginning, one would select people with numbers 29, 8, 7, 46, 24

D2: FREQUENCY POLYGONS AND PIE CHARTS

1 (b) Plot (2500, 1), (7500, 9), (12 500, 10), (17 500, 13), (22 500, 3)

2 (a)

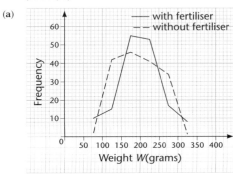

(b) Increases mean weight; decreases spread

3 (a) (i) 9% (ii) 162°
(b) (i) 25° (ii) 38%
(d) Wholemeal: higher fibre (7% compared with 2%) and lower carbohydrate (38% compared with 45%)

4 (a) 28% (b) 13.9 cm

5 (a) 10° (b) 1.75 km² (c) 28%

D3: HISTOGRAMS WITH EQUAL AND UNEQUAL INTERVALS

1 (a) Missing values are 115 and 105

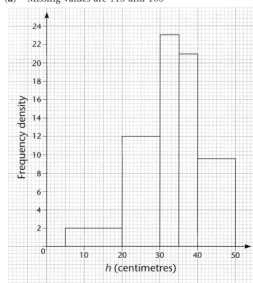

(b) 34 seeds

2 (a) $x = 2$ **(b)** Missing entry: 15

(c)

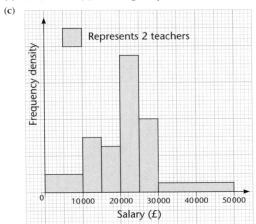

3

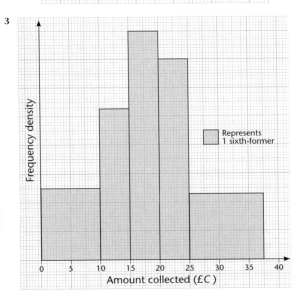

4 Frequency densities: 0.1, 0.68, 0.8, 0.64, 0.56, 0.12

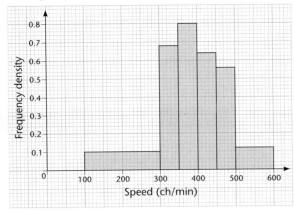

5 (a) 1, 7.5, 9.5, 4, 1

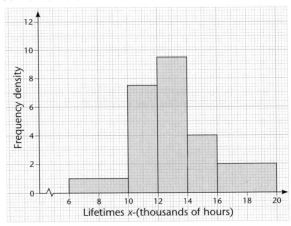

(b) $\frac{24}{50} = 0.48$

(c) Second company; more bulbs last longer

D4: SCATTER DIAGRAMS AND LINES OF BEST FIT

1 (a)

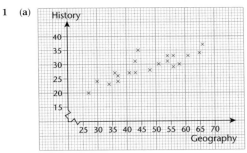

(b) About 33 marks

(c) There is evidence for positive correlation between the marks for the Geography and History tests and, so, the statement is false

2 (a) and **(b)** Negative (inverse) correlation

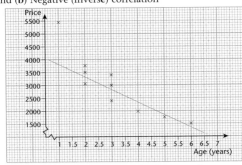

(c) About £2600   **(d)** Just over 2 years

3 (a) No; there is evidence of negative correlation, which means that good bowlers are good batsmen

(b) B

(c) G

4 **(b)** Positive   **(d)** Just over 70%

    (e) Student A

5 **(b)** Positive

    (c) Plot (1.31, 10.1)

    (d) Bournemouth, Saunton, Southsea

    (e) Fishguard

D5: MEANS OF FREQUENCY DISTRIBUTIONS

1 1.2 hours

2 2.748 cm

3 **(a)** 5.16 letters

    (b) 5 letters; 5 letters

    (c) **(i)** The medians of the two books are the same
            The range is larger in Book 5 so there are
            some longer words in Book 5
            These long words might cause difficulty

        (ii) The range is the same for both books
             The median for Book 2 is smaller than that
             of Book 4
             Book 2 is probably easier to read than Book 4
             because it has a greater number of short words

4 **(a)** **(i)** $20 \leq t < 24$ **(ii)** 23 mins

    (b) 14 mins

5 **(a)** 171 cm   **(b)** 5 ft 7 ins

D6: CUMULATIVE FREQUENCY, MEDIAN AND INTERQUARTILE RANGE

1 **(a)** 1740 mm   **(b)** 1615 mm, 1850 mm

    (c) About 92%   **(d)** About 8%

2 **(a)** 10 years, 58 years   **(b)** 41 years, 49 years

    (c) 45%, 77%   **(d)** 10%, 40%

3 **(a)**

Weight in grams	Frequency	Cumulative frequency
$0 < w < 10$	52	52
$10 \leq w < 20$	157	209
$20 \leq w < 30$	125	334
$30 \leq w < 40$	71	405
$40 \leq w < 50$	51	456
$50 \leq w < 60$	44	500

(b)

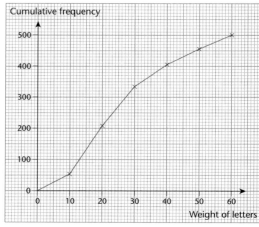

(c) Median is about 24 g

(d) About 70 letters

4 **(a)**

Length of call in minutes	Frequency	Cumulative frequency
$0 < t < 1$	52	52
$1 \leq t < 2$	204	256
$2 \leq t < 3$	109	365
$3 \leq t < 4$	33	398
$t \geq 4$	2	400
Total	400	

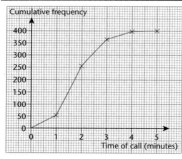

(b) Between 1.6 and 1.8 minutes

(c) The correct figure is less than 2.5 minutes
      (300 → 2.4 approx.)

5 **(a)** Cumulative frequencies: 2, 20, 47, 65, 77, 80

    (c) 1997: 48, 40, 57, 17

    (d) 1996 (upper quartile must be 60)

D7: STANDARD DEVIATION

1 **(a)** 12.1 cm, 0.6 cm

    (b) Only about 5% taller, but more consistent height

2 **(a)** 2.2 °C

    (b) **(i)** 292 K   **(ii)** 2.2 K

3 (a) Mean = 32.2; standard deviation = 7.82

(b) Standard deviation = 15.64

4 (a) Mean = 493.5; standard deviation = 10.6

(b) 483.5 (subtract 10); no change to standard deviation

(c) B; some emissions are very high

5 (a) Mean = 1.4 days; standard deviation = 0.8 days

(b) Second class take longer and the time is more variable. Some second class letters arrive before some first class letters.

(c) Increase mean by 1; does not change the standard deviation

6 (a) (i) Happy   (ii) Happy

     (iii) Doc   (iv) Dopey

(b) (i) No change   (ii) No change

     (iii) Grumpy   (iv) Sleepy

7 (a) Mean = 4.59%; standard deviation = 0.18%

(b) 9.18% and 0.36%

8 (a) Mean = 232 kWh; standard deviation = 39 kWh

(b) 209 kWh, 35 kWh

9 (a) Standard deviation = 20.9

0–20	20–30	30–40	40–50	50–60	60–100
20	20	30	50	40	40

(b) C (standard deviations are: A 25.4; B 26.1; C 16.8)

D8: BASIC PROBABILITY

1 (a) 58 boxes   (b) $\frac{5}{64}$

2 (a) 0.6

(b) Events are not exclusive; probabiity of lime or green paper = 0.5 (because all lime biscuits are in green paper)

(c) 15 biscuits

3 A: $\frac{1}{13}$ B: $\frac{1}{8}$ C: $\frac{2}{3}$ D: $\frac{1}{40}$ E: $\frac{1}{2}$ F: $\frac{3}{13}$

4 (a) (i) $\frac{1}{2}$ (ii) $\frac{1}{2}$ (iii) $\frac{1}{4}$

(b) (i) $\frac{3}{16}$ (ii) $\frac{3}{8}$ (iii) $\frac{1}{2}$

D9: ESTIMATING PROBABILITY

1 (a) $\frac{11}{80}$ (b) $\frac{69}{80}$

2 (a) Tracey: 0.22; Harmeet: 0.27

(b) Harmeet's estimate is likely to be more reliable, because his sample was bigger

3 (a) 0.22

(b) 0.35

(c) 293 red counters

(d) 235 red counters

(e) The answer to part (d), because it is a bigger sample

(f) Yes; he should obtain a better estimate
Exceeding the number of counters in the bag is irrelevant

4 (a)

Number of spins	Total number of 7s	Relative frequency
First 50	13	0.26
First 100	23	0.23
First 150	27	0.18
First 200	38	0.19
First 250	105	0.21

(b) Likely to be the last one, i.e. 0.21, because this uses the most data; in fact, the probability is 0.2

5 (a)

+	1	2	3	4	5	6	7	8
1	2	3	4	5	6	7	8	9
2	3	4	5	6	7	8	9	10
3	4	5	6	7	8	9	10	11
4	5	6	7	8	9	10	11	12

+	1	2	3	4	5	6
1	2	3	4	5	6	7
2	3	4	5	6	7	8
3	4	5	6	7	8	9
4	5	6	7	8	9	10
5	6	7	8	9	10	11
6	7	8	9	10	11	12

(b) Relative frequency: 0.03, 0.05, 0.088, 0.108, 0.136, 0.174, 0.132, 0.108, 0.086, 0.06, 0.028

(c) Set B; the relative frequency is largest for score 7
Table for Set A shows that the probability for scores of 5, 6, 7, 8 and 9 are the same
Table for Set B shows the largest probability is for score 7

D10: PROBABILITY OF COMBINED EVENTS INCLUDING CONDITIONAL PROBABILITY

1 (a)

(b) (i) $\frac{25}{324}$ (ii) $\frac{5}{27}$ (iii) $\frac{67}{162}$ (iv) $\frac{95}{162}$

2 (a)

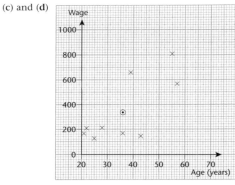

Peter $\frac{2}{3}$

Meeting

0.6 or $\frac{3}{5}$

Carlotta

No $\frac{1}{3}$

Meeting $\frac{3}{5}$

Meeting $\frac{1}{4}$

No

0.4 or $\frac{2}{5}$

No $\frac{3}{4}$

(b) (i) $\frac{2}{5}$ (ii) $\frac{3}{10}$

3 (a) $\frac{1}{11}$ (b) $\frac{19}{66}$ (c) $\frac{7}{22}$

4 (a) $\frac{1}{12}$

(b) (i) $\frac{1}{3}$ (ii) $\frac{1}{4}$

5 (a) (i) $\frac{1}{4}$ (ii) $\frac{1}{3}$

(b) $\frac{3}{4}$

6 (a) 0.09   (b) 0.41   (c) 0.51

7 (a) $\frac{1}{6}$ (b) $\frac{1}{2}$ (c) $\frac{1}{9}$ (d) $\frac{80}{81}$

MISCELLANEOUS EXERCISE

1 (a) Type y (b) Polygon is more spread out

2 (a) 36 years   (b) £338

(c) and (d)

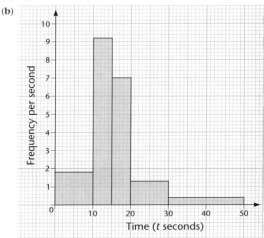

(e) The mean is not representative
There are 5 people with comparatively low wages
where age makes little difference
There are 3 people earning a lot more, of whom two
are significantly older than anyone else
So, although at first glance there is some indication of
positive correlation between wages and ages, there is
not any strong evidence for it

3 (a) 3, 10, 11   (b) 1, 2, 3, 7, 7

4 (a) No, because there are significantly more boys than girls
in year 8 (A 10% sample gives 8 or 9 boys and
6 or 7 girls)

(b) 15 pupils

5 (a) 13 biscuits (b) 6–10   (c) 30 students

6 Table entries: 32, (20,) 18, 4

7 (a) $\frac{2}{23}$ (b) $\frac{35}{69}$ (c) $\frac{185}{276}$

8 (a) 65.5 kg
(c) 66 kg
(d) 46 kg, 84 kg
(e) 73 kg – 57 kg = 16 kg
(f) Seems reasonable; 15% of women weigh more than 78 kg
well above the ideal weight
(g) 36%

9 (a) Curve to go through (5, 1), (12, 15), (15, 30), (21, 44)
and (37, 59)
(b) £9
(c) About 17 students

10 (a) (i) 0.144 (ii) 0.256
(b)

11 (a) $\frac{1}{10\,000}$ (b) 12

12 (a) Adrian   (b) Chris   (c) Jan   (d) David
(e) Chris

13 $\frac{3}{8}$

14 (a) £2300
(b) (i) £5010   (ii) £2300

15 (a)

(b) 23.8 hours
(c) 8.5 hours
(d) 14-year-olds watch more television; 14-year-olds are
more variable about the amount of television watched

COURSE REVISION EXERCISE 1

1 (a) 5.5×10^{-23} g
   (b) 3 people per household

2 (a) $a = 3$ (b) 99
   (c) $2^2 \times 3^3$

3 (a) $\frac{5}{33}$ (b) $\frac{53}{198}$

4 (a) Rational   (b) Irrational
   (c) Rational   (d) Irrational
   (e) Irrational   (f) Rational

5 (a) 43 Key Stage 4 and 57 Sixth Form, using the ratio 3:4.
   (b) E.g. number the students and then select numbers randomly

6 (a) $d = -4.2$ (b) $a = \frac{15 + d}{3 - d}$

7 (a) (i) $12a$ (ii) t^7
       (iii) 32   (iv) $\frac{1}{3}$
       (v) $\frac{27}{64}$
   (b) $3\,(x - 4y)\,(x + 4y)$ (c) $\frac{6\,(b + 2)}{b\,(b + 5)}$

8 (a) $(4.5, -0.75)$
   (b)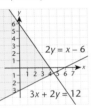
        $2y = x - 6$
        $3x + 2y = 12$

9 (a) No, because area is multiplied by 4 when length is doubled
   (b) Halve the diameter means divide the volume by $2^3 = 8$
        So 8 small spheres have same volume as one large one

10 (a) 24π cm^3 (b) $\frac{2}{3}$ cm

COURSE REVISION EXERCISE 2

1 (a) $r = 7.21 \times 10^{10}$ (b) $p = -0.095$

2 (a) Upper 28.6 cm, lower 28.2 cm
   (b) Upper 49.43 cm^2, lower 48.01 cm^2

3 (a) $x > 10$ (b) $-3 < x < 3$
   (c) $x = -4$ or $x = 7$

4 (a) H1, H2, H3, H4, H5, H6, T1, T2, T3, T4, T5, T6
   (b) $\frac{1}{4}$
   (c) $\frac{1}{6}$

5 (a) 86°   (b) 13.5 m^2
   (c) 32.4 m^3

6 (a)
t	0	1	2	3	4	5	6
h	6	8	9.5	10	9.5	8	6

   (c) 1.37 a.m. and 4.23 a.m.

7 (b) $x = 3.68$

8 (b) Diagonals of kite are at 90°
   (c) 4.07 cm, 16.1 cm^2

9 (a) £4348   (b) 10 years

10 (a) Mean = 55.3° F, standard deviation = 6.8° F
   (b) Widths: 10, 4, 4, 4, 8
        Heights: 0.6, 1.5, 2, 1.25, 0.625
   (c) Higher in June; less variable

COURSE REVISION EXERCISE 3

1 (a) 50 000
   (b) 80
   (c) (i) 1.35×10^{-10} (ii) 3×10^{20}

2 (a) 632.5g   (b) 25 cm

3 (a) and (b) E.g. $2 + \sqrt{5}$, $2 - \sqrt{5}$
   (c) E.g. $3 + \sqrt{2}$, $5 + \sqrt{2}$

4 (a) 14.925 m
   (b) Could have just about been a tie

5 (a) (i) $y = 54$ (ii) $x = 1$
   (b)

6 (a) $x = -2$, $y = 5$ (b) 3, 4, 5, ..., 12

7 (a) (i) $125t^3$ (ii) w^9
       (iii) 3^{10} (iv) $\frac{1}{9}$
       (v)   64
   (b) $x = 5$ or $x = 9$

8 (a)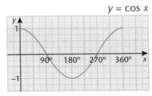
        $y = \cos x$
   (b) 318°

9 (a) $p = 128°$, $q = 52°$ (b) 20°

10 (a) (i) $\frac{35}{144}$ (ii) $\frac{37}{72}$
   (b) $\frac{31}{66}$

COURSE REVISION EXERCISE 4

1 (a) $2^2 \times 3^2 = 36$ (b) $2^3 \times 3^5 = 1944$

2 (a) 2.478×10^8 miles   (b) 1.56×10^9 miles

3 (a) E.g. 0, 7   (b) E.g. 5, −5
   (c) E.g. 3, 12

4 (a) 12.2 miles   (b) 2.7 miles

5 $x = -2.8$

6 (a) 19, 23; 48, 63
   (b) and (c)
        $4n - 1$ (144th term); $n^2 + 2n$ (23rd term)
   (d) In the first sequence, all terms are odd
        In the second sequence, all terms are 1 less than a square and 1001 is not square

7 (a) Table of values

x	-2	-1	0	1	2
y	9	6	5	6	9

(b) $x = -1.4$ or $x = 1.4$

(c) -2

(d) $26\,cm^2$

8 (b) BE = 4.6 cm, AE = 5.4 cm

(c) $31\,cm^2$

(d) $9.4\,cm^3$

9 (a) 1.25 km

(b) (i)   1.5 km   (ii)   185°

10 (a)

Height (cm)	Cumulative Frequency
25	3
30	20
35	44
40	74
45	96
50	119
55	130
60	135

(b) 39 cm

(c) 16 cm

(d) 18–19%

(e) Second is more consistent in height

(f) 5.1×10^{-5}

COURSE REVISION EXERCISE 5

1 (a) -1 (b) $x = 2 + \sqrt{3}$

2 (a) 5, 0.5, 50

(b) (i) 5^6 (ii) $5 = 5^1$

(iii) 5^3 (iv) 5^2

3 $\frac{9}{50}, \frac{2}{11}$

4 (a) $\sqrt{2}$ (b) $6\sqrt{3}$

(c) $20\sqrt{2}$ (d) $\frac{1 + \sqrt{2}}{2}$

(e) $24 + 12\sqrt{3}$

5 $Cos\,x = \frac{5}{\sqrt{28}}$, $sin\,x = \frac{\sqrt{3}}{\sqrt{28}}$

6 (a) $(-1, -4)$ should be $(-1, -2)$

(b) 3

(c) $y = 3x + 1$

7 (a) (i) $\frac{b^4}{a}$ (ii) $6t^4$

(iii) $\frac{3y + 4x}{x^2y^2}$ (iv) $\frac{3y}{4x}$

(b) (i) $S = 24$ (ii) $T = \frac{RS}{S - R}$

8 (b) $x = 5$

(c) $y = 2$

(d) Half turn about (5, 2)

(e) Vertices of E are $(-1, 3)$, $(-1, 6)$ and $(-2, 5)$

(f) Reflect in $x = 2.5$

9 (a) 36°   (b) 270° and 202.5°

10 (a) Blue 8; yellow 4; purple 8

(b) 40 times

(c) $\frac{4}{25}$

COURSE REVISION EXERCISE 6

1 (a) £700   (b) £27.83

2 (a) 7.4×10^7 years   (b) 1150 people per km

3 (a) 300 Hz   (b) 1200 m

(c)

4 (a) 82   (b) 12 or –12

(c) $\pm 3\sqrt{A - 1}$

5 $y = 3.5x^2 + 7.5$

6 (a) 7.1 cm   (b) 23°

7 (a) £10 872

(b) £6000 to £8400

(c) £6000 to £8400

(d) (i)   Mode or median

(ii) Probably mean, but it depends how intelligent the people you are negotiating with are

8 (a) $x = 4.5$

(b) $x = -2.28$ or $x = -0.22$

(c) $x = 4$ or $x = -1$

9 (a)

(b) (i) $\mathbf{a} + \mathbf{b}$ (ii) $\mathbf{a} - \frac{1}{2}\mathbf{b}$

(c) $x = \frac{5}{3}, y = \frac{2}{3}$

10 (a) AB = 18.5 and AF = AE = x (tangents from A)

(b) (i)   BD = BF

(ii) BD + DC = $(18.5 - x) + 2.5$

(c) $(x + 2.5)^2 + (21 - x)^2 = 18.5^2$

$\Rightarrow 2x^2 - 37x + 105 = 0$

$\Rightarrow (2x - 7)(x - 15) = 0$;

$x = 3.5$ gives a height of 17.5 feet

NDEX